The Alabaster Girl

With all best wishes!

Zan Perrion

BUCHAREST

ZAN PERRION

The Alabaster Girl

Numinous and luminous
something that can never be
fixed in language
beauty is my life force
I could hang all day
in its current like a bird

ARS AMORATA

This book is a work of fiction. Names, characters, places and incidents are products of the author's imagination or are used fictitiously. Any resemblance to actual events or locales or persons, living or dead, is entirely coincidental.

Published by Ars Amorata Press

ISBN: 978-0-9920166-0-9 (Paperback Edition)
ISBN: 978-0-9920166-1-6 (ePub Edition)
ISBN: 978-0-9920166-2-3 (Kindle Edition)

Edited by Clare Kent
Cover Design by Andrei Craciun
Cover Art by Egor Lapko

www.arsamorata.com
www.zanperrion.com

For Jennifer

Contents

one

The Way of Beauty

There are four things I know about women
I will tell you three

A journey on a train is a curious affair, rigid, precise, scheduled to the minute, tightly fixed in time and space, a cloistered captivity, and yet... open and easy in a way, flowing with romance and fluid possibilities... slow-rocking, dreamy and free.

I read your book, she said.

I know.

A book about women.

Yes.

Why women?

The greatest subject on earth.

Well... there are lots of interesting subjects on earth.

Yes, and reduced to their essence, most subjects resemble one another, do they not? They converge. They are the same. Through all of time, only a handful of fundamental themes have ever occupied our minds.

And "women" is one of those fundamental themes?

The beauty of women, yes. The mystery that is woman, an obsession we all share.

Is that true for everyone?

Well, let me ask you this... when men gather together, what kind of things do they like to talk about?

I don't know. Sports? Cars? Their careers?

Things like that, for sure. But that's not all. What else do men constantly talk about with other men?

Women, of course.

Exactly. Men talk about women all the time. Never ceasing. So now then... what about women? When women gather together, what do they generally like to talk about?

Men.

Yes, and?

Well, our relationships with men, actually.

Of course, and what else?

Women.

Precisely. Women talk about women as much as men talk about women. Maybe even *more* than men. Think about it... men talk about things that generally interest men, and women talk about things that generally interest women, but the only subject we all have in common, the one thing we all talk about without ceasing, is women. Look at any magazine rack. The men's magazines have women on the cover and women on every page. The women's magazines? Women on the cover and women on every page.

That's funny because it's true.

So, naturally... a book about women.

Outside the window, a palette of soft greens is floating by. The occasional farm house. A road or two. The train has left the city.

Did you write the book for men? Or for women?

I wrote it for me.

For you?

Yes.

Say more about that.

Well... I guess I just want to remember my love affair with women when I am old. So I wrote it all down. A *billet-doux* to myself. It's pretty scattered... you read it, so you know. Just a few thoughts, impressions, blowzy prose, fleeting vignettes. Fanciful navel gazing, really. Nothing more.

Maybe so. But it hit a nerve out there. It was intriguing enough that I wanted to interview you.

To ask me a few questions.

To ask you some questions, yes.

I accept.

The only thing you can do on a train is... be on a train. That's about it. A forced sybaritic dream, a luxuriant over-abundance of time. You are captured there, frozen between departure and arrival, and there is nothing to be done about it.

The article I am writing will be for women.

Yes, I know.

When I pitched this story to my editor, she joked that it would be like one of the hens interviewing the fox.

She did, did she? Maybe it's more like sitting down with the vampire to ask him why he is torn between his eternal love for you and his desire to destroy you.

Neither of which I feel from you.

You sound surprised.

No... I just... well, you have a formidable reputation. A professional ladies man.

Yes well... today is my day off. You can relax.

There really is no end to a journey on a train. It stays with you, a part of your heart forever. You remain, in a way, on that train for the rest of your life.

What would you like to know?

Everything.

Everything? Okay, how's this... I lost my virginity at fourteen, lying on my back in the bed of a pickup truck with an ashtray on my chest. Her name was Allison, she was eighteen, and what can I say? She liked to smoke, I guess.

Oh yeah?

Yeah. And since then my life has been a blur, a veritable forest of women... thousands even... the glistening body of Brynda Johannsdottir beside a Gjain waterfall in Iceland... a three-day roller coaster ride at the Dnipro Hotel in Kiev with Tatiana and Irina... a life-saving, hypothermia averting night in a sleeping bag with a Sherpa named Honey on the slopes of Everest... I could go on and—.

Is any of that true?

No.

Too bad. It would make a great article.

Do you want a great article... or do you want the truth?

I would love the truth.

The truth is fairly banal, I'm afraid. How does the fox catch all those hens? He pretty much just runs right into the middle of them and there they are, all around him.

Yes, but what is he thinking at the time?

Ah... what is he thinking?

That's what I want to know. The mindset of a master seducer.

I see. Well, your curiosity is sweet and you seem wonderfully sincere but as our good friend Robert Frost once said... those woods, my dear, are lovely, dark, and deep. Do your interview. I will give you nice answers.

Listen, I am here on this train with you because I really *do* want to know.

Well, I suppose I am kind of stuck here with you, aren't I?

Yes. Frost also said that we have miles to go before we sleep.

Ah, that he did.

I am right here... with you... I'm not going anywhere.

I see. And we do have to talk about something, don't we?

Yes.

Outside the window, a palette of soft greens is floating by.

It's going to be a long journey, girl.

Yes.

Do you really want to know?

Tell me everything.

Very well then...

And outside the window, like half-remembered dreams, the soft greens float on by...

ಶಿಂಣ

Sit back and relax… I will sing you the song of women.
What women? you ask.
All women, I answer.
Even me? you ask.
Especially you, I answer.
And what will you sing to me? you ask.
Ah, my love, I will sing to you of hidden truths. Yes, hidden truths
and secret secrets.

I will sing to you of beauty, for the song of women is, first of all,
a song of beauty. This we must understand, for it is beauty that is
missing from this earth and from our hearts. Beauty is the only
thing that will save this broken-down old world, the only thing
that can recreate the spirit of aliveness in all of us again, in both
men and women.

What is beauty? Is it an evocation of harmony and symmetry? Or
is it an awakening of the ragged disorder of desire in us? Is it innocence? Is it holiness? Is it a quality of the object observed? Or is it
inherent in us, the observer? Perhaps beauty is not inherent in the
object, nor in the eye of the beholder, but in a dance of the two?
Who knows? Each must answer alone. One thing is certain: beauty
has a holy vibration.

Beauty is truth, truth beauty—isn't that how Keats described it? Yes.
There you have it. If it is not beautiful, it is not true, and if this is so,
then beauty is the *only* truth. Which is to say that what draws our hearts
is the only truth. Which is to say that what we desire is the only truth.

In mythology, Beauty always arrives as a guide. Obscure pathways
are illuminated, difficult times are softened, conflicts are harmonized,
and every ray of new light leads the warrior on gently from adventure
to adventure, from wisdom to wisdom, from abundance to abundance. Beauty fills his heart with the sweetest anthems of gratitude.

All women are beautiful, in a way that transcends mere features and forms, and yet most women no longer believe in their beauty song, just like most men will never learn to hear it. We have all forgotten how to connect to the transcendent beauty of women, the celestial essence of the feminine, but it's there all right, a rhythm all around us.

And you, my love? Can you hear it? Can you hear the glorious, eternal song of women? The harmony and symmetry of the lullaby of beauty? Do you still believe in your beauty? Well, listen for a while and you soon shall.

Few men will ever learn to hear the beauty song of women. But if their hearts are sincere, they will hear it. And when a man learns to hear the beauty song of women, the whole world opens up for him. He becomes aware of beauty, he becomes alive to beauty, he becomes alive to truth.

Here is a secret, my love: when a man chooses to live his life in sync with the rhythm of women, the song of beauty, he is universally loved by women, and he becomes a *lover* of women, the greatest lover a woman will ever know. The greatest lover *you* will ever know.

So sit back and relax... I will sing you the song of women, which is really the song of beauty, which is really the song of truth, which is really the song of you.

ഇൽ

All beautiful things must end. Otherwise they are not beautiful. A simple truth, suspected by most, acknowledged by few. I pause for a moment to consider this small bunch of wild flowers I tied together today with a string. Yes, it is a quiet truth, a universal truth.

I pretend now to hide the flowers behind my back, then tap on her door. I know that when she opens the door she will pretend to be surprised by this artless bouquet that I pretend to hide, and I love this about her and that this is the way of all women.

She opens the door with a flourish, excited, inviting, shining like she does. What's that behind your back? Oh this? Just some flowers. She claps her hands in delight and gathers the flowers and me into her home.

She is superb, this woman, this quintessence. I watch her now as she shifts the flowers about in a blue vase. Her serenity is infectious and calming, like the warmth of the sun on a balcony in the morning.

Observe a woman in profile, intent on a task; it is one of the unsung wonders of the world. Watch the way she touches her hair, how she pushes it back from her face, curving it around the contour of her ear, a subconscious gesture when it gets in her way. And notice your delight when her hair falls right back down again as she leans forward. Some women have no idea the effect they have on men; it is beauty in repose, and it is wonderful.

You... painted on this moment, impressionist's swirl...

We all have one perfect image when we are reminded of someone who has touched our lives. It is the first image that swims into view every time we think of them in the future. I realize now, watching Emily arranging those little wild flowers in that little blue vase, that this is the image of her my mind has forever captured, the vision that will return on those mornings when I awake and suddenly miss her, or when I happen to drift through her perfume again somewhere, someday.

She pauses now, as I watch, trying to decide if she is pleased with her arrangement, discovers she is, then turns to me, her eyes dancing. I am unsure which is more endearing: her breathtaking natural beauty, or her complete innocence concerning it.

"I just have to finish getting ready," she is saying now, twirling toward her bedroom on a cushion of grace, all smiles and light steps and knowing. I smile in return, unnoticed, for

she has already disappeared. She wants to make a good impression, for everything to be perfect between us.

Well, not to worry, Emily... you already have and it already is...

"There's a bottle of wine on the counter," she calls out from her bedroom. "I forget how to pronounce it, but it's the kind you like, the Italian one. I won't be long, I promise."

"Take your time. This—" I glance at the bottle, "—Sangiovese and I will get to know each other."

I pour a glass of the wine and look around the room. Everything is perfectly arranged, simple and elegant. There is comfort here in her home; not comfortable things, just an abiding sense of comfort, subtle and woven throughout. There is a fireplace in one corner. There is a portable easel by the window with a painting just begun, the inchoate figure of a woman. There is a bookshelf with books and trinkets and trivial things, all arranged and composed just so. Everywhere are candles (of course) and small pictures in small frames, pictures of family and friends and trips to London. Everything is neat and everything is clean and everything is correct. I take it all in, this little home, this wicker and pillowy comfort, this essence of Emily.

There is a kindness here, a sanctuary, something ancient, something necessary, something that calls to me, something that I don't have in my life, something that I eternally long for. This is a place of creation, of knowing, of serenity. This is a place of beauty. I feel like I could stop right here right now and rest, in this quietude, by this fireplace, with this woman, with my head on her breast, as she strokes my hair forever.

I sit down and spread out upon her sand-colored sofa, my feet heavy on her wooden coffee table, careful not to disturb the meticulously arranged green apples in their wide and shallow bowl, and raise the glass to light.

Ah yes... Sangiovese, the Tuscan courtesan with a shadowy past...

Here's what I've learned in my life: to truly experience anything, to experience things in their entirety, all the senses must be engaged. A woman is like a fine wine of the rarest vintage. It is not enough to merely glance at the wine in the glass, then toss it back without a care or thought. Instead, one needs to take the time to let the wine relax and breathe, to observe its clarity and complexion, to admire its superb body, to draw in its exquisite bouquet with every breath, savoring it deeply, and then—and only then—should one take that first anticipatory sip, drinking it in slowly, mindfully, attuning the senses to all of its quixotic subtleties, its texture, its nuance... experiencing it... breathing it... living it... fading into it.

This is the secret to living and loving: everything must be experienced on all levels, everything must be explored, every invitation accepted, every experience fully immersed. When we travel to another city, why do we stay on the tourist track? How dreary to see the world this way! Far better to discover the rhythm of the place, to touch the city's fabric with our hands, to absorb its culture through the pores of our skin. Who, after all, can say they've been to Paris when the only thing they remember is the Eiffel Tower?

It is the same with women and it is the same with wine.

I hear her voice from the bedroom now, soft and low, singing to herself. I lean back and close my eyes.

Emily is, to me, the highest form of art. There are some women you encounter in your life that shake your foundations. Because there are women like her in this world, I believe. I believe in the kindness and gentleness and goodness of the female spirit. When I consider my life in the company of all those rare and beautiful women, surrounding me with such boundless beauty and grace, I can only conclude that everything good in me has accumulated from my time with them.

Because of women like Emily, there are poets and artists in the world. Because of her, I am in love with all women.

I raise the glass to light and I know. I know that wine and travel, wild flowers and women can only be truly experienced in their entirety, that all the senses must be engaged, and that, ultimately, all beautiful things must end.

Otherwise they are not beautiful.

I give it about a month.

Maybe two.

— The Alabaster Girl, *page 14*

ഇൻ

My lifelong proximity to women has imbued me with a simple and abiding philosophy: *I move toward beauty in all its forms, art in all its forms.*

And to me, the greatest manifestation of beauty and art in this world is women. My entire life is a dedication, an official ceremony, a monument, to the song of women. Is not the curve of a woman the greatest creation of a benevolent God? Is not the smile of a woman the greatest source of inspiration on earth? How can one possibly resist the disarray of desire that beauty invokes? How can one devote his life to anything but a study of the poetics of women? It makes no sense to me to strive for anything else. I defer to Plotinus: "This is the spirit that beauty will ever induce, wonderment and a delicious trouble, longing and love and a trembling that is all delight."

Your beauty manifests itself in many forms, my love. It is there in your personality and charm, it is there in the essence of your nurturing spirit that bathes and cleanses and forgives us men, it is there in your smile that seduces our hearts, it is there in the delicate dance of relationship with you, and because the gods love us, it is there in the way you look to us in the moonlight.

The beauty song of women is a love song. This is my truth. I *love* women. I don't give a damn what others think of me. Let analysts analyze. Let psychologists murmur and suggest. Let moralists tut-tut

and wring their hands. Let man-haters roar. I move through life
without apology, without defense, without regret. I am wondrously
in love with women, in love with the very *idea* of women, and if
your heart is sincere, you will understand exactly what that means.
This is what I live. This is what I love. This is what I believe. This is
my religion, my saving grace. This is the air I breathe.

When I am gone and they are scattering my ashes to the wind, let
them look up to the sky and say, "Yes, he was a scoundrel, a *flaneur*,
inconsistent, ridiculous, excessive, but oh, he lived a life! A *winged*
life! He loved freedom and beauty above all. His greatest fear was
mediocrity. He was immensely curious, charmed, and enchanted,
on an adventure, itinerant, having enormous fun in life, never
needy, never attached to the outcome, never serious, but always
sincere. He was in love with the voluptuousness of life and its
immense potential. Above all, he was a lover of women. He loved
women completely, from the sea to the sky. He was fascinated by
the essence, the glory, and the magical omnipotence of women.
He had no other hobbies. Women were his poetry, his music, his
reading, his travel, his sport."

And wow, what an adventure! What extraordinary women I have
loved; I have danced with angels on this earth. My angels, my
beautiful girls, how I celebrate them, how I adore them, how I
miss them all, and how I dream of them still, like the rain dreams
of the sea.

œ∞αœ

There is something fundamentally beautiful about women that is
more than their outward appearance. It's something else entirely.
And what is that something else? *Gratitude*. True beauty has a profound sense of gratitude. A gratitude for life and a gratitude for
love. A simple thankfulness, a kindness, a grace of spirit in the
heart. As Nietzsche put it, "The essence of all beautiful art, all great
art, is gratitude."

The notion that a beautiful woman is a throwback to a different, more simple time is both a cliché and true. There is a certain worldliness in true beauty, an ancient spirit, a knowing. Beauty is not light-headed, uncaring, frivolous. Beauty is not "Look at me! Look at me!" Beauty cares, has empathy, is tinged with sadness.

Beautiful women are secretly lonely. We think it's because they are intimidating to others. This may be true, of course, but there is something else here, something a little more fundamental, something beyond the obvious. Beautiful women are lonely because they are never fully included in the lives of others. Men are rarely honest with them about their intentions and women are a little unsure of them, a little suspicious, a little mistrustful, a little wary. Beautiful women are placed upon a stage, up there, away... away from the nodding, whispering, murmuring audience. They are politely non-included, set apart.

True beauty is so rare that when you encounter it—in nature, in art, in people—it breaks your heart a little. True beauty stops us in our tracks, we catch our breath, we are still.

ജ്ഞ

There's a difference between hot women and beautiful women. Hot women are everywhere; they abound. They are beautified, not beautiful. Beautiful women, on the other hand, are rare and a real mystery. Hotness speaks to our impulses. Beauty speaks to our imagination.

All men notice when a hot woman enters a room. But all women (and only a few men) notice when a beautiful woman enters a room. Women secretly admire beautiful women. There are no greater admirers of beautiful women than other women. Women dress, wear makeup, wear designer clothes for other women... rarely for men. Men don't care at all who designed the shoes, the dress, the purse. They don't even notice. Does she look good? Yes. Are the dress and shoes removable? Perfect.

Hot women get hit on. Beautiful ones rarely do. Why is this? It's because men understand hot women; they are a known entity. Men know what to do with them, or more precisely, what they would *like* to do with them. Hot women have a front side and a back side. No mystery there whatsoever. Beautiful women, on the other hand, possess a complexity, a depth, a nuanced grace, that confuses most men. Men have no idea what to do with them. So beautiful women are politely passed on by.

This is why bars and clubs are infinitely depressing to a beautiful woman. Her encounters with men come in only two flavors: the drunks, oblivious, who leer and lurch, spray-painting their beer breath upon her, and the sober ones who shuffle their feet, clear their throats, avert their eyes.

Hot women are attracted to "shiny objects": money clips, camera lenses, fancy watches. All you have to do is flash it better or more profusely than the next guy and you're in. This is something men can understand, for there is logic here, and structure. A road map to follow: *acquire shiny objects, acquire hot women*. Simple. One for the left arm and one for the right arm? Sure, why not?

Beautiful women do not care about these things at all. They are attracted to only one thing in men: *beauty*. And what is the beauty in a man? A lifelong devotion to a personal passion, a passion larger than him, larger than her, larger than the whole wide world, a passion that radiates from his pores until the day he dies. This is the beauty of men. And this is why beautiful women are forever in love with starving artists, musicians, dreamers, iconoclasts. They love these men because they, too, possess a certain, rare beauty. They, too, are set apart.

ഈൠ

And what do you do? she asks.
I turn to her.
She is glorious in a butter-colored dress.

Treasure hunter, I say.
She laughs and I like her.
And what is the treasure you seek?
Beauty.
Ah, I see… and how will you know when you have found it?
I always know…
— The Alabaster Girl, *page 18*

૭૦ભ

There is a subset of men who move among women with ease. Who are these men and why are they allowed to roam unhindered in the land of women? What causes women to be drawn to them like proverbial moths to the flame? What qualities do they possess that compel women to allow them liberties not afforded to other men? We assume it is things like animal magnetism and confidence, the ability to light up a room with sheer force of presence. But what does any of this mean? Why do these men seem to have this presence while others do not? The answer is simple: these men love women with all their hearts.

A man who loves women is loved by women. This is a law of the universe. Let me say that again: *A man who loves women is loved by women.* This is a motif that is embroidered upon everything he says and everything he does. Therein lies the power. And the difference. All radiance, all confidence, all charisma that these men possess is a natural result of their deep, abiding, and thoroughly irrepressible love for women. And women, in turn, love these men through all the days and nights of their years.

Men who love women inhabit an entirely different sphere, a realm outside the usual mass of men. They are the secret, the unknown, the mystical ones. They move freely in the land of women. They move around the periphery while other men mill about the center in confusion.

Women recognize when they are in the presence of a man who loves women, who chooses to celebrate them, who chooses to see them in a certain light. They willingly step into that light, for he is a man who loves women, that rarest of men, and women always, *always* respond to a man who loves women.

A man who loves women delights in his desires. He *loves* that he loves women. He presents it for all to see. He proclaims it to the world without restraint. He never apologizes for the fact that he is a man and she is a woman and that he loves women. He never hides it *ever*. In fact, he can't help it. It is impossible to suppress. His love of women is always on his lips and shining from his eyes. If a woman asks him something like, "So… what made you decide to visit this city?" he smiles to her and says, "Why? Because I love women, that's why. What's your name again?"

A man who loves women never needs to dominate a room by being loud or boisterous or ridiculously animated. He stands out, yes, but he doesn't *stick* out. The greatest forces of nature are quiet ones. Although his energy is electric, palpable, a vital current, he is at all times poised, calm, and radiant. He is *exceedingly* generous—with his time, his money. He shakes hands readily and firmly. He nods to all the men, welcoming them freely, including them in his story. He winks at all the girls. Everyone feels noticed—*really seen*—in his presence, which is, of course, the greatest gift a man can ever give to others in this world.

A man who loves women treats all women the same, giving each of them his full attention, kissing their hands and winking all around. It doesn't matter at all what he says. What matters is the way he says it. When he focuses on a woman, there is no one else in the world. He includes. He shares. He leans in to her, giving of himself, and inviting her to share of herself in return. He smiles with his eyes and his whole being. And he makes sure that every other woman sees the special attention he is lavishing on her, for their turn will come.

A man who loves women has an effect that is pure alchemy, everything transmuted to gold. Women transform in his presence, for there is something about him and the way he looks at them, something that makes them, well... *soften*. They soften, my love. They become girls again, in his presence.

A man who loves women has no need or desire to take anything from a woman, and yet would happily share everything with her. His respect for her is supreme and yet if she spends any time in his presence at all, he will bend her over without hesitation. Oh, you know all this, don't you, my love? All women do. Men don't understand this and women do.

A man who loves women is impossible and impertinent and any continuance with him is entirely out of the question. And yet... women can't stop thinking about him. They call all their girlfriends and say, "I met this guy last night... I can't stop thinking about him."

Other men? Other men openly dismiss him, yet secretly admire him, a reluctant veneration, like a pagan deity in whom they are unable to believe.

ഇരുജ

Does she not sleep? Each time I awaken in the night she is still close to me, smiling at me, stroking my hair. She only smiles, saying nothing, saying everything, surrounding me in her aura of hidden things. An island girl, dark-skinned and opulent, belonging to different constellations than I will ever know, a distant girl from a distant land, a land of sand and sarongs, of topaz and tango.

She guards me in the night, watching over me, cradling me tight to her breasts, protecting me in my dreams. Her breath-hum is all around me, an unseen force with no beginning and no end, like the hot wind of this beautiful country that created her. I close my eyes and listen to her heartbeat.

Her purity is so pure it cleanses me, her sweetness so sweet it makes me cry. She is eternal.

I can only think that if a man has never experienced a moment like this in his life, a moment surrounded by the whirling flowerness of an island girl, with the scent of orange blossom salt on her skin, her body the color of café-au-lait and as hard and smooth as porcelain, and little bits of sand still flecked all about her knees, then he needs to stop his life right now and find it. Only then has his life been lived, only then can he smile up to God and say, thank You, now I understand, now I have seen the majesty of Your works, I have touched my feet upon sacred ground, and now it is enough, I can kiss the sky and die.

No wonder Gauguin went to Tahiti to paint.
— The Alabaster Girl, *page 20*

૭૦૦૨

Beauty needs a witness. This is the secret to success with women. The secret to the art of love. It is what separates true lovers from pickup artists, one-night-stand cowboys, and heart-breakers with a whole bouquet of empty promises. It is also what sets true lovers apart from all the nice guys huddled around women trying so desperately to figure it all out.

Beauty needs a witness. This is the only thing a man ever needs to know. If he learns this, he learns everything. His life gathers force and focus and he is propelled onward with art and grace, like a sail upon the sea.

To seek beauty in women, and only beauty, is the thing that will save a man. All he has to do is look for and then describe, with his words and actions, the beauty he sees in them, and he is saved. Every step toward beauty moves him away from the teeming multitude of boys and into the rarefied realm of men. Every turning toward beauty saves his life.

A boy looks for all the ways that he can impress a girl. A man looks for all the ways that she can impress him. A boy seeks to maximize the way he appears in her eyes. A man seeks to maximize the way she appears in his eyes. A boy wonders what she thinks of him. A man wonders what he thinks of her. A boy asks himself, "Where is she on a scale of one to ten?" A man asks himself, "What is beautiful about this woman before me?" A boy asks himself over and over, "Does she like me? Does she like me?" A man asks himself over and over, "Do I like her? Do I like her?" A boy is in his head. A man is in his heart. A boy observes himself. A man observes *her*.

A man who loves women actively chooses to be curious about them, to make them feel lovely in his presence, to make them feel appreciated, to make them feel desired, to make them feel noticed. He turns to a woman and he thinks, "You are altogether lovely, my dear. That is how I see you. That is how I choose to see you." For it *is* a choice. We can choose to see ugliness in everything or imagine beauty. Rose-colored glasses? Unwarranted optimism? So be it. To choose to see the beauty in a woman is a choice that any man can make.

ഇരു

Sometimes when I talk to a group of men, I ask them this question: "Who here loves women? Absolutely *loves* women? Raise your hand!" And it is remarkable to see the shift in the energy of the group. Their postures straighten, their hands shoot up to the sky, their smiles burst forth and fill the room, their faces shine like a light, an almost holy light, like a celestial choir about to break into song. They are more animated, more effervescent, nodding their heads at each other, and laughing at the change in all of them. Yes, they sing out, of course we love women! So then my next question is, "Wow, why don't women ever see this side of you? Be more like this in the presence of women and they will *adore* you!"

There is a remarkable truth and clarity to loving women, and in celebrating the fact that you do. To celebrate a woman the first time you meet her, the first time she joins you for coffee or wine, the first time she shares your bed, a celebration that continues the next morning, the next month, every year she is in your life, and every time your paths cross again in the future. For it truly is a celebration, in every sense of the word. As in, "Look at you, my angel... how absolutely radiant you are to me today!"

Any true success a man will ever have with women comes from a belief that *all women are beautiful*. There is no other way. All women *are* latent beauties, like the color white that contains all possibilities. What a sublime shift in perspective this is for a man! A sublime shift in the way he sees women, and a sublime shift in the way they see him. To see every woman as truly beautiful, not as an object, not as something to acquire, not as something to possess like a pet or a boat.

When a man believes that all women are beautiful, they will believe it too. They become beautiful again in his presence, for a woman enthralled or delighted or in love is *always* beautiful. That's the way it is and the way it has always been. A man who knows this and who takes the time to discover the beauty in women, moves from being a passive observer of beauty to a participant, a creator, and well... let's just say that women everywhere will open up to him in amazing ways.

I am not implying that women are only beautiful in the presence of a man. No, your beauty is always there, my love, like a flower in a forgotten meadow, but most men are too busy looking at the outside to ever really see you. For a true lover, every encounter with women is a chance to see the beauty in them, to uncover it, for it is already there, discovered again in his presence.

And wonder of wonders, it is reciprocal, for like magic, or perhaps design, the transcendent beauty of women is the only thing that can inspire men to great things, the only thing that can make men truly feel alive.

two

The Way of Seduction

I like the honey
I run from the bees

Where shall we go today? Oh, where shall we go? New cities bring new promises and new beginnings. Oh, glorious, ineluctable journey on a train! Because why not? If we are not moving forward, we are dying, are we not?

You've been described by the media as the "world's greatest seducer," she said.

It's true.

It's true that you're the world's greatest seducer?

No, it's true that I have been called that. I have no illusions about myself. They slipped through my fingers along the way.

How would you seduce me?

Well... I could tell you the truth about me, but to seduce you, I will tell you the truth about you.

Can you seduce any woman?

Well, let me put it this way. My *belief* that I can seduce any woman is not necessarily related to my actual *ability* to seduce any woman. Ah, but why not err on the side of optimism? Why not choose to believe it? It's as valid as any other invented assumption, is it not? Who cares if it's true or not? It doesn't matter. The light is better over here.

Is that a no?

Let's just say it's the finest of all my illusions.

The shimmering, crayoned, scrambling hills rush by. There is no time to wait! For opportunities, for money, for success. These things are just going to have to catch up. Or not. For we are going anyway.

Do women know you as well as you know them? she said.

Women always know me. They can see me coming a mile away. They always understand me. Men do not, and women do.

What about the real you?

What do you mean by the real me? The private me? Or the public perception of me?

I mean the *real* you.

Aha.

Do women ever get to see that part of you?

Of course they do. They know. Women know. An intelligent, perceptive woman can instantly detect an impostor, a poser, a pretender. She can smell a hidden agenda from across the room, and the moment a man enters her presence, she puts him to the test, the tip of her sword at his throat. "Who goes there?"

But not you?

Like I said, women already know who I am.

So again let me ask... who are you?

Who am I? Who am I? An interesting question. For what you are really asking is... who am I to presume to know anything about women? Who am I to speak of beauty?

Yes. Who goes there?

Ah, *touché*...

ଡ଼ଠଓ

I am not like other men. I know certain things about certain things. I know women. I look at you and... I know you. Oh yes, I do. I know you, my love. And though you may not admit it, you know me too. You have known me all your life. You know exactly who I am. You know exactly who I am not.

I am not your future boyfriend. I am not your future husband. I am not your future anything. Those positions in your life will be filled by other men with far more talent for those respective roles than I. No, my love, I represent something entirely different.

I am your lover. I am your secret affair. I am the bandit, the pirate, the gypsy. I am the Bedouin riding hard across the desert in white and flowing robes. I will gather you up, my love, I will adore you, I will adorn you, I will praise you, I will serenade you, and when the lights are quiet and your serrated beauty flickers in the shadows, I will caress your hair and lay you down upon silk, upon clouds, and I will put the full weight of my body on your body, and you will bear witness to the picture-perfect reflection of you and me together. This I will do and more. I will delight in your delight. I will give you everything, everything of myself to you entirely, an exhilaration of you and me. You understand all this, don't you, my love? Yes, I can see in your eyes that you do.

∞∞

I have a power in me. I can feel it in my bones. I have seduction in my soul. I have soft words cascading from my lips. I have delightful intrigue in my fingertips and the dance of joyful liaisons in my step. I have a calm assurance in me, an assurance that, given an hour or two in a quiet place, I can seduce any woman. Yes, *any* woman. Yes, even you.

This power is so strong in me that I can announce to you that I am about to seduce you, then pirouette lightly to the side, listening quietly to your proclamations and protests, and still delightfully succeed with you. This is because as soon as my intentions—and your protests—are in the air, I know exactly how to deal with everything. And what's more, you will believe, in your cautious charm, that it was all your idea.

I have many ways to seduce you, my love, delicate and rhapsodic by turns. I know what to say next, what to do next. I am so finely calibrated to your signals that I have a kind of sixth sense. I know what you are thinking and what you are about to say. I know what makes you sad, I know what makes you happy, I know what you desire most, I know your entire history.

I know the language of women. I am at complete ease in the land of women. I have spent years listening to your heartbeat, my love, and I know women better than any man I know. My intuition is finely honed. In a room full of people, I can tell what is possible with every woman in the room, without even looking. In fact, I consciously do not look at certain women because otherwise, well, you know… it's on. A gay friend of mine once said to me, "I have the same intuition about men that you have about women. I have never met a straight man who has this quality. No wonder women respond to you."

A lot of people have a fear of being alone when they are old. Not me. I never worry about being alone when I am old. It has never even crossed my mind. This is because I have the notion, whether false or true, that no matter how bald or fat or toothless or moth-eaten I become, well hey, as long as I can talk, I will *never* be alone.

This is how I seduce you, my love. Not with apples and ribbons, but with words. All women are different, yet all women are wonderfully the same. They still respond to the same things they have always responded to. Different words, perhaps, or a different tone of voice, a different cadence—but they *all* respond.

I have the requisite dexterity, fleetness, and lightness in my words to take a woman places in her mind that she has never been. Every sonorous syllable is laser-lined, razor-sharp, yet velvet and inviting, a cascade of wildly dispersed musical notes on an inevitable path toward coherence, a path full of surprises, even for women who have been there before and think they know the way.

A man falls in love with his eyes. A woman falls in love with her ears. I know exactly what to say to you, my love, and exactly how to say it. I know what to say to you if you are strong and used to being in control, and I know what to say to you if you are quiet and shy and demure.

If you mistrust men or are bitter because of men, well, for me that is the easiest. The fishing, as they say, is better in troubled waters. I know how to make you believe in men again, as presumptuous as that sounds. Don't like men? No problem. You *will* like me. A myriad of paths to travel, but all leading to the same sacred temple.

Other men might be better at telling stories or getting phone numbers or entertaining you, but sit down across from me, my love, for an hour or so and I am without equal. In an hour I can explain your very soul to you. I can take you places in your mind you have never imagined. I can change the night into day and the day into night with my words. I can bring the stars to your feet. I can weave a net that catches us up together, breathless, a luscious wondrous net of words, cascading, tumbling, folding in upon us, a whisper of words to you and to the air all around us, a beautiful anticipation that is impossible for either of us to resist.

Can attraction be created? Is it possible to create chemistry, *ex nihilo*? Oh, if men only knew what is possible with women! It doesn't mean that I can bed every woman, of course, nor that I want to, but it does mean that, if I desire, I can speak to a woman's dreams in a way that no man ever has before. If I strike, I rarely miss.

Ah, you might think, who does he think he is? If so, I understand, for these are bold and provocative words! But there is no desire in me to provoke. I am not trying to convince you or anyone of anything. There is no hint of presumption at all in what I say. There is no sense in me that I am God's gift to women, or that if a woman does not accept what I have to offer, well then, it's her loss. For it's my loss too—I really liked her! No, none of that "I am the prize" nonsense. There is only a quiet kind of assurance, a knowing, that floats all around me like cherry blossoms in a garden. I can feel it falling gently everywhere in the air.

Now then, it's certainly not because I possess anything special as far as looks or intelligence that makes this possible. No. It is simply my willingness to embrace an undiminished belief in the beauty of women, a willingness to recklessly submit myself to the desires of women, a willingness to allow myself to be thoroughly seduced by women, and a willingness to dash myself upon the rocks of the sirens, with unalloyed ease and delight.

Idealistic? Florid? Over-the-top? Sure. So be it. I have no time to respond to suspicion or cynicism or pessimism. It's too wonderful over here where I am standing.

My proclamations are sure, my generalizations are sweeping, and I speak volumes about all women when I, of course, have not been exposed to all women. What would the women on the windswept steppes of Kazakhstan think of the things I say, for example? There surely is a vast difference between the heart and mind of a devout Muslim woman and the heart and mind of a Western girl who has spent twenty years in the dating world. Ah yes, for my foolish presumption, I will be duly pounced upon and pummeled, I suspect, and rightly so. "Who does he think he is," they will say with righteous indignation, "a man trying to describe the heart and mind of women?"

And they will be right. I am not a woman. It is not my place to describe the hearts and minds of women. I will do it anyway, of course, and I will be set upon and clawed and pummeled, and I will take my lumps accordingly, bowed but unrepentant, beaten but unquenched.

ഇരു

I step into the elevator on the nineteenth floor in Las Vegas, and here they are before me. Two shining beauties in, oh, their late fifties or so, shimmering into view. And wow, they look great! Glistening evening gowns, red lipstick, hair professionally coifed, the whole nine.

I smile at them and they brighten. I say, "Look at you two beauties here before me... absolutely ravishing! What, may I ask, is the occasion?"

They brighten even further (I didn't think it was possible) and say, "We're joining our husbands downstairs for a formal event, so we got all dressed up."

The elevator starts its descent and I wink at these two stellar angels, "You know what, girls? Why don't you call your husbands and say you're not feeling well, and that you won't make it to the event? Then sneak away and party with me!"

And oh, those two... how much more alive they are now! All smiles and delight and shining eyes. The elevator stops and they step out and away, laughing and waving back to me, as bright as sun-reflected snow.

Trying to pick them up? Of course not. Did I have a hidden agenda? Not at all. They knew all this. They knew the spirit of what I was saying. They knew that I am simply a man who sees beauty in women, that I saw beauty in them, and because I did, they became even more beautiful. Just for me.

This is what I love. This is the gift of life that women give to me and that I give to them. A perfect exchange. I make them feel desirable, they make me feel inspired, and it has nothing to do with seeking a specific outcome. The interaction is the only outcome that matters. That is everything right there. There is nothing else.

— The Alabaster Girl, *page 23*

৪৩

Women always know men better than men will ever know women. This is something men do not understand. They think they can fool women, but they are mistaken. Women have been reading faces their whole lives.

Women can see right through me. And I would have it no other way. I love it when I am in the presence of a woman who can see into my soul and who understands my nature completely. This pleases me greatly, for I am in my element and I can relax.

Women are always on my side. Even ones I barely know. They facilitate things for me. They introduce me to other women. "Ah, you will love my friend," they say. "Excellent. Bring her around," I say. And they do. This is because women recognize a man who truly loves and delights in women, and there is something in the heart of a woman that wants to assist that delight in some way, to make it happen for him. Women are inherently generous to men who love women. Women want men to succeed. Women want to take care of men. Even mothers are on my side, offering to introduce me to their daughters.

Men, on the other hand, are suspicious of me, thinking that it can't be as simple as I make it out to be. And that's okay. I don't need men to understand me. Also, young women are sometimes challenging in a you-couldn't-possibly-seduce-me type of way. And that is also okay. I am completely at ease and perfectly unfluttered when men are suspicious or young women are challenging.

Older women? Older women *love* me. They smile and nod and wink. They laugh and shake their heads. "Ah, if only I was younger," they say. Older women are instantly on my side, defending me, explaining me, understanding everything I say and do. This is because they completely get it. They see me coming a mile away. Show me a seventy-year-old woman and I will show you an accomplice.

Women trust me because I am trust-*worthy*. They accept me because I am not trying to impress them or prove anything. I allow myself to be vulnerable to women, admitting that I am not perfect, admitting that I need them, admitting that I desire them—and women respond with trust and affection.

Women accept me for the way I am. That's all I ever need. I never seek validation from men. I seek it only from women. I don't need praise or understanding or acceptance from men, but I feel lost without it from women. Women provide me with my checks and balances, for I am extreme and spontaneous and ridiculous, in need of occasional recalibration.

ഇറോ

So, there you have it, my love. I can connect to a woman's heart directly and openly, win her trust, gain her affection, and all without the slightest trace of presumption or manipulation. Which, of course, one might argue, is the ultimate form of manipulation.

Yes well… I know about manipulation. I have great potential for manipulation, for I can see things as if I am floating above. I am always aware of the climate of the situation, which way the prevailing winds are about to blow. I can sense the relative positioning and movement of all the people and elements in a room. I can see it all like it's in slow motion. I can see how things are likely to unfold, as in a game of chess, where one can see several moves ahead.

I see everything, absolutely *everything*. At a party, club, or restaurant, I know where every woman is at any given time. It might not seem like it if you were to observe me, relaxed as I am and not looking around all that much. Oh, but I miss *nothing*. I have a radar, a sixth sense. The eyes-in-the-back-of-the-head cliché. I can be leaning in and talking closely to a woman directly in front of me, fully engaged, and yet I always know where everyone is, what they are attempting, what they are thinking, what they are saying, who likes who. I miss nothing.

There was a time, my love, when I was not clear at all in my intentions with women, when I tried to come in under the radar, to hide my secret plan. I made feeble attempts to get what I really wanted but would never say. I would try everything to win a woman over. I resorted to schemes and trickery and careful elision. The great seducer! I thought I was being seductive when I was just being manipulative. I would beckon hither and disappear yon. *Come into my parlor, said the spider to the fly.*

Manipulation is a stain. Oh, how I have wrestled with this in my life! I've had to rip it out, tear it away from my body, away from my soul, like smoldering cloth, and cast it down before me in the dirt. I don't want to convince, to adjust, to weave words. I want to just *be*. My lifelong quest has been a quest for clarity, for plain speaking, for speaking my truth, whatever the hell that is.

The wonderful thing you discover is that there is no need for manipulation ever. Authenticity is the only truly seductive thing in this world.

৪০৪৪

Three pretty maidens all in a row. I like the one in the middle. The music in this crowded lounge is driving and deep, but not too loud. Beautiful people everywhere. I am sitting on the arm of the sofa occupied by these three pretty maidens all in a row, and I am engaged in a fun conversation with the girl nearest me, but occasionally smiling and winking at the other two.

I love this dynamic. Women are a delight to me; every encounter is a brush with beauty and wonder. Here I am again in my empyrean element, immersed in the evanescent radiance of the female spirit; I wade into it like a little boy wades into the sea.

Three pretty maidens all in a row. I engage all three, I include them all, but I am mostly talking to the girl nearest me—because of proximity more than anything else. We continue to talk, about nothing really. We share a few jokes and the other two are listening and laughing and gradually being drawn into the conversation.

I like the girl in the middle, so a shift will happen soon. I smile at her and she smiles at me. Perfect. I know how this will unfold. I have been here before. Her friends like me, she likes me, I like her, and all is right with the world.

Then suddenly, it happens. On the periphery of our little foursome, our thoroughly engaged and engaging little group, I see him.

Michael...

This can't go well. Michael is like the annoying mosquito that buzzes around your head all night, but you're just too damned tired to get up and squish it. I spent some time with him only once or twice before, and in that short time I found him to be unbelievably pessimistic, misogynistic, cloying, and disrespectful to women. Suffice it to say that men like him are immediately off my radar. I have nothing in common with men who do not like women.

Yet here he is, hovering around, the little mosquito, eyeing the three girls and me, sizing up the situation. And suddenly, with a flourish, he alights.

"Hi guys."

I level my gaze at him, "Michael..."

Mosquito boy leans into me abruptly, and in a nasal, ex-aggerated stage whisper—purposely loud enough for my nearby girl to hear—he says, "What are you doing, man? You trying to pick up a fat chick? She's faaaat!" And just like that—before I can react—with a self-congratulatory half-laugh, half-grunt, he buzzes off through the crowd.

I am stunned. I immediately look down at the girl beside me—my nearby girl, my engaged and engaging girl—and I see her face fall, ever so imperceptibly fall. She recovers at once, looks up at me, and smiles.

And my heart breaks.

Yes, it's true that she is fat. And yes, it is obvious to all. She knows it, I know it, her girlfriends know it, Michael, the little prick, could see it. I look again at the face of my nearby girl, this wonderful, kind, voluptuous girl, who has graced my life for the past fifteen minutes.

And my heart breaks.

Once upon a time, she was someone's little girl. No father ever looked down at his little girl, sleeping in his arms, and wished she would grow up unwanted and rejected and alone someday. Her daddy's quiet wish for her, his secret prayer, was that she would have a good life, that she would be loved and adored, that she would grow up radiant and happy and pretty.

I stand up and take her by the hand. "Let's go for a little walk, shall we?"

And so we do. We circulate and perambulate, arm in arm, throughout the lounge, in and out of various rooms, up and down stairs, everywhere actually. We shake hands and greet people we know and people we don't, we smile, we nod, we dance. We share laughs and a bit of wine, tipping more than we should.

For the rest of the evening, my nearby girl and I are inseparable, insuperable, the life of the party, the funny couple, the gregarious couple, the engaging couple, le beau monde. Everyone is envious of us. Everyone is amazed by her. Everyone sees what a beauty she is.

I make sure of it.

> — The Alabaster Girl, *page 28*

ℰ◯ℛ

There are some who do not understand me and my love affair with women, and because they do not understand, I have been called an entire nursery rhyme of names:

> *A player, a womanizer,*
> *A raconteur, a rake,*
> *A heartbreaker, a lady killer,*
> *A libertine, a fake…*

Ah yes, I have been called all these things, my love, and it makes no difference to me whatsoever. I do not care what others think of me at all. It is not my responsibility that others are comfortable in my presence. I will not withhold my energy or suppress myself in any way. I will not shrink from allegations or blame. I have no need or desire to defend myself. I ask for neither forgiveness nor absolution. These are not confessions, for there is no repentance. While others wring their hands and cast aspersions and fingers at me, crying out *J'accuse!*—I sit quietly and look them straight in the eye.

Women are my greatest defenders. They have always been and always will be. The villagers might chase after me with pitchforks and torches in the middle of the night, but there are no women in their midst. Why? Because women know the truth. Women recognize me for who I am and they quietly embrace me. Suspicion falls away and they sheathe their blades, for I am on their side.

Women accept that I am not like other men, and because I am not, they open everything to me—their hearts, their minds, their bodies. They allow me liberties not afforded to other men. Other men are made to prove the sincerity of their intentions through a series of dinner dates and hoops and subliminal tests, while I am simply allowed to pass. That's the way it is, and the way it has always been throughout the ages. My kind is ancient, created by women, all women.

I am a lover. I love. I am loved. I am a friend to women, a believer in women, a student of women. I am the one who doesn't stay, I am the one who reignites passion, I am the recipient of the gifts of careless men. I am the greatest listener a woman has ever known.

I exist because of men, not because of any capriciousness of women. I exist because men no longer seduce their women, because they no longer seduce their wives. This is why the women they love, love me. Women understand that passion is essential to their lives and they will seek it out and they will find it, whatever the cost. So my kind is necessary and has always been necessary, like a floor trader keeping the market liquid.

ஒ⊘

But you are a *seducer*, some will say. Yes, well… aren't we all? At what point did that become a term of accusation? Is not every interaction in life, in essence, a seduction? Who seduces? Who is seduced? Is it me? Or is it her? Can we ever know? As Yeats described it, "O body swayed to music, O brightening glance, How can we know the dancer from the dance?" We are all the dancer. We are all the dance.

So yes, I am a seducer. And what of it? What is this awareness that I have, this intuition? Is it possible to use the power of seduction for good and not for evil? Is it possible to seduce without manipulating? Is it possible to put myself forward as my true self—truly authentic, truly passionate, truly desirous—and still be loved for it? Am I allowed to present to the world the full sexual manifestation of myself? Or must I hide my true nature, dial it down? If I am being my true self, is it my fault if a woman falls in love with me? And then is it my fault if her man feels betrayed? Where is the fine line of intimacy between a man and a woman—before it tips over into a physical act? How far do you push it? What is the nature of this power? What is gained? What is lost? What is next? These questions fuel my entire life journey.

Hylas and the Nymphs, Odysseus and the Sirens, me and the women of the world… what am I supposed to do? I have no choice. I am a *slave* to my love of women, willingly bound. Just look—*look!*—at the arabesque of light that surrounds and illuminates women of all ages. How can one not be forever transfixed by such shimmering luminance? Am I the seducer? Or am I the seduced? Is it possible to cast a spell when you are under one yourself?

Of one thing I am certain: one can never be a seducer of women if one is not seduced *by* women. To seduce, one must be forever seduced. There is no other way. Oh, to be seduced, caught up! This is the thrill of life, of living! And I am not alone in my helpless fascination. From Casanova: "I don't conquer. I submit." From Camus:

"I don't seduce. I surrender." So yes, I am the seducer. But more than that, I am the *seducer seduced*.

෨◌෭

Here you stand before me in my apartment in Kiev in your best red dress and your best pearl earrings and your best bright makeup, presenting yourself to me, giving to me everything of you that you can, wanting so desperately to find a good man, a good husband. You are so radiant, so honest, so present here with me, and it shakes me to my core.

We were out late last night so I know how tired you are tonight, how completely exhausted you are, how you just traveled all the way across this great city to see me again at this crazy, late hour, how you had to work at two jobs today because it is necessary to do so if you are to survive, and how you have to get up so early in the morning to do it all over again tomorrow.

Yet you never once complain or show how weary you really are. You are remarkable. When I mention this to you, how completely exhausted you must be, you hold your head high, smiling and bright, honest and proud, and you look at me with steady, clear eyes. We are used to it here, you say. All women work two jobs. We have no choice.

What a glorious woman you are! What a magnificent Ukrainian princess! Other men, encountering you, see a girl dressed to party; and they straighten their ties and smooth back their hair, hoping to score, because they think the reason you are so wonderfully arranged is to present the possibility of sex, if they play their cards right.

But yours is not the casual, trifling, hook-up mentality of men and women in the West. It is so much more than that for you, and I see the truth in your eyes. I see the real you. There is no guile in you. This is serious for you, almost life-and-death serious, as it is for a lot of women in Ukraine.

You are the beauty queen, the queen of beauty, in a land

flowing with milk and honey and impossibly beautiful women, but you know that it is just a matter of time before advancing age catches up to you, betrays you, that impetuous, impertinent wave crashing over you, pummeling down upon your striking beauty, the only currency you have ever known, crashing it into the sand, with a new wave of pretty, younger women right behind you, stretching along the shore for as far as the eye can see, eroding and smoothing away every trace of what you once were.

You stand before me, knowing that you can't do it anymore, and I can see that in your smiling eyes. I can't shake the feeling that you consider me to be your last chance at real happiness before you give up and become some boring, foreign banker's wife. It takes my breath away, and I so love you, Natalya. Wow, I adore you, girl.

— The Alabaster Girl, *page 31*

„кё

The word "seduction" causes us to flinch. We remove our glasses and, looking down, wipe the lenses, inspect them with furrowed brow, then wipe some more… seduction, we say, no, not good, not good. We toss the word seduction onto the same trash heap as words like manipulation, guile, and deceit. But seduction is a wonderful word. It needs to be rescued, redeemed, dusted off, and placed back upon the shelf, under glass and well-lit.

Dictionaries have two definitions for the word seduction. One: *the act of leading astray.* Two: *something that attracts or charms.* Have we forgotten that second definition, my love? For there is a quiet beauty in the notion of seduction as something that attracts or charms.

Seduction is not manipulation. It is not base trickery or uncouth deceit. It has nothing to do with getting you to do what you don't want to do. It allows you to do what you already want to do. It smooths the path, picks up the stones, lays down a cloak before you in the mud.

Seduction leads the holy crusade against the creeping compromise of mediocrity, because seduction is honest. Seduction will save us from our sins against beauty, because seduction is our real selves shining. To be seduced is to be amazed, caught up, transformed. It is the ultimate calling of our hearts, the only true romance. And we are missing it on the earth, in all our relationships, in our entire lives. We are missing the seduction of our women, the seduction of our wives, the seduction of ourselves, the seduction of our very souls.

ಬಂಡಾ

The number one genre of books sold in the world today is romance. And why is this? Because women everywhere are no longer seduced by men. Because men no longer seduce their wives. Because we settle. We settle in our careers, in our relationships, in all aspects of our lives. We color everything beige and we call it good enough.

Women everywhere are asking, "Where are the real men?" And the men are over here in the corner with their beige careers, their beige relationships, and their beige attempts at love-making, saying, "Oh well, it's good enough." This is how we live our lives, somnambulating, devoid of any real passion, any real seduction, any real romance, any real love.

Women are complicit in their own seduction. They don't need convincing. There's a yearning in the heart of woman that is rarely addressed. They want to be seduced and seduced well, to be caught up in a whirlwind, a romance, an intrigue.

Every woman deserves a lover. A woman with a lover is transformed. A woman with a lover is more beautiful than she has ever been and more beautiful than she will ever be. A woman with a lover is always youthful and pretty, no matter her age. Everything about her—her countenance, her complexion, her composure—is more alive, more bright. Her face shines, her step is light. There is something marvelous about her and no one is quite sure just what it is. They can't quite put their finger on it. Oh, but they *all* can see it. A blossomed woman draws the gaze of every woman and every man as she walks along the street.

Women are waiting to be seduced again, to feel something, anything, for men to show up as men, for men to rediscover their role in the dance of life. Women are secretly cheering for men, wanting them to be excellent, wanting men to know that they are on their side. Please be successful with us! Be excellent with us, woo us, seduce us, make us believe again!

Women want to be generous to men, and they are—they are massively generous to men who love women, who delight in their desires. Women give. There is no need to take. There is no need for conquering or controlling. This is another thing that most men don't understand. It is not man against woman. It is the two of them together against the world.

ಬಿೂಲ

Seduction is a dance, an ancient dance, a timeless dance, a dancing in the moment. That's what it is. Men and women dancing together as they always have, entangled for all of time in joy and heartbreak and ecstasy and hope. It is a dance of clarity, of honest communication and the intricacies of sub-communication. It transcends age, race, everything. It is intuition as an art form. It is ease and delight. It is curiosity. It is gratitude. It is a welcomed hint of danger. It is unrepentant, direct, overt, audacious. It is subtle and elegant. It is joyous, charged, electric, rushing, magnetic, subdued, restrained, intimate, respectful. It is the love of man for woman, the love of woman for man, the love of ourselves, and the love of life. It is the culmination of all things good: the masculine, the feminine, the divine, everything coalesced, abundant, and in perfect form. Yes, seduction is a dance, a luscious, effusive, sensual, sexual, never-ceasing, sacred dance. I am man. You are woman. Talk to me. Tell me things.

Think of the tango. The dance of strangers. Is this dance not the very embodiment of seduction? Would we say it is composed of manipulation and lies? No, we would say that the tango is as honest and passionate and broken and beautiful as anything in the whole of our experience.

Tango is intimacy, intimacy between a man and a woman, intimacy in the way we used to use that word. A man and a woman aligned, synchronized, charged, so close together and yet so respectfully distant, without needing to fall over the edge every time.

Tango is entire. It contains everything, all the secrets. The man leading, hands high, confident high, and the woman serene, feeling everything, eyes closed. For three minutes, that woman is his and his alone. For three minutes, that man holds her dreams—and everyone else be damned.

Tango is life. All other dances are entertainment. If a man wants to know how a woman should be experienced, the tango is all he needs. Even a cursory spectator experience will teach him more than all the books and dating advice in the world.

ഇൻൽ

You come to see me every day, bringing everything of you to me—your love of cooking, your love of good coffee, your love of dancing, your love of painting and art—you bring it all, everything of you, into my presence, every day, laid at my feet.

You show up before me shining, a true beauty, beautiful in my presence... simply because I asked for it.

Ours was a meeting of minds. You, an exotic dancer, an expert at manipulating men, at exploiting them, at using all the nuances of feminine wiles at your disposal, and knowing just how fundamentally weak and pliant men can be in the wake of a resplendent female body.

You approached me that night in the same way you had approached all others before me, and I looked you in the eye as you stood before me and quietly said to you, "I am not like other men."

You sat beside me then, silent, like a bird on a branch in the rain, and I looked at you and you looked at me and we stayed like that for a long time, without a word, the layers melting away.

"I understand your heart," I said to you, and you believed me immediately in the midst of all that crushed velvet and those crimson lights, and you cried a little, and you told me everything, all your stories, all your hurts, all your abandonments, all your betrayals, through all of your life, and how you no longer believed.

And I, because I understood your heart, said the only thing I could say, "I am right here with you and I hear every word you are saying. Yes, you have been hurt and yes, you have been abandoned and yes, you have been lied to and yes, you have been betrayed. But not here. Not with me. Not in the presence of me. Not ever. Outside of us, sure, be mistrustful of men if you must, be wary of men, but not here. Look into my eyes, sweet girl. I don't even know you, I'm leaving Austin in about a month, and I may never see you again. But if I ever do see you again, understand this: I will only see you as maximally beautiful. I will only see you in beauty, from now and forever into the future, and because I do, you will feel beautiful, like the most beautiful woman in the world, infinitely lovely again. This is my invitation, my promise to you. You are beautiful. Never forget it. And so... show up that way. Show up beautiful before me, as the beauty I see."

And here you are now, weeks later, coming to see me every day... in a little sun-dress, absolutely radiant and absolutely lovely. Beautiful for me.

Simply because I asked for it.

— The Alabaster Girl, *page 33*

ഇൗരു

Society heaps a deserved measure of reprobation upon so-called pickup artists and one-night-stand cowboys, those who are only looking to score. This makes sense to me, for these men are taking something ineffable from women, and giving nothing in return. They are hit-men, contract lovers, a single shot to the head and they disappear into the night.

A pickup artist is out to win, to conquer, to take. He has one goal in mind: to get laid. Little consideration is given to his chosen "target," for she is interchangeable, just another pawn in his game. Actually having a relationship with a woman? Well, they just haven't thought that far ahead. Pickup artists are like dogs chasing cars: they wouldn't have a clue what to do with one if they caught it.

Men who fancy themselves to be players are simply takers. Sure, by trial and error, any man can learn a few tricks, can discover ways to get to first base with a girl, can try for second, and maybe even steal third. And maybe a man's definition of success is the *quantity* of women he can bed. But what of it? What then? Has he won? Has he conquered? Is he a man? Is she looking back on her encounter with him and smiling to herself the next morning? Is she going about her day in a haze, gazing dreamily out the window and thinking of him, of them? Is she constantly checking her phone to make sure he didn't try to call and she somehow missed it? Is she inspired, alive, swept up in emotions and possibilities? Is she decorated with gladness, adorned in bliss? Does she speak his name softly to herself, like a sacred incantation? Will she cherish the encounter with him for the rest of her days? If not, then what was the point? Yes, he got laid, but what has he gained?

There is an entire doctrine out there of pushing through a woman's resistance. If the pickup artist's stainless-steel technique is precise enough or his onslaught of words is strong enough or coercive enough or confusing enough, she will eventually "give in" and the "seduction" will be complete. Men of this ilk congratulate themselves on their prowess, at how skillful they were to get another "lay."

This isn't seduction. This is psychological warfare, wearing down a girl's resistance until she is bone-weary and it is easier to give in than to continue to resist. Where is her delight in all of this? Where is her breathless excitement? Where is her chance to wake up in the morning beside him all happy and shy and cuddly?

These men—or let's call them what they are: boys—don't care about any of this. They trample about all over the place, like a field they deprive of vital nutrients, scorched earth, taking advantage of a woman's openness. She is led to believe one thing and discovers another. And when it happens, she is saddened a little more and her belief in men dies a little more. These *soi-disant* ladies-men play with emotions, play with hearts, play little boy games. They manipulate endlessly and they end up hurting hopes and muddying the waters for the rest of us.

A real man *never* takes. His only desire is to share, to inspire, to beautify the experiences of himself and everyone around him. His ecstasy is derived solely from her ecstasy. If she doesn't feel like a queen, he doesn't feel like a king. A boy makes his girlfriend jealous of other women. A man makes other women jealous of his girl.

A real man is not motivated by quantity, scratching triumphant the number of his conquests on the bedpost. His motivation is quality, not quantity. He believes that all women deserve passion. And he knows they are not getting it from the men they are involved with. By seeking beauty in women, he corrects this imbalance, creating a kind of poetry with her, a connection, a magnetic attraction that is impossible for either of them to ignore or forget. He has love affairs, yes, but never conquests.

We are responsible for our impact. When a woman trusts a man enough to open her body, her emotions, and her heart to him, well…

that is a profound thing. That is something that can never be taken lightly. She has entrusted him, in a way, with her soul. She has said to him, I give to you a part of myself. A romance artist will cradle her heart-song and her emotions in his hands, holding her up to the sky, setting her ever so gently upon a cloud, ready to catch her if she falls. He dare not let her fall! For he will damage her heart and her future dealings with men, and she trusts him not to. There is something sacred here.

Some might infer from my words that women are frothy, emotional creatures that need saving, and if so, they are spectacularly missing the point. Women don't need saving. Not by me or anybody else. Women are remarkably resilient. They simply want to be in the presence of men who see them as equals, who see them as lovely, who are authentic, who don't play games, who represent something—*anything!* Men who stand on this earth as men. Romance artists. Dance partners. Lovers of women. Real men.

ഇരു

There have been countless times when I am talking to a pretty girl and I know I can have her in my bed. I can see it in her eyes, in the way she touches her neck, in the way she plays with her hair. I can feel it in the air. All I have to say is one or two little words and she is mine, and yet… I just shake her hand and smile and tell her it was nice to meet her and I get the hell away.

Why do I turn away from her? I don't know. Sometimes, I just can't be bothered, I guess. I look into her eyes, and there is no mystery there. It's like I've been there before, if you know what I mean… like I already know everything about her, the way she is, the way it will be with her. I know, just by looking into her eyes and observing the way she carries herself, exactly how she will feel in my hands, exactly how she will smell, exactly how she will taste… for I have been there before, I have smelled her before, I have tasted her before. I have heard her stories a thousand times on other lips. I have already touched her body in every conceivable way. I already know what positions she prefers. I already know if she will be animated in bed or if she will just lie there on her back and starfish. I look at her and… well, she is so sweet and she is so kind and I have nothing for her, nothing to give to her, no words to say to her. I can't even take one step toward her. It's like the restaurant is open and I am hungry and I have money but I just can't be bothered to go inside.

Shakespeare wrote, "She's beautiful, and therefore to be wooed. She is a woman, and therefore to be won." What more can I say? Is that not enough motivation and reason right there? And yet I turn away. Spinoza suggested that a hatchet, when not in the hands of a carpenter, ceases to be a hatchet. It is only a hatchet—imbued with "hachet-ness"—in its utility as a hatchet. What does that make me? What kind of a lover turns away from women? What kind of a womanizer doesn't womanize? What am I to do? Am I just bored? Ah, who knows? We never notice a spoon until it is bent.

A wise woman once said to me, "The only thing that gets you hard these days is your purpose." Oh beautiful, wise woman. It's so true. I am too caught up in my relentless pursuit of beauty to ever dabble. Look away, look away from mediocrity, for it is catching!

☙❧

I see you there across the room, through the crowd. My friend is saying something to me and other women flow by, but oh, let him talk, and oh, let them flow, for all is ignored. I only see you.

These are the moments I live for. Snapshots of beauty, swatches of grace…

A stare without staring. A smile and a nod to my friend. Slowly it dawns on him that I am not listening to him in the slightest, nor shall I. He stops talking and follows my gaze, to see what I see. And what I see is you, my lustrous-eyed lover… oh yes I do.

*Lover? How can we be lovers? After all, we haven't even
met! Yes well...*

*And at this exact same moment in time, as if summoned,
you glance in my direction, a dreamy wandering softness,
a sweeping pass across the room and me, and then... a
pause... and back to me. One one thousand, two one thousand, and now down and away. Yes, you see me too, my
scintillating Titian goddess... and now you know.*
—The Alabaster Girl, *page 35*

છાલ્સ

Women have a sense of abundance when it comes to sex. A woman
can walk into a bar or a lounge and be reasonably assured that *someone* there would agree to go home with her. Most men do not have
this sense of sexual availability, this sense of abundance. They *hope*
it might happen. This is why they call it "getting lucky," because
they are surprised most of the time when it happens.

Because women can have sex whenever they want, because they
can have that guy and that guy and that guy, they tend to look
for something different, something beyond the crowd. They look
for, and rarely find, a man of excellence, and an experience that is
transcendent, connected, meaningful.

What's interesting is that the more sexual abundance a man has, the
more he becomes like a woman. He begins to view the world with
the same weary, yearning eyes of a woman. A simple sexual experience is always an option, and because it is always an option, it is
no longer an option. He sees women all around, and yet he, like a
woman, looks for something more.

I also find it interesting that a woman will not have sex with someone
she doesn't like. A surprisingly large percentage of men will. A man
might find a woman's personality grating or her attitude insipid, but
if he is horny enough, and no one will ever know, ah... why not?

Isn't the desire for a one-night stand essentially a desire for mediocrity? Because if the other really is that great, wouldn't we want to see them again? If I am interested enough in a woman to want her in my bed, then I will *want* to see her again. I have no desire to become physical with a woman if I can't experience her fully. I want to delight in her aspect, in her mind—not just her body. I don't want or need "just sex." I've been there many times before and the landscape can be, at times, bland and boring. Instead, I need to commit to her and the experience freely, entirely, without suppressing myself in any way—even if it is only for one night.

Sex with a random woman I don't really care about, well, isn't that just glorified masturbation? As Hunter S. Thompson wrote, "Sex without love is just as hollow and ridiculous as love without sex." A one-night stand is just plain old gymnastics, a workout, hanging onto the ceiling fan and spinning around and all that. And then what? Wake up in the morning with the overwhelming urge to chew my arm off like the proverbial coyote in a trap rather than wake her up? The walk of shame? No, not for me. Might as well go to bed with a magazine.

My constancy is the highest constancy. I am faithful above all men. Others might think I am afraid of commitment, but my commitment is the loftiest commitment. Because some men don't want a commitment, they only seek out one-night stands. For me, the opposite is true. Because I don't want a commitment, I stay *away* from one-night stands. For what shall I do with her tomorrow? I can't just flounce away like nothing happened.

Ah, who am I kidding? If a woman is sweet and kind and she crawls into my bed, well hey, everybody stand back… I am still a gunslinger. I have only one gear: forward, and only one speed: fast. I love the succulence of a woman's body more than just about anything in this world. I never meditate to recharge; women are my meditation. A woman's body is a sacred temple that I have worshiped at for years, a place of meditation that quiets my soul and infuses my heart with clarity and joy. But I won't expend any effort whatsoever to try to pick her up or convince her or chase her down just to get in her pants.

I understand, of course, that sometimes men and women just want to have a physical fling with no strings attached, recreational sex, a little fun with no emotional attachment. In a perfect world, everything is clearly implied and clearly inferred. There is an understanding and everyone knows the score. But it is one thing to have a one-night stand. It is another thing to spend a night together.

A single night and nothing more. Oh, but that's not a one-night stand. Not at all. It's just that sometimes the twin villainy of logistics and circumstances whirl us away from each other before we are ready to be whirled away from each other. Ah, but the time with her was real… as real as any there ever was, an exhilarating and momentous celebration, a memorable occasion, and although we would have loved to continue the dance with each other, it just wasn't meant to be.

Oh, how many moments glisten in my memory like jewels in a tiara, nights with women who possess that rare and wonderful feminine spirit that I adore. So yes, a woman who inspires me and makes me laugh, whose mind is a delight to me, whose spirit stirs and excites me, who smells absolutely wonderful? I want her… right then and there.

I have known the perfumed pillow of many a pretty girl, the kind of girl that men desire. Now I look for something more, something behind the eyes. The way she looks to me, the smell of her hair, and the curve of her body, are all part of the attraction, of course, but her spirit, her mind, her mystique… oh, that is another level completely. I need to desire her mind as much as her body… no, even *more* than her body. I need to desire her very essence.

There is a light that shines from within certain women, a nurturing light that washes over the hearts of men, cleansing them, baptizing them in a way. In her presence, all is forgiven. What calm radiance! What a gift of grace!

This is the only thing I desire from a woman, the only thing that makes me pause, the only thing that makes me look at her and wonder what is possible with her. It has nothing to do with her outward appearance and everything to do with her transcendent, iridescent, natural beauty. When I encounter a woman like this, I love her so much; I would do anything for her. Well... almost anything.

೩೦೦೪

You understood no English and I no Portuguese and I muddled along in Spanish which helped not at all and you smiled in golden sunlight before me on the sand.

And you danced and laughed before me with parted lips and parted legs and you feathered a long and silken cloth through your fingers and around your lissome waist and into the air and around and around like a ballerina. And the sun of Ipanema smiled down proud upon us and bathed us like children and beamed upon us, as if she loved it.

Do you remember that day and night of dreams, Valéria?

You love your country with an incandescent longing, in the way that all Brazilians do, and I could see it in the way you breathed and moved and touched the earth that day, like you couldn't get enough of it and you wanted to consume it and it amazes me still, your fierce love of Brazil, and it seems to me that Brazilians are the greatest patriots in all the world. Rich, poor, saint, thief, it doesn't matter... they all love their country so much.

And sunrise and sunset converge and day and night are one and the people worship their sun and the land of bossa nova and bunda settles into its beloved and raucous rhythm.

I watched as you danced before me on the sand, with your caramel skin and adamantine eyes and I, too, wanted to consume you and everything around me and in Brazil.

And every now and then, all these years later, this image of you in the sun suffuses upon my picturesque reverie.

I trip through my dreams toward you and your several

secret smiles...

I will never forget the moment when the sun began to set that day, how in the precise instant that it first knelt to kiss the horizon, everything paused—the sea, the sand, the lovers, the sky—and all stood and faced toward the benevolent sun setting, and the decades-old ritual began anew, with the entire beach clapping and cheering and thanking the sun, grateful for the day and the warmth and the goodness bestowed. And you, oh daughter of Brazil, dishevelled and barefoot and wild and free, dancing beside the opalescent ocean, in that golden moment with your golden hair, around and around and into the air like a slow-motion dream.

Yes... that was a pretty moment...

Mellifluous time flow over me and cleanse me of her smile.

A pretty moment indeed...

Surround me with your dulcet calm, and hide me for a while.

— The Alabaster Girl, *page 38*

ജ്ഞ

There is nothing a woman can do or say that will make me stay. Women want promises of promises and I am not a promise of anything. You want to buy my heart but it is already sold. In order to go out with you, I would have to break up with *me*. And oh, I am too caught up in my own ridiculous notions of freedom and romance and adventure.

Even though I have been looking for you all my life, my love, in everything and in every place, no matter how close I come to you, no matter how many times I find you, I cannot stay. No matter how much I desire you, no matter how much my heart yearns for you, ah, my dear, my darling one... I must go. And I will adore you for the rest of my days.

The writer Evelyn Underhill described it like this, "He goes because he must, as Galahad went towards the Grail, knowing that for those who can live it, this alone is life." Do you feel the weight of that, my love? The truth of that? Maybe you will never understand, but this is my truth. I go because I must. Something out there calls to me, something ineffable, and that call is far more important to me than any desire for you. My heart is caught up in a myriad of possibilities and impossibilities. I must go away upon the sea.

Is it possible to completely and utterly love someone even though you know it will end, and even though you know there will be others? A woman stroking my hair is profound, yes, but can just about anyone do it? Ah, who knows? It is a wonderful thing to encounter a great desire that is devoid of neediness. I think profundity has its own completion point, which does not require permanence. I don't know—maybe it isn't possible to teach that to a woman. Maybe she has to experience it for herself.

The future is always great intentions and nothing more. The only commitment I can honestly give is to be fully present, fully engaged, fully real, a promise to stay true to myself and to *never* misrepresent. This, my love, is the only way a relationship can last.

There are those who will analyze what I say and do. It is obvious, they will say. He is the little boy lost, they will say. He is seeking unconditional love from women, they will say. He is seeking approval from mother, they will say. He wants to be the charming boy who can do no wrong, they will say.

I don't mind. Go ahead and categorize me, figure me out, analyze away. Assign me my Jungian archetype. I accept. Or create for me a new one, perhaps, for what am I really? A King? A Warrior? A Wizard? A Lover? Who knows? Who cares? I am just laying it out there, presenting the light I have been given, flatly, without comment. Well, actually… with a great deal of comment.

Will this ever change? Will I ever just someday… stay? Sure, why not? I morph. I change. But not because of the opinions of others. I will never artificially attempt to correct some supposed imbalance in my soul just to align myself with society. I hearken to criticism, but blithely ignore judgment. I err consistently on the side of optimism. I love life. I love women. I love love. This is the only nobility of my character. For everything else, bind me to the mast and administer the lash. I can take it.

ഇൠ

What kind of man does not stay, my love? Let us simplify and suppose there are two kinds. The first kind is the man who simply will not commit because of his fears—fears of intimacy, of rejection, of showing his true self. That sort of thing. He doesn't mean to hurt a woman. In fact, he doesn't mean to run away at all. He really does enter the relationship with the best of intentions. But when the intimacy that is required and the opening of his heart that is required overwhelm him, he runs away. Or he sabotages the relationship, attacking it internally, until she finally leaves him. Even though he doesn't know it, this man is afraid of commitment and everything that commitment implies in our spectacularly uncommitted era. He's not a bad guy. He's sincere but misguided. And now she is sad and frustrated and feels like she wasted all that time in her life and must begin all over again.

The second kind of man is a man who plays with her heart. He has his fun with no regard for her. He promises all kinds of things, then runs away, laughing. Though he never tells her, he has no intention of staying or giving of himself in any way. Instead, he takes. He manipulates. He is not truthful, either to himself or to her. He has no core strength, no masculinity, no conviction, and no empathy. In fact, he is *afraid* of women. He may not even like them. He simply uses them in an attempt to validate himself, to show off to other men, to prove something to himself and to the world. He uses them, tires of them, then dumps them when something better comes along. This man dishonors all men. He is a coward. His failure as a man is complete. And now she is angry at him and disgusted with herself that she fell for it all over again.

I am simplifying, as I always do, a complex concept. But I think we can agree that society pretty much lumps all men who do not stay into the category of "cad." These men are examined under a microscope and automatically and immediately proclaimed to have a fear of commitment. After all, they say, if a man is not afraid, then surely he will commit to a woman. An unafraid man will *want* to stay.

But is this true in every case? Can we imagine another perspective that might be equally true? Is there perhaps a *third* kind of man who does not stay? For what shall we do with all the iconoclasts, the dreamers, and the treasure hunters of the world? The men who are not part of the madding crowd?

Imagine the heart of a man like this, my love. He goes because he must, because he is caught up in something greater, something ineluctable, something wondrous that calls his name, something that draws him ever onward to all his magnificent horizons. Simply stated, he *must* go. So now... is this a bad thing? Is it possible that his love of adventure and freedom is simply stronger, more ebullient, more exhilarating, and more alive, than any desire to stay? Could it be that this man has no fear of commitment at all? Could it be that his commitment is the highest form of commitment—a commitment to the truth that is his truth? Could it be that a woman knows in her heart that, contrary to other men, he will *never* leave her? Even if he must go?

A true lover of women never misrepresents. He never takes. He only shares—he shares his heart with her fully, he shares his vulnerability with her fully, he shares a relationship with her that transcends all relationships she has ever had with other men. It is honest, pure, giving, and passionate. His desire to stay is strong but his desire to go is stronger. He must go, for this is his full truth, his full heart, his full vulnerability. He is not running away at all. He believes in her, he loves her. But he must go. He knows that if he stays, if he quiets his spirit for her, if he calms the warrior in him, it will slowly kill his heart, kill the light in his eyes, and just as surely, kill her desire for him. And though she won't admit it, in her heart she knows this as well. For this is the very thing she loves about him.

A woman wants it both ways. This is what leads to all the heart-rending. She is attracted to the valiant, exciting, feral heart of the adventurer, but once she catches hold of him, she tries to tame him, domesticate him, settle him down, and once he is stuffed and mounted, she has inadvertently quieted the very essence in him she loves the most.

A woman can never change a real man. He can only change of his own volition. He can only change because he *chooses* it, because he looks at her and thinks, "yes, this is where my heart lies." She can, however, change a weak man; he will change just to please her, because he is too insipid or too timid or too bland to do anything else. Just go with the flow.

Creeping compromise. We are not really committed to our relationships at all. We climb into the nearest boat simply because we are tired of paddling alone. We loll around in the doldrums, looking for a clean way out, a better boat, for the wind to pick up. Even sexual intercourse is domesticated, negotiated, negated, scheduled, compromised, with the whole sordid affair dwindling away into nothingness. Sexual desire giving way to a kind of sexual despair.

Man was once wild and free, was a lover, a fighter, a rocker. Woman sets out to tame him and the moment she succeeds, she resents him. The truth is, women love the spirit of the untamed stallion. They love to see him run free—just not too far. They want him to love the smell of the grass and the clover—but in this nice, fenced-in area. They want him to prance and caper with easy stride, yes!—but over *here*.

No woman wants a dispirited, broke-back horse plodding along behind her on a string. She wants him to be tamed, yes, but not broken. She wants him to love to be near her always, but to never lose the Spirit of the West in his soul.

৩৩৪

We think that women have a monopoly on the desire for romance, but it's not just the women. Why do men do anything in this world? Why do they build the Taj Mahal? Why do they go to sea? Why do they write a sonata? Why do they cry over a painting? Given the myriad of choices, why do they choose this pair of shoes rather than that pair of shoes? Why do they do any of these things? For fame? For money? For power? No, they do it all for romance. Which is to say, they do it for their dreams, for relevance in their lives, for meaning. Locke said, "Beasts abstract not." In other words, humans are the only romantic ones.

We are all starved for romance, for seduction, for passion. We want it so badly that it makes us cry. Oh, how we yearn for a romantic path through our days, for relevance in our lives, for our lives to have an impact. Our hearts ache to be caught up in something greater than ourselves, to be seduced, to seduce ourselves and others, to desire something—*anything!*—so much that we would die for it.

This is the essence of romance. And we try so hard to find it. We scatter about this earth, to every wind, pursuing an infinite number of endeavors, pursuing fulfillment of the romantic yearnings of our hearts, getting lost in whims, choosing this pair of shoes rather than that pair of shoes. We are all starved for romance. It is the fight of our lives.

And where is it? Where is romance? Where is seduction? Where is passion? Where are men of grace and purpose? Why do men apologize for being men? Where is the spirit of men? Where are the treasure hunters, the adventurers, the heroes? Where are the real men? These are the questions women everywhere are asking, and men are not.

We used to believe in adventure, we dreamed of treasure as boys, of rescuing the princess, did we not? And where is it today? Our desire for adventure has been replaced with obligations. Our desire for treasure has been replaced with the accumulation of needless things. Our excitement and audacity have been replaced with hesitation and apologies. Our fun and play have been replaced with cynicism and manipulation. Our masculine edge has been replaced with a cloying niceness. It's like we're not even the protagonists of our own story anymore.

And the women? Whatever happened to grace? Lost in the darkness, I'm afraid. Everywhere are women in short skirts and perfect outfits and perfect makeup, dancing and prancing on tables and runways. We see female shapes and forms all around us, yet so little femininity. Hair, lips, and breasts can all be purchased, but that's not femininity—that's renovations. Where is the essence and the tenderness of the feminine? Where are the beauties, the courtesans, the muses, the nurturers, strong and caring, lovely and radiant?

In our culture, true femininity and true masculinity are as rare as ghost orchids. We are completely uneducated about our greatest gifts: our authenticity, our passion, our romantic hearts.

three

The Way of Discovery

I see myself in pictures four
I am not like that anymore

A journey on a train. An interstitial fragment of time between the station we left behind and the station yet to come—between cradle and grave, really. Where is this train going? Where, for that matter, does any train go? Who knows? Who knows? As long as it goes.

Some would say that it is easy for you, she said.

Easy in what way?

That you're a natural.

A natural? Yes, I've heard that, but what does that mean?

It means you were born with it.

No one is ever born with it. Every man who is good with women is good with women because he has learned it. Am I a natural? Well, sure... as natural as any man who has ever taken the time to learn about women, I suppose.

So it can be learned?

Of course it can be learned. But not like most men think. It is simple but not easy. It takes a lifetime of learning.

But your reputation precedes you. You can't blame men for thinking it is easier for you than for them.

The only difference between me and other men is that I've been thinking about these things for a lot longer. That's it. Some men, noticing my constant proximity to women, think I have some magical ability, that I was born gifted with women, that I jumped out of my mother's womb and started kissing all the nurses. They work themselves into a lather trying to figure me out. "Hey," they say, "it's easy for him. He's a natural. He was born with it. He can walk into a bar and take any girl home. He's slept with hundreds of women. No, thousands, I bet! He has multiple girls, one for each day! Girls in every city! A whole harem of girls! And I'm sure he has threesomes—or even *moresomes*—with girls, guys, everything. A perpetual orgy!"

Is any of that true?

Well, for one thing, I've never been with any guys.

Why not?

Not my style. Only one penis per fantasy, thank you very much. The last thing I am interested in is a sword fight!

And the rest of the allegations?

Ah, sweet girl, I have nothing to prove.

All of the greatest stories of history involve journey. This is because every journey is, in essence, a journey into oneself, into the soul. The only important question to ask is this: Is it a journey from chaos to order… or from order to chaos? Because it's always one or the other.

Have you always loved women?

More than anything else in the entire world. I've never had any other hobbies. I absolutely *love* women. Always have, always will.

But surely lots of men love women.

True, but not like this. Everything I've ever said or done in my life has been in the context of women. I remember once being asked by some friends to join them on an epic three-week fishing expedition off the coast of Vancouver Island. "We will cast nets," they cried out, "and grow beards and rage against the elements!" And my first thought was, "Yes! Yes! Fantastic!" And my next thought was, "Uh, wait… there will be no women out there…"

And did you go?

No.

ഇൻൽ

My story is as simple and common as flowers in a field. I have distant memories of me as a little boy, when it was good, and then when it wasn't so good. Like so many of us, I wasn't pushed out of the nest when I had enough feathers and was old enough to fly. Instead, I tumbled out of the nest too early when the nest simply fell apart. And this I did not understand.

At five years old, I was disconnected from my father, my mother, my brothers and sisters, and thrust alone into the bowels of an egregious system of foster homes, where I was beaten, where I was not allowed to touch anything, where I was not allowed in certain rooms, where I was locked in dark closets for hours while "the people" went to town. And this I did not understand. I taught myself how to count to a hundred while locked in a closet. There I was, this little boy sitting alone in the dark, and I sort of just figured it out. And I was afraid, so afraid, too afraid to say anything. I never said a word.

After a few years of this neglect and sadness, I was somehow (I'm still not sure what transpired) reunited with my mother and my siblings, and we grew up together in the deep forests of the far north. We were poor. We shared the same clothes. We had no running water. We bathed only once a week, in melted snow, with each of us six kids, one after the other, oldest to youngest (I was in the middle), in the same two inches of increasingly sullen and opaque water.

And there were other things... sinister things. Drunken parties, violence, detritus. Our dogs were shot, our kittens drowned, our horses beaten with two-by-fours. My mother was knocked unconscious before our eyes, hospitalized a time or two, by a succession of men in trucker caps. We, in turn, were whipped into glassy-eyed submission. Yes, my love, I've seen a few things.

And yet, when I think back, when I memory surf, none of these dark things come to mind. I only see the good. For I escaped... escaped

like a dream—a sylvan dream—into the forest. My hyperborean
childhood was magic to me… the summer barefoot days… sneaking
through the incandescent, birch-white forest… creating immense
kingdoms out of rocks and sticks… swimming with my brothers and
sisters in our beloved swimming hole that was, in retrospect, a shallow scum-swamp, teeming with leeches and limb-ensnaring weeds.

Oh, how I loved the forest! I swear to God it's still in my blood.
Adventure! I spent my summers in a tepee, and I can still smell
the pine-smoke. I wore deer-skin moccasins with leather sinews
crisscrossed around my ankles like a legionnaire's sandals. I had a
rabbit fur hat that I wore every single day because I loved it and
because I made it. I caught Dolly Varden trout in the slow-moving
Wolverine River with a willow pole, a simple hook, and a piece
of cheese. I learned what wild plants to eat and how to start a fire
without matches. I made snowshoes out of poplar saplings and twine,
and lean-tos out of spruce boughs and determination. I climbed
mountains and cliffs and crags and trees. I traversed impossibly
swollen rivers on slippery moss-logs like it was nothing, like it was
a carefree, cursory stroll and common. I was brilliant with an ax.
My prized possession was a long-bladed knife, ever present at my
side in a leather sheath that I had made. Yes, I embraced the forest
with all my heart. Oh Canada! I loved it so much. I wanted nothing
else forever and ever.

I laugh when I think about it now because I am such a city-slicker
today, a *soi-disant* sophisticate, cosmopolitan and urbane, gliding
dexterously throughout the cities of the world; no one would ever
guess that I was just some poor, uneducated, snot-nosed *gamin*
from the forest!

∽✄∾

I was at home in the forest but not so much in society. When I finally
emerged as a young man from my poverty-wild childhood into the
vast and modern world, I felt inferior, embarrassed, inadequate. I felt

misplaced and awkward; I had none of the trappings of life—money, education, life-plan—that would tend to make one confident on any level. I had little knowledge of social graces, for I was socially uninstructed. I was about as ready for the world of adults as a twelve-year-old with a milk mustache and his dad's ID.

But oh how I loved girls! I loved them to the "depth and breadth and height my soul could reach," to exaggerate a little and steal a phrase from Miss Browning. I just didn't know how to interact with them. I was spectacularly, how shall I say... *ungifted* with girls in my early years. I would see a pretty girl from a distance and be smitten by her, absolutely sure that I was in love with her—*true* love, mind you—and that she was "the one," only to have her virtually ignore my existence. Not that it took much effort on her part. I was mostly too scared or too shy to approach her on any level anyway. I had no confidence whatsoever, and never once did I believe that I deserved a girl like her or that she would ever want anything to do with me. So, I consistently rejected myself on her behalf, saving her the trouble.

I spent those dismal years as a young man in neediness and despair, constantly love-sick, wishing, hoping, vacillating, and clingy. I was the prototypical nice guy. I was a virgin until relatively late and even then I think she was just taking pity on me. If a girl displayed even the slightest passing interest in me, I was all over her like a cheap suit. I was afraid to lose her, aching for her, one hundred percent available for her, and because of that, of course, she quickly wanted nothing to do with me.

And there were quite a few... Ah yes, it is embarrassing to me now, my love, and painful to relate. I was a marvelous "dater." I was the perfect "boyfriend"—just give me a chance and you will see! I got down on my knees and I promised those girls the world, and when they waved me away with contempt or unfiltered pity, as they invariably did, I begged them to please don't leave me, give me another chance, I'll do anything! Ouch. It still makes me wince. I was so paralyzed by those early interactions. I was so lost and alone.

What changed? Who knows? I spent those early years wandering around, lost and confused, with sporadic, unsuccessful forays into the land of women. I would look in the mirror and wonder why. Why? I loved women so much; why was it so difficult for me to relate to them? Or them to me? Why? Why were my experiences with girls not what I wanted them to be? Why was I so awkward, so clueless? Why was it so hard to be desired by a woman? Why was I so pathologically undesirable? Why was it this way and not another way? *Why?*

At some point, every man needs to stand in front of the mirror, look himself in the eye, and ask himself the big questions, the hard questions, the immense questions. The question I asked myself was this: *Have you ever been a woman's fantasy? If not, why not?*

This, to me, was as profound a thought as any ever posited by the mind of man. Every woman is fantasizing about somebody. Every woman is looking out her window or lying in her bed dreaming about somebody. Was it me? Had it ever been me? Ever? If not, why not? The weight of that thought broke my heart. Because, yes… why not? Every woman is dreaming about *somebody*. Why not me?

There is a magnificent shift that needs to happen, a choice. Anything less is wishes in our pocket. Two thousand years ago, the Jewish scholar, Hillel the Elder, asked a question of the ages, "If not now, when?" Indeed.

I set out to change it, to change everything, to change the way I related to women and the way they related to me. No matter what the cost! I would cast away that erstwhile nice guy of the past.

Epictetus advised: "First say to yourself what you would be; then do what you have to do." I knew exactly what I wanted to be. I decided that I would become *the greatest lover a woman has ever known*. I would become a woman's fantasy. She's dreaming about somebody. It might as well be me.

੪੦୯ଓ

We meet the way I meet most women—through another woman. The scene: rooftop lounge of the Gansevoort Hotel in New York City, three-tiered appetizers, Pinot Gris (straw, pear, delightful!), the city evening blue and warm and vibrating with music; an evening when you just know something magical is going to happen.

We have just started in on this bottle of excellent wine when the two of you arrive, a great-looking couple, full of apologies and introductions. He is dressed in—well, whatever—but you...

You aren't wearing anything exceptional, just a simple dress, elegant, pellucid blue. But the way you wear that simple dress is not simple, the way it dances and shimmers about your body. And the way you smile, beatific, inviting, lips of red, red, red. (Why don't women wear red lipstick anymore?) And the way your dark hair falls, insouciant, upon your shoulders. Yours is the beauty of a wildflower in a remote place, untrammeled and pure. It is all so... startling. That's the best word I can think of to describe the effect that you, splendid girl, have on our little group. We are all startled.

After the requisite introductions and nods and shaken hands, the evening carries on as these evenings do. We order more food. We order more wine. We eat the food. We drink the wine.

At some point, I excuse myself—for no reason at all—and wander onto the vast veranda overlooking this vast city on top of the world, the summer breeze warm and whispering and slow-motion. I lean over the rail for a long time, looking out on the city and taking it all in, unwilling to move until I have absorbed the essence of it all, until I have accepted the meaning of it all, the meaning of you in your simple dress, the meaning of this summer breeze, all warm and dark and slow-motion, the meaning of this sparkling city vista, and me on top of it all.

I turn around after what seems an eternity, lost in thought, the city behind me now, and I lean back, propping myself against the rail, my arms outstretched on each side like I am embracing the whole rooftop lounge and everyone there (and I am). I watch the people glide, neon streaks, angels all of them.

And there you are, in the middle of it all, in the middle of the people, in the middle of the music, still sitting at the little table. You are bewitching and exotic in an unclichéd way, not perfect like the airbrushed cover of a magazine, but there is something about you, something magical, something wondrous, something daring, something more... something more, but what? You are mythic, a mystery. You are Tristan's Isolde, you are Dante's Beatrice, you are Blake's Tyger, burning bright, in the forest of the night. You are lithe before me in your simple dress of pellucid blue and your gypsy necklace and your insouciant hair and your silver hoop earrings, a possessor of quiet beauty, classic beauty, beauty in repose, the luminous kind that steals a bit of your soul.

Oh, what is the plan of the universe? There are moments in time, infinite moments, when God looks down upon you and says, here you go, this is for you, today it is all for you, yes you, six billion on the planet but today is your day, this moment is your moment, when all of life's mysteries are revealed to you and only to you... and look! here is even a soft wind, just for you.

I watch you, smiling and serene and laughing with the others at the table. I watch as other men near the bar, in awe and with great intent, hover on the periphery, angling for an opening to approach you. And I watch your date, poor soul, his paralyzing infatuation so painfully evident, sitting close to you, trying his best to be confident and witty, and scanning your face for approval every time he opens his mouth. I watch how oblivious you are to all this attention from the men that hover around you, and how kind and considerate you are to him, engaging everyone at the table with equanimity and grace.

I watch you and as I do, your eyes find mine and the whole scene pauses and the pause makes me smile because we both know. Your eyes, alive with soft secrets, never leave mine. They speak to me somehow on this warm, blue New York evening, teaching me things about you, ancient things. I discover everything about you in an instant, in this infinite pause as I look into your eyes. I see the way you sleep, with your hair wild about the pillow. I see the way you cry in quiet times when you are sad and lonely (all beautiful girls are secretly lonely). I see the way you clap your hands in delight at simple little gifts. I see all of this as I look into your eyes and from this moment, I know, and you smile to me because yes, I know and you know I know.

Without a word, you stand up from the table, your hapless companion half rising from his chair, unsure if he is supposed to follow, and you walk straight toward me and out onto that vast rooftop balcony. And now it is just the two of us, and here you are, my girl from this moment on, and we turn around together, without words, and look eight stories down and straight out forever upon this great city.

Was it Kundera who suggested that vertigo—the twinge of fear we feel when we look down from a great height—is not the fear of falling; it is, rather, the desire to fall? We are not afraid that we might fall; we are afraid that we might jump. Yes, this seems about right. It is not knowing what we are falling into, yet standing on the very edge anyway, so afraid and yet so willing. We try to reason with ourselves, others warn us to be careful, and all we can do is lean out even further, overwhelmed by love potions and magic. We don't know and yet we exactly know. It is a euphoric loss of sensibility, an exquisite madness that takes over all our senses, and yet it is somehow correct, this vertiginous love-falling.

— The Alabaster Girl, *page 42*

ℬℭ

I realized if I was going to be a woman's fantasy, first I had to find out what her fantasy was, and there was only one person who could tell me that… *her*. I became a student of women, voracious, devoted, dedicated—a voraciousness and devotion and dedication that have never left me. In the same way that I studied and learned the Queen's Gambit opener in chess as a child, I devoted my years to studying and learning the intricacies of the hearts, the minds, and the ways of women.

I made a choice those long years ago to venture into the land of women, and I never left. I have had spectacular successes and spectacular failures in the land of women. George Bernard Shaw said, "A man learns to skate by staggering about making a fool of himself; indeed, he progresses in all things by making a fool of himself." That's exactly what I did. I staggered about like a fool for an egregiously long time. But I stayed. That is the main thing. I stayed and stayed. No matter what, I stayed in the land of women.

Born in me as well, all those years ago, was an intense love of life, a resolution to escape from ordinariness, an immense curiosity about the world and the way it works, and a deep compassion for anyone who is honestly seeking a better way.

Sure, I have other interests… but no, not really. I have dipped my feet in various oceans, I have had a few dangerous escapes, I have touched the face of art, I have shared sublime and esoteric philosophies with sublime and esoteric friends, I mess around with a guitar now and then, and I even jumped out of the sky once, but my only real interest, my only real abiding love, is women. I have never lost my delight and profound adoration for women. All my life, while other men were over there, drinking beer and cheering or cursing at sports or whatever, I was over here engaging with all the women. Sometimes I think I am the greatest student of women the world has ever known.

ഇൻൽ

I am often asked, "What did you read, or what did you discover, or who mentored you in your life, that gave you such an understanding of women? What was your epiphany? What was it that caused you to finally 'get it'?" Well, the truth is, I had none of these things. I had no epiphany. I had no reference points, no seminars, no mentors, no anything. I've never read a self-help book in my life. Nor any books on love or relationships. No, none at all.

Women taught me about women. They have been my only teachers. I have lived all of my days and years in the company and the arms of women, listening to their hopes, their dreams, their stories. I spent every waking moment sitting at the knee of women, as it were, asking a thousand questions, and they whispered their secrets into my ear. All I did was listen.

I have nothing original. Everything I say to men has been stolen from women. My gift is simply the gift of translation. That's all it is, really. Simple translation. I will stand up somewhere, say a few things, and the men will come up to me after and say, "Wow, that was profound. I've never heard anything like that before. I took a ton of notes." Then the women will come up to me and say, "Uh... we've been saying this for years!"

ഇൻൽ

Above all, I am devoted to my own learning. I am an eternal student. I have no answers. No one does. All I have are excellent questions. All I do is describe what I have seen. If a man's heart is sincere, he will see it too. I will give my whole experience, my whole history, my whole heart, to men who are searching and sincere. I will share with them everything I know. Which is not much.

Every day I learn something new about women and the way they weave in and out of the lives of men, like golden threads in a medieval tapestry. Sometimes, I think I know nothing at all, and I sit around and scratch my head like everyone else. Other times, I think I can see just the tiniest pinprick of light through an opaque veil, hinting at the vast, unexplored realm of knowledge that lies beyond, like the stars that only become clear in our peripheral vision. Yet at other times... I know all.

I know the secrets of women, my love. I see them in their natural light. I see them as they really are. I see right through their makeup, their attitudes, their insecurities, their shields. I see the way they cry sometimes when they are lonely in the night and wishing the phone would ring. I see all their hurts, I see all their dreams, I see all their desires. I see it all.

And because I see it all, I am a great friend to women, a great defender of women, a rebel for their illustrious cause. Because I see it all, I believe. I believe in the transcendent beauty of the female spirit, in the magnificent enveloping power of women, in the feminine aura that bathes and cleanses us, in the gift to the world that women both possess and suppress. I believe in women even more than they believe in themselves.

ଽଓଔଓ

Supple, catlike, a natural grace that defies description. Oh, I would love to have, on this evening, a girl like you. What qualities do you possess? I don't know, but put every little detail together and you complete into a dreamy dream, the kind of dream that wakes a man suddenly in the night, inspired and ready to write.

Your friends are sexy, desirable, and all the men here are watching them. But you... you shine... quietly like a distant star, a hidden gem of beauty.

The way you move... the way you move... fixed upon my reverie. All else falls away.

The way you move...

*I have seen it now, beautiful girl... I have seen it now and
my heart is gladdened. I can rest assured, knowing there
are women out there in the world like you. I will stand in a
good way for the rest of my days, knowing this.*
— The Alabaster Girl, *page 45*

෨෬

Can the art of love be learned? Can any man become the kind of
man that women love? Can he learn ways to increase his aura, his
charm, his confidence, his attractiveness quotient with women? Can
he invent for himself an exciting and new *joie de vivre* that makes
him irresistible to women? Can he learn to live a life that is passionate, compelling, admired and desired? Sure, why not? Charisma
is not innate. It is practical magic, something you create, through
conscious practice.

Success with women is not an accident. *Any* personality type can be
magnetic to women. It stems from a realization that we already have
within us all the necessary strength and courage. And it is a choice
to acknowledge ourselves and our fears, and then—and this is the
important part—to move forward anyway. The difference between
men who are successful and men who are not is that successful men
examine their hearts, realize there is something they care deeply about
and desire, and take decisive steps toward it. They take steps *forward*,
always and forever forward, in spite of their fears and doubts, and
no matter what the cost. That is the only real answer for men, the
only singularity.

Love is an art. Beauty is an art. Celebrating women is an art. And
as in any art, there is theory and practice. Theory can only get us
so far. We can read about it, study it, and dream about it for years,
and yet never experience it. To become a master in any art, we must
embrace it daily and lifelong. Most of us are too afraid to try. But
we must try, forever try, if we want to understand. We must try and
fail. The brush must be picked up.

80Q8

There is a passage in the book of Proverbs that describes the four things too wonderful to comprehend: "The way of an eagle in the air; the way of a serpent upon a rock; the way of a ship in the midst of the sea; and the way of a man with a maid." These things truly *are* wonderful. And incomprehensible. And simple. And worthy of contemplation. These things have never changed through all of time. We don't need to add more layers. We need to strip them all away.

Nothing I am saying is remotely new. There is nothing new under the sun. Our society has forgotten basic truths, ancient truths, about love and relationships. Everything has been said before, but because we forget, everything has to be said again.

It is simpler than we think. We just need a return to first principles, as Aristotle advised. There are layers of culture and history and circumstances that constantly change and yet, like mathematics and music, the basic principles of men and women never do.

Ever notice that no one invents a new musical instrument? Why doesn't someone announce the invention of a completely new *acoustic* instrument? Sure, there are instruments being invented and demonstrated all the time, but not *embraced*. We've electrified and amplified everything, but does that constitute a completely new instrument? The last truly original non-electronic instrument was the saxophone, invented by Adolphe Sax in 1846. The saxophone has a distinctive, instantly recognizable sound, and has been embraced in all kinds of genres and celebrated in orchestras and jazz halls everywhere. The saxophone is ubiquitous; anyone in the world can go buy a saxophone and buy books for it and take lessons. There hasn't been anything new in over a century and a half. Why is this? It's because the principles of generating musical notes have remained the same throughout the history of humanity. Every musical instrument is a variation of blowing air through a hole or banging on something stretched. There are no other ways of making musical sounds.

৪৩৫

I have a far away memory of sitting on a swing as a boy when a little girl my age came over and sat on the swing next to me. She turned to me. She smiled to me. Oh, how I remember! What exalted beatitude! I couldn't take my eyes off her. To me, she was an angel shining, blessed and serene, on clouds of glory. She was the most beautiful thing I had ever seen. And I, of course, I was too scared to say anything. To me, she was perfect and I was not.

I have never forgotten that first brush with beauty. When I lifted my eyes to that girl those many years ago, awash in all my trepidations, I lifted my eyes forever to the greatness of the female spirit. I've never looked away. In fact, that pretty much sums me up. I am still just that little boy in the swing, enamored by the wonder of female energy. I felt so undeserving of her smile, so small and insignificant, yet I seek her beauty to this day.

To me, there is no other pursuit or aspiration in life more worthy than rediscovering that magic and wonder again, rediscovering one's soul, rediscovering how wonderful it was to sit there beside that girl in the swing.

৪৩৫

Women in Amsterdam are glorious to see, riding every-where on their bicycles, and you, no exception, came riding to meet me on your bicycle, in your little black dress and your pearls and heels, and you were impeccable and won-drous to behold.

I watched you on that starry night from the open-air table. I watched you park your bicycle and straighten your dress, and I watched you as you entered the candlelit restaurant, searching for me in the soft darkness. I waved my hand, but you couldn't see me there, and then you did. And we sat together under the stars that evening in Amsterdam, and we shared the wine and shared the candlelight.

This was, of course, not really a date, but an interview, contrived to appear like a date, so you could write about the "experience" for your monthly column. It was a fun idea and I liked it very much.

The first thing I did (do you remember?) after I poured you a glass of wine was... I looked into your smiling eyes, and I reached across the table to touch the back of your hand with the tips of my fingers, and I said to you, "So tell me... who is this pretty blonde girl sitting across from me? You came on a blind date with me, you crazy girl."

You laughed and leaned in toward me, "Well, it's more of an interview than a—"

"And you wore this stellar, little black dress just for me?" I smiled as I reached under the table and tapped your knee, so slight and feather-soft that it was virtually unnoticed, a physical connection with you, wonderfully respectful, but enough to let you know... enough to let you know.

"Yes, just for you," you joked, and you touched your neck, and you were so soft in the lambent candlelight with the softness of your pearls.

"I usually begin by asking questions about the things that—" you started to say, but I interrupted you again, because... well, because I had seen you touch your neck and the softness of your pearls.

"Tell me something interesting about you." I said.

And you, suddenly demure and silent, looked down, twisting the stem of your wineglass on the table.

"Well... I'm not sure... something interesting about me? Mm... I don't really—"

"Mirjam."

"Yes."

"Tell me something you've never told anyone before."

And then you did, Mirjam, you did. Only five minutes into our pretend date, you looked into my eyes across our little table, and you told me something you had never told anyone before, and you searched my face as you did, with the stillness of a deer beside a stream, then you looked down again and you watched the candle-flame for a while as it curtsied and pirouetted before your breath.

"I can't believe I just told you that... I've never told anyone before..."

Yes, I know, Mirjam. And our whole pretend date was like that, wasn't it? We talked, did we not? With the stars and the wine and the pearls kissing your neck and the voice recorder beside the plate. Yes, we talked into the night, long after the recorder had switched off. You had planned to ask me the usual interview questions, and you did not; all we talked about the whole time was you. And you didn't notice at all, did you, that all we talked about the whole time was you? That is, until the tape recorder switched off, and then you realized that you had not yet asked me any of the questions you had planned to ask me, and it startled you, and so you did.

"What do you talk about to the men who come to hear you speak?"

"What do I talk about? I will tell you. Look around us now and see everything here... really see it all. You want to know what I talk about to men? I talk about this," *and I waved my hand over the whole scene around us, like a conductor reaching for the woodwind section.* "I was a profoundly poor and scared little boy who grew up in the wilderness of northern Canada, with no opportunities and no understanding and no sense that I was ever part of anything really. And I look around now and here I am in Amsterdam, with you and your pearls and this glass of fine wine, on this warm evening, underneath these stars, and I wonder how can this be? How did I get from there to here? And something inside me is filled with wonder, and it is profound, and here I am, Mirjam, with you, in this city, and it shakes my foundations because it is so magnificent, this whole experience, with you on your bicycle in that dress and those heels. I look around*

me and all I see is beauty—the beauty of you and the beauty
of a poor kid from the wilderness sitting here now with you,
and a knowing that anything is possible in this whole wide
world, and the most amazing thing I can think of that I could
be experiencing right now is this moment with you.
   "That's what I talk about to men."
                      — The Alabaster Girl, *page 48*

ଡ଼ଔ

"Teach us how to get women," men call out to me. "Teach us what to say, what to do. Shortcuts, fancy tricks, how to get her panties off in *three easy moves*! Teach us all these things." Yes, well, there are no shortcuts. To be a lover of women is not a set of tricks or fancy tap-dancing. It is something you believe, not something you say. It is something you are, not something you do.

Men are always looking for the ultimate answer, the singularity, the epiphany that will make them finally—*finally!*—successful with women. The magic pickup line. The perfect thing to say. The perfect thing to do. A transference of some kind to the other side of the curtain of understanding. Well, no one ever jumps out of bed one morning and *Ta-da!* now they are good with women.

It's like the ancient *sorites paradox*: Imagine a beggar sitting on the sidewalk with a tin can. Is he rich? No, we would say he is poor. Oh sure, he might love the sunshine and his freedom to sit there with his can and is therefore arguably richer than most, but materially, we would say he is quite poor. So what if you give him a dollar? Is he now rich? No, we would still say he is poor. What about another dollar? Nope, still poor. What about another dollar? And another? And another? At what point would we say, "Ah, that man is rich." Which dollar makes the difference? Certainly if we continued to give him dollars until he had one million dollars in his can, we would all consider him rich. But what if you took one dollar out? Is he now poor again?

I always imagine everything on a continuum, from left to right. On the left is where we were. On the right is where we want to be. Somewhere in the middle is where we are. On the left is a sense of scarcity. On the right is a sense of abundance. On the left are our doubts and fears. On the right are our hopes and dreams. On the left is our comfort zone. On the right is our freedom. On the left, we are followers. On the right, we are leaders. On the left, we are wishers. On the right, we are creators. On the left, we stand alone and lonely. On the right is the land of women.

We start out alone, with only our hesitation and self-talk. As we venture further into the land of women, we find ourselves venturing further in our understanding. As we learn, as we practice, as we fight the good fight, as we move from left to right on our journey, we discover something remarkable. The continuum keeps going, forever, beyond the land of women, beyond everything we thought we wanted, beyond what we can possibly see. We find ourselves once again standing alone. Not alone and lonely like before, but tall and assured, in our strength, in our truth, in our masculinity, needing no validation from women or anyone ever again.

სიდ

So, what do you do?.
I'm on a mission
A mission?
Sounds exciting
What is your mission?
Shhhh...
— The Alabaster Girl, *page 51*

სიდ

I am often asked: What do I say that other men do not say? What do I do that other men do not do? I have no clear answer to any of this, for who, as they say, has seen the wind? It is almost impossible to describe it in words. It is foolish to even try. I can only hint. I can only guess. I can only wonder. There is no clear algorithm to follow, there is no "You start by saying A; if she responds with B, then you go to C." It is all about intuition and sub-communication, feel and flow.

So what does that make me, my love? A philosopher? Ah, too lofty a garland for my head, I'm afraid. A philosopher *manqué*, perhaps, a wannabe *poète*. But that's about it. I prattle on about beauty and when I do, men look at me and think, "Uh, that's great… but how can I use any of that to get a girl in my bed tonight?" Men want and need practical advice, and since I have a tendency to wax poetic and wane practical, they are not sure what to make of me.

I have no illusions about myself. I am not enlightened in some mystical way. I am not a guru. Not at all. I'm just a scoundrel over here in the corner winking at all the girls. I don't have some noble, world-saving motivation. I just like women. And yes, I am aware there's a long tradition of mystics with painted reputations and aw-shucks grins, winking and pretending that they're just fools. Not because they haven't thought some deeply profound thoughts, but because they know that ultimately, every seeker has to find out for himself, has to discover his own truth. So take it for what it's worth. The only difference between me and other men is that I have been studying the poetics of women for a lot longer, and if men want to observe the little dance that I do in order to learn something, well, that's okay.

Instruction is great for cooking or calculus. But not for affairs of the heart. Why? Because it is all a mystery to us. Anyone who pretends to be a guru when it comes to love is delusional. Listen to those with great questions, not answers. Wisdom does not come from having an answer for everything. It comes from having a question for everything.

Men look to me as a teacher, it's true, but I'm not really teaching anything. I have nothing to teach. I only describe what I have seen, and the only thing I have seen is beauty. I'm just waving my hand around in the air and pointing at things that excite me. It's not like I set out one day to stand upon a celestial mountain and cast my light, *ex cathedra*, down upon the multitude. It's more like I was part of the multitude and somehow got pushed higher and higher up the slopes.

In reality, I don't really know. None of us do. Oh sure, there are others with a message, voices from other wildernesses. But we are all just approximating our version of the truth, are we not? I may be right. I may be wrong. The only interesting thing to me is the conversation itself, the wonder of the question, the what-if, the unabashed joy of seeking—and loving—the mystery of it all.

∞⚮

Ah well, what can I do? I am torn… shall I conquer the world? Or save it? The truth is, I don't have any answers. I just ask good questions. If men want to call me a teacher, okay fine, but then let me supply the definition of what I teach: *I teach men that women are beautiful.* Which is to say, I teach men how to be lovers.

And why not? No one is ever born in full armor. We can take singing lessons, dancing lessons, writing lessons… but lessons on how to love and be loved? No? Well then, what are we supposed to do? Are we expected to just "know" these things, like baby sea turtles who are born underneath the sand and yet head unerringly to the sea?

Men listen to my words. Or they do not. Either way is fine with me. I am not devoted to their comfort in any way. I am nothing if not extreme. I am prone to purple prose and curlicued sentiments. I say great and grandiloquent things to men. I proclaim. I speak in absolutes. I say, "This is how it is." Then I say, "This is how it needs to be." Then I wander off for a few months to some distant corner of the planet, and when I come back I say something entirely different. To quote Whitman, "Do I contradict myself? Very well then, I contradict myself. I am large. I contain multitudes."

And women? I have nothing to teach to women. Not that women have all the answers, of course. Women are just as confused and lost as the men. But it's not my place. I am not a woman. I can't say to women what they should do, how they should change, how they should be. "Hey girls, you're doing this... when you really should be doing *that*." How insolent, how supercilious is that?

All I can do is talk to women about the goddesses I have known and the way they made me feel. I can only describe what I have seen. I can only describe the kind of rarefied beauty that seduces me. It is not my place to explain a woman's experience to her. I can only explain *my* experience to her. I can only elucidate the qualities in a woman that make me pause. And what makes me pause, my love? Devotion. Absolute devotion.

Some men claim to be feminists. Huh? I am not a feminist. That space needs to be left to those who are qualified to speak for it: the disenfranchised and marginalized voices of women, the women who, until recently, never had a say. I have nothing meaningful to contribute. I have a man's point of view and, what seems to me, an abundance of advantages and opportunities in comparison. I don't know, for example, what it's like to be fearful when walking down a crepuscular street. Nor have I been sexually violated. Nor have I been raped. So no, I could never presume to enter into the "safe spaces" of women. Even if invited.

Ȫȫ

Men complain bitterly about the flat-out rejection and abject dismissal they endure at the hands of women, that whenever they get up the nerve to approach a woman, they run the risk of getting systematically shot down. Yet they turn around and do the exact same thing to any girl they are not attracted to, dismissing them out of hand and ignoring them like they don't exist. "Her? Nah... she's only a five, maybe a six on a good day."

A woman is a woman is a woman. And every woman is *my* woman. That's the way I *choose* to see it. I may discover that she is not, but that is my *starting* assumption. They are all my girls. When you believe that, they start to believe it, too. This is the perspective I choose to forever inhabit, for it is glorious here! It lends a certain tone to my voice, a swift-sure lightness to my steps, and the air is easier to breathe.

Ah, but she might have a man in her life, some will say. Yes, she might. Yes, I assume she does. But that's not the point, and not my concern. It doesn't mean that I am interested in somehow "stealing" her away from her man. It just means that her personal situation is irrelevant in this flash-moment of time.

Are women ever really 100% single? They complain they are, of course, but most women that are at least somewhat pleasant to be around have a guy of some stripe somewhere. A woman has a husband or a boyfriend or a guy she is kind of seeing or a guy she is kind of dating or a guy she is kind of sleeping with or a guy who likes her and she tolerates or a guy she can call. To wait for a woman to be completely single before talking to her is to wait a long, long time.

All women notice the way a man treats a woman. Always. They see everything. I never take a woman for granted. I never dismiss a woman because of the way she looks. And this has nothing to do with pursuing women or trying to pick them up. Women, like men, are beholden to the vicissitudes of life: sadness and loss, fading dreams, tone-deaf relationships, stultifying careers, and mind-numbing responsibilities. My only desire when I talk to women is to impart a little joy into their lives again, thereby imparting a little joy into my own. There are still good men in this world, as if to say. I need nothing from women in return. Or to say it better: I already have everything from women in return. Women understand all this; they know the difference between a guy who loves women and a guy who is trying to pick them up. Or dismiss them.

Women can smell other women on a man. They know. They know who spends time in the company of women and who does not. And whether women admit it or not, there is a kind of intoxication that results, a mild but lingering curiosity, a subconscious raising of one eyebrow. Hmm, what is it about this particular guy?

Women beget women. They are like seagulls. They see one pecking and they all come running. Am I the only one who has figured this out?

ಬಂಇ

I lean in to her and smile.

Come out with me for a drink tomorrow night. I will pick you up at seven.

I can't. My boyfriend wouldn't like it.

Oh hey, I understand... let's make it eight then.

She laughs and dashes off through the crowd.

I am completely unrestrained with women and having enormous fun, and even though I love to amuse myself above all, it is crucial that it is fun for her as well. Otherwise, I fail.

She looks back and smiles.

I turn and look around. She will come back.

You can say anything with a smile and a wink. I know and she knows that my little invitation is all in good fun. She, after all, has just let me know she has a boyfriend. That is fine. We can still dance the dance of desire, skirt the edges. No one is harmed, and everyone is seen. I am under no illusions whatsoever that she will accept my playful invitation. And neither is she.

And here she is now, walking toward me again. Ah, how excellent everything is.

I smile and wink and pick right up where I left off.

Hello, sweetie. Did you miss me?

Hardly. I don't even know you.

Where are your friends?

Over there.

I like it that you came back to see me.

I didn't. I had to go this way anyway.

To see me?

No!

Yes, you did. You're a bad girl, aren't you?

She laughs. No!

A little bit?

She pretend-slaps me on the shoulder. No!

Oh yes, you are. I can see it in your eyes. You're definitely bad. You know what? I'm starting to like you.

Yes... and again... I have a boyfriend.

Uh-huh. That's very interesting. You know what else?

What?

I have two bottles of champagne at home...

Oh yeah?

Yeah. One to drink and one to pour all over your body.

She laughs.

You never give up, do you?

Of course not! It wouldn't be the same if I did, now would it?

No... I suppose not.

— The Alabaster Girl, *page 55*

ဢၐ

A lot of men want to know, not a lot want to hear. Skepticism is good. Suspicion, I cannot abide. I will not spend one second of my time trying to convince men of anything. I never give my light where it is not invited. I never say a single word to men about women unless they sincerely want to know. How can I? It is not my place to impose my philosophy upon others. It is not my job to try to adjust the "error of their ways." What right do I have to try to correct some supposed "imbalance" in the world, straightening picture frames in the houses of others? This is the height of presumption, is it not?

I have nothing to say to men who have no real love or empathy for women. I have nothing to say to men who misuse or abuse women. I have nothing to say to men who do not like women, let alone those who hate women. Men who do not like women don't even exist on my radar. These men don't understand me at all; they never will, and frankly, my dear, I don't give a damn. They can glower and fume all they want. I'll be over here, talking to all the girls.

෯෬

Why do I bother to describe to men what I know about the hearts and minds of women? I wonder about that sometimes. Who knows? Maybe it's as simple as this: I am in awe of the extraordinary beauty I have seen in women and want others to see it too. "Look there," as if to say, "can you see what I see, my friend? For if you could see even *one-tenth* of the beauty I see in a woman, you too would be seduced, you too would believe, you too would live your life surrounded by boundless beauty and grace."

Maybe I don't really care about other men. Maybe I just want a fair fight, like the pre-Columbian tribes of Central America, who would, from time to time, covet another tribe's lands or women, and decide it was time to take them. First they would announce their intention to wage war, but then, because they believed there was no honor in defeating a weaker enemy, and besides the gods determined the victors anyway, they would hand out shields and clubs and arrows to the enemy tribe. Once everything seemed to be about right, as evenly balanced and as fair as possible, then and only then, would they attack.

Maybe I am not doing it for men at all. Maybe I am doing it only for women. Maybe it's my subconscious gift back to women for the great love and memorable experiences they have given me in my life. Helping women by helping men.

Maybe I am doing it only for myself. Maybe it's because when I was young, I had no clear message. I had no teacher. I had no mentor. I had no champion. I had no man in my life who was my hero, who I admired, who I worshiped. No one taught me how to be a man. No one taught me about women. No one took me aside and said, "This is how you hold an ax, son, and this is how you write a poem, and look here, this is a woman and in the presence of one of these, this is what you must do." So maybe I just want to give something like that to others.

Maybe I have compassion for anyone who is lost and seeking, the downtrodden, the underdog, because, well... that was me. Maybe, in some way, it's the talk our fathers never gave us.

four

The Way of the Natural

I disentangle myself from your stories
to pour more wine

Forward! But do we ever arrive? Do we even want to arrive? Out there, a soft-bedded landscape beneath a long, loping sky... rising, falling, in our peripheral vision, and guiding us ever on. And to where? To home? Or to away?

Is there someone out there who thinks she's your girlfriend? she said.

That's a great question. Very clever! It's an entirely different question than "Do you have a girlfriend?" A great question that cannot be avoided.

And the answer?

No.

Have there been many?

Yes.

How many?

Many.

Somewhere ahead is our destination. Straight ahead like a bullet shot, can't miss it, that inevitable destination of ours... but for some reason, it feels so elusive, slips the mind. There is something so familiar about this girl... an inquisitive spirit... an attentive kindness in her eyes.

Are you a pickup artist? she said.

No, pickup artists are skilled at picking up phone numbers, not women.

Then what are you?
A romance artist.
What's the difference?
Empathy.

ଚ୍ଚ

What is the secret of attraction? It is well and good to talk about a magnetic personality, but what does that mean, really? What makes a man irresistible to women? What qualities cause women to fantasize about a man? What is the essence of charm? Why do men like Casanova still fascinate us today? Why do women always gravitate toward certain types of men, inviting them willingly into their lives, their arms, and their dreams? Is it looks, power, money?

We have this notion that all men who are successful with women must have something going for them that the average man does not. Well, that notion is correct. However, contrary to everything we have been led to believe, it is not looks, power, or money.

These are the things most men concentrate on—an accumulation of externalities, so to speak. And why not? A man with power and money will be surrounded by women, of course. Is that success? Perhaps. Is he loved? Ah, who knows? Maybe he is. All we know for certain is that men spend their lives trying to increase their personal power, thus increasing their influence, thus increasing their perceived value to others, thus believing that all this will make them appear more "lovable" to women. This is not new; it is a simple concept that we all understand.

But is there something else? Yes, my love, there is. If you press me for an answer, I will say this: the kind of men that women universally adore possess an inimitable love of life, a sense of aliveness, an irrepressible audacity, and an overwhelming sense of fun. And more than anything else, they possess a supreme and ever-abiding love and admiration for women.

There is something magical about the heart of a man who loves himself, loves love, loves life itself. There is a surging rush of curiosity and wonder and mystery in his every step. His is a life poetic, filled with the spirit of elegance and gratitude. The words are light on the page, a lightness and ease, a welcomed breeze about the whole experience. All women and all men are drawn to him, for he is a man of conviction, of honor, of purpose. And this sets him apart, miles apart, from other men. He is labelled by all, in hushed tones and with a modicum of envy, as a "natural."

"Why is it that we can get phone numbers, but you get women who love you *forever?*" I will say it again: *men who love women are loved by women*. Men who love women are hymned far and wide, adored and doted on by women. Men who love women view the world with different eyes. Men who love women smile and wink at all the girls, for they possess a secret, a secret of the universe.

A lover of women is a lover of life. That's just the way it is. It might be possible to love life without a love of women, but it is not possible to be a lover of women without a love of life. It's like spelling. People who are not good at spelling may or may not be intelligent, but people who are good at spelling are *always* intelligent.

ഇരു

All men who love women have the same way of looking at the world. They all have the same traits, and these traits have been constant throughout all of time. What is interesting is that other men have *none* of these traits. A man either has all of them or none.

Many have tried to unravel the tapestry of men, but no one has ever managed to successfully tease out the threads that belong exclusively to the lovers of women. I shall try.

There are plenty of men who possess a certain facility with women, but those who possess a masterful understanding of women, and the hidden arts of love, are exceedingly rare. In all my years, I have met exactly two. These two men, from entirely different backgrounds, have the greatest facility with women I've ever seen—a smoldering understanding, an intuition approaching my own. Theirs is a life of abundance, an abundance of women, the kind of life that men everywhere dream of every day.

Women can tell in an instant who has women in their life and who does not. So can I. Game recognizes game, as they say, and these men… well, I recognized them immediately. A knowing nod, a clear-eyed assessment, a shaking of hands as peers. I get it, you get it, we both get it. Yes, indeed. Behold, a brother-in-arms before me.

One is European and has spent his life traversing the world as a high-paid escort for lonely women of means. The life of a gigolo. Now then, although one might bridle at the morality of his chosen profession, one cannot deny that his years of practice in making women of all ages and sizes feel special and beautiful, of sitting and listening to them and their stories, and of touching them in caring ways they have never known, would tend to make him highly attuned to the majestic symphony of the female spirit. Which is my only point.

The other man is a fellow Canadian. Women hover around him like a rock star, and it is phenomenal to behold. Oh, and he isn't a rock star. He drives a city bus. The bus driver. And yet he has a quietly seismic effect on women. They *adore* him. They give him everything. They take care of him. They defend him. They seek him out and miss him when he is not around. They bring all their girlfriends around to meet him. Mothers tend to jokingly keep their daughters away from him, but love him just the same. He is magnanimous and inviting to all around, generous to a fault, kind and gracious. Above all, he is highly, *highly* sexually charged, concupiscent to the core. Everything he says to women, young and old, is a manifesta-tion of his virility. He is here to lay waste to all the land, scorched earth, all or nothing. Everything out of his mouth and everything he does informs the world around him of only one thing: I am here to bend you over, if you desire it. And you will love it. And yet every woman who meets him feels thoroughly safe and protected in his presence, like he is a magnificent, well-fed lion, calmly protecting a little gazelle from harm. This man will be surrounded by women until the day he dies.

In the presence of these men, something is invoked in the hearts of women, something placid, something ancient, a direct summons to the brightest aspects of female nature. These men command *attention* from women—in every connotation of the word—and women rush to comply.

ৠ৹ঙ

Here is a sublime secret of the ages, the secret of men whom women eternally love: *They are father figures and little boys—simultaneously!* There you go. I've never heard anyone say that before, but I am convinced it is true.

Leadership and vulnerability, a lightning combination that is utterly impossible for women to resist. It is the greatest strength of these men, their triumph, the defining characteristic that sweeps all other men unceremoniously into a corner forever.

Because they are simultaneously father figures and little boys, these men are the only ones that can reconcile the seemingly irreconcilable duality of the nature of women: the madonna and the whore. They appeal to *both* sides of the feminine mystique. A woman wants to be put in her place by a leader and, at the same time, she wants to take care of him immensely. She wants him to stand guard at the mouth of the cave, fire-torch in hand, majestic and defiant against the elements in one moment, then crawl into her lap like a kitten the next.

Do you understand the impact of this, my love? The broad-spectrum, dual nature of these men is an overwhelming notion for a woman, a shattering, unprecedented, thoroughly welcomed assault on her senses and her heart. Oh, what possibilities, what profound and boundless enlightenment this is for her, for him!

When a woman enters into the presence of a man who embodies both the indomitable spirit of a warrior and the inimitable spirit of a child, she will respond to him with her entire being, her entire body, her entire life. She will *never* leave it. She will love this man forever.

It is a perfect balance, a tightrope they traverse with ease. The leader side of them is never aggressive or controlling; it is firm and in command. And the boyish side of them is never mewling or pitiable; it is playful and beaming and in need of a bath.

These men command attention in pleasing ways. Given the right circumstances, they can get *any* woman into bed. Never by coercion or convincing or conniving; but by making her feel, with every breath she takes, that she is a true beauty and she is highly desired. Their sexual nature is always direct and on full display, but it is forever accompanied by a gracious generosity and profound respect. They have a knowing about them, charm is ever present, and a graceful escape is always proffered.

All sexual aggression is sexual frustration. Women are buffeted by winds that should be directed outward. Men who love women can afford to be extremely sexual because they have no sexual aggression in their soul. There is nothing frantic about them. They are bastions of stillness and grace, but still highly sexual. They are dangerous, yes, but never to her. Simply put, a woman always feels safe in the presence of these men. Women only feel afraid if they think they might lose their ability to choose.

Other men, awash in sexual urgency, simply do not have the light touch necessary. They invade women, occupy the land by force, then spend all their time trying to suppress the rebellions and uprisings. They come from a place of frustration: either needy and begging for sex or indignant and demanding it, a hand that is either limp and clammy or an iron fist. Never the requisite velvet glove.

ଈଔଷ

A quiet day of writing in a café in Taipei. There is a man next to me, a table or two away, sipping tea and reading I know not what, but the cover, amusingly to me, is vaguely suggestive of "Don Quixote." A man on a horse... is that a windmill? Or a tower? It's hard to tell.

A pretty girl walks in. He doesn't see her, for his back is to the door, but I do and I watch as she walks up behind him. She is smiling and smiling. And what's this? She is holding something small and blue in outstretched palms, cradled delicately before her like a little girl might hold a baby bird, and now I see that it is a little wrapped gift. With ribbons.

She stops near him, just behind his shoulder, and sing-songs his name. "Chen..." He doesn't hear or doesn't notice so she sings out again. "Che-ennn!"

And now he hears and now he turns his head and I watch as he swims back into the room (from La Mancha?) and he looks at her and he does a double-take and I see his mind processing, registering, swimming back into the room. And now a smile blossoms across his face and his eyes light up and sparkle and he glances down at the gift, then up to her eyes, then back to the gift, then back up again to her shining eyes, and he sits straight up in his chair and he turns his full body and his full attention to her, his book down, page-lost and forgotten.

Is this a special occasion? His birthday? I have no idea. It is simply an unexpected, surprise gift from her to him. With ribbons.

I marvel at the simplicity and completeness of his transformation. His posture, his energy, everything about him, has changed. He was calm before and now he is not calm, a shift from quietness to aliveness, from studious contemplation to wide-eyed wonder. He is thoroughly surprised and delighted at the mischief in the air. "For me? Wonderful!" as if to say.

A woman is like a surprise gift to me. This is the way I see it. In fact, this is the way I see all women. This is the delight I feel for every woman I encounter. This is how I react when I first meet her, and this is the way I react every time I see her again.

A surprise gift from a beautiful friend. The same expressions of wonder that come naturally to me when surprised with a gift are the same expressions that come naturally to me every time a woman comes into my sight. How glorious! All for me!

Imagine if all men had this sense of wonder and delight for every woman they encounter. Imagine if they had it in their relationships! And what a difference it would make if a man were to celebrate his lover, his girlfriend, his wife, as a surprise gift to his life.

A gift from a beautiful friend, surprising him on this day, every single day.

— The Alabaster Girl, *page 57*

ଚ୦ଔ

What about men who are good-looking, my love? They have an unfair advantage, do they not? Well, maybe they do, but only for a few minutes or so. Ultimately, a man's physical appearance is such a small component of attraction for women that it barely registers. In fact, it doesn't really matter at all. Women are not attracted to men who are good-looking… they are attracted to men who are *attractive*. Big difference.

A woman is attracted to the way a man chooses to move through life and how he perceives the world around him. She is far more attracted to the way he makes her feel than the way he looks. She is far more turned on by his mind than by his appearance. A man's mind is his greatest, most attractive, most erotic feature.

This isn't to say that women don't notice or care about the way a man presents himself or the way he carries himself. The first thing a woman notices about a man are his extremities: his head, his hands, his feet. In other words, his hair, his nails, his shoes. These subtle clues speak volumes to women, for they are indicators of how a man views himself and the world around him. Part of the attraction for a woman is knowing that he finds it important to take care of the little things, to look his best.

So yes, it is a wonderful thing for a man to learn how to dress well and how to groom himself well, and he has no excuse whatsoever for not staying in shape. After all, walking is free! These are all great things for a woman to see in a man, and it's not only because it makes him more physically attractive to her; it is because it portrays to her mind his sense of self-worth. Which, I suppose, amounts to the same thing.

∞)(∞

Some of the most famous lovers in history were, by most accounts, average looking, or even quite ugly. Look at some of the portraits of Casanova, for instance. Or photographs of Jean-Paul Sartre. Not physically attractive at all. But the auras of these men were intoxicating, mesmerizing, breath-taking, to volumes of women.

Casanova described it like this, "I was not handsome, but I had something better than beauty—a striking expression which almost always compelled a kind interest in my favor…" And one writer said of Sartre, "Women fell for him because he knew how to explain their soul to them." Even Voltaire said, "Give me five minutes to explain away my ugly face, and I can bed the queen of France!"

Sartre, for example, was renowned for his philosophy but almost more renowned for his prowess with the Parisian ladies. Yet he was, by all accounts and evidence—and by his own admission—notoriously ugly. One leg was shorter than the other, causing him to lurch when he walked, his eyes were big and loopy, flailing around in random and opposite directions, and he was barely five feet tall. And yet women loved him, desired him, fell at his feet.

It was no accident. Sartre deliberately and painstakingly developed his confidence and persona. He looked at his life, realized that he could either wallow forever in his limitations, or he could do something about it. He dreamed for a long time about being adored and desired by women, until finally he made a conscious choice to become just that. Through sheer force of personality and deliberate choice, that's exactly what he did. He became what he always dreamed of being: a ladies man.

We have absolutely no excuse. Some guy said to me recently, "I feel like I'm too short for women to ever be attracted to me." I told him the only thing he was short on was the courage to get out there and put himself into the land of women.

Almost everyone can think of a guy they have known who seemingly had nothing going for him—not good-looking, not in shape, no money—and yet he was constantly surrounded by women. His secret? His assumption that all the girls are *his* girls.

&ᘍC

It has been well said that you don't have be impressive… you just have to be interesting. So how does a man become interesting to women, my love? By being interested in *them*. Casanova said, "Love is three quarters curiosity." Behold! The fundamental ingredient for dynamic interactions and sublime relationships with women: *curiosity*.

Curiosity is the wonderment of life. It is the sense of adventure in our soul. It is learning to cultivate profound interest in the journey itself, the learning, the surprises. It is the essential ingredient in every dynamic interaction in life. It is infectious. And it is, in turn, massively attractive to women.

Curiosity is underrated. Curiosity is misunderstood. It is not about seeking answers. It is about seeking *mystery*. Always and forever seeking mystery. A great life is one of mystery, not answers. We have this packet of answers in our hand. Now what is the greater mystery?

Intelligence is curiosity. It is that and only that. If you are curious, you are intelligent. If you are not curious, you are not intelligent. In fact, politically correct be damned, I will say it straight: A general lack of curiosity is a general lack of intelligence. I will even go so far as to say that a general lack of curiosity is the *worst* of all traits.

We are automatically good at what we are truly curious about. The effort of learning is halved. A man who is curious about women, or anything really, is always paying attention, always fully engaged, always learning. While other men are looking for ways to impress women, a curious man is looking for new ways to understand them.

Curiosity is alchemy, transforming a pedestrian encounter into a truly engaging experience. It imbues all of our interactions with a sense of ease and delight. It is the only tool a man needs on a date with a woman. It negates any worries about what to say, what to do, how to be. And it is the only thing that will ever keep a relationship alive and interesting. It solves everything. When there is genuine curiosity in an interaction or a relationship, everything will flow.

Curiosity is a form of creation. What does it create? Why, curiosity, of course. Curiosity begets curiosity. If all men had a spirit of curiosity, the world would change. Imagine a man who is genuinely curious about his wife and children, excited to gather them around him at the end of the day. "Tell me, my loved ones, about your day." Yes, genuine curiosity allows everything to unfold and spread out before us like a picnic on a sunny day beneath a tree.

Curiosity is a gift, a gift from a man to the world. It is about him learning to be genuinely interested in a woman. It is about being puzzled, amazed and enchanted by her, this amazing woman sharing this part of his life. He is listening, engaged, and interested. He is fully present with her. He is drawing her forth in return. By sharing himself with her, she will share herself with him.

"But what if I am not really curious about women?" men say. Then *get* curious. You can always find something in any woman to be curious about. Curiosity is a choice. We can all choose to be more curious, more interested, more engaged. When we choose curiosity, choose to view the world with a real sense of wonder and delight, our curiosity deepens and strengthens.

Men want a greater experience with women, but all they have to do is look for ways to be curious about women and their lives will change. Women will *adore* them. Even sprinkling their conversations with the phrase, "I'm curious…" is immensely powerful. "I'm curious… why did you move to this city?" or "I'm curious about those shoes…" And then… just listen. It sets a beautiful tone for the whole interaction. She will call all her friends and say, "Wow, I met a man who really listens!"

Genuine curiosity is a trait of all great lovers. It is impossible to be truly adored by women without it. True lovers are immensely curious about women, always listening to them, always looking at them with a sense of wonder. True lovers want to know, want to know, *want to know*. Tell me things. Tell me your stories. What do you love? What do you love? I can't even begin to describe how mesmerizing this is to women.

ဆၢ

I am not like other men.
Oh, really? How are you different?
I am honest. I don't play games.
Is that so?
Yes. If I like you, I will tell you. If I want you in my bed, you will know it. If you give me your phone number, I won't

artificially wait three days. I will call you tomorrow.

Well, that's all very interesting, but I don't give out my number to strangers.

I didn't ask for it.

She laughs.

I don't even know why I am talking to you.

I know why.

Why?

Because you are my lover.

She laughs again.

I don't even know you.

Oh, yes you do. What we have between us is age-old. We were meant to be lovers. It is in the stars.

Oh, really?

Of course!

What makes you so sure?

I can see it in your eyes and in the way you touch your hair. It's just a matter of time.

Why are you so interested in me?

I don't know.

There are lots of pretty girls here.

That's true. Maybe it's because you have the second most beautiful eyes I've ever seen.

What? Second most? What do you mean by second most?

Ah, it's a long story. Let's just say it involves three continents, a riding crop of the finest Moroccan leather, and private lessons in the lost art of knife-throwing.

She laughs.

Are you serious?

No.

Aha! I thought you said you were always honest.

Yeah, well, I thought you said you never give out your number.

I didn't give it out.

Not yet.

— The Alabaster Girl, *page 60*

ഇറയ

Men have this notion that they need to talk about *themselves* in order to be interesting. After all, if they only talk about and listen to her, well, isn't that tantamount to neediness, to supplication, to putting her on a pedestal? Uh, no. Not at all. A true lover never talks about himself when he sits down with a woman. How can he? The truly interesting subject is sitting right there in front of him. Hello, beauty… tell me about you.

Sometimes a man on a date with a woman will rapid-fire a bunch of inane questions at her, like a persiflage-spewing, polyester-clad salesman, not really listening to her and not really wanting to know. He is only thinking about the next thing he is going to say, and he is waiting for her to stop talking so he can say it. It's all about him, and how he can impress her. He brags about himself, he talks non-stop, slowly burying her with shovelfuls of unremarkable personal information sludge. "Yes, and when I lived in Cincinnati… and my other car is… to the gym three times a week… I don't mean to brag but when you're good at it, it's actually pretty easy…"

Ah, but that's not curiosity. That's not being interested or interesting. That's not real listening. That's smarmy and invasive. That's a job interview. Maybe if he can just say enough impressive things about himself, she'll hire him. Might as well just hand her his resumé. Where's the fun? Where's the joy? Who is this delightful girl in front of him? What is interesting about her? What is she passionate about? What does she believe? What does she love? What is the dream?

She will match his energy. She will rise—or descend—to the level of the interaction. She will give back to him exactly what she receives. If he is distracted, distant, dry, platitudinous, monotone, not really paying attention, and sitting stiff, she will respond in the same way. If the conversation is all surface, just a dispassionate exchange of pedestrian information, then so is the whole experience. The time spent with him is mostly uninteresting and devoid of life. But if he is genuinely curious about her, a little more quizzical in tone, posing questions more searching than the general interrogations of others, she will come alive, animated, poised, and focused on him; the whole conversation is elevated. She will be caught up, transformed, in the magical juxtaposition of him and her in that time and space.

It seems to men that women never seem to know exactly what men want and need. It's because we never explicitly state our desires. We expect her to just know what we want and then we are frustrated when she doesn't. If men were ever lucid enough to ask why, women would look at them in surprise and say, "Well, it's because you never asked!"

Women are marvelous reflectors. They will respond and meet a man exactly where he is at. They will treat him exactly in the way he asks to be treated. It's that simple. It is up to men to create the kind of experiences they want with women. It is up to men to describe to women exactly what they desire from them and exactly how they want it to be. This is the supreme task of men when it comes to women. We teach women how to treat us. Women only give us what we ask for, even if we have no idea we asked for anything at all.

⁎)(⁎

And sometimes… no, all the time… how do I say this without being misunderstood? Ah, let it be misunderstood, for it is subtle and it is wonderful. When I am talking to a woman, I interrupt her. Constantly. I break her train of thought, her sentences, in mid-phrase, all the time. And she doesn't even notice.

Don't get me wrong, my love. I do not interrupt her in order to impose my opinions or to hear my own voice or because I think I have something more interesting to say than her. No, not at all. I interrupt her to clarify, to shape, to enlarge the things she is saying to me. "Wait a minute," I will lightly tap her arm, cutting her off in mid-sentence, "You said you love to paint… more than anything else in this world… tell me more about that."

Or I will cut her off for fun, just to shift gears a little, taking the conversation somewhere completely different and new. She might be saying, "Yes, I moved here to Montreal three years ago and—" I tap her arm. I smile. I look in her eyes. "I love the shape of your lips…" And straighten suddenly, sitting back in my chair, "Sorry, you were saying? Montreal?" A wonderful diversion, a digression, a short-circuit across her frontal lobe, or something like that. In a good way. It has the same effect as kissing her suddenly, unexpectedly.

It might sound counter-intuitive, but interrupting this beauty before me does not come across to her as rude or offensive. Not at all. Instead, my little innocuous interruptions, my gentle asides, create a natural ebb and flow between us. Interrupting her amplifies the connection, sprinkles magic all around us, and electrifies the air, a palpable frisson.

Am I listening to her? Oh yes, my love, I am *really* listening. I am right there before her, hanging on her every word. Because of her, I am omnipresent, omniscient, enchanted. This is listening on a superior plane. It is active listening, interactive listening. It is sharing my experience of listening to her *with* her. "I'm listening to you, my love, and here is what I am hearing," as if to say.

ഇരു

What are you? Some kind of gypsy?
Yeah, kinda.
Or a pirate?
That too.
Well, which one?
I'm a gypsy pirate.
　　　　　— The Alabaster Girl, *page 64*

ഇരു

I am asked all the time: What is your method? What do you do or say to women that is different from other men? Ah, well… the truth is, it doesn't really matter what I say to women at all. In fact, my method is: there is no method. If pressed, however, I will say that my method is this: *I put invitations into the world, and I leave them out there.* That's all I do.

Putting invitations into the world is the essence and foundation of the way I interact with women, my love. Everything about me is an invitation. Life is a dance and I am inviting her to dance. If she accepts, then I am inviting her to shine. I will not grab her hand, lift it up, and spin her dizzy round and round by force. No, I will lift up her hand and invite her to step into the space between us—an invitation to twirl, to be the beauty, to wow the crowd. The important part is that she must step *willingly* into that space. If she accepts my invitation, then I will lead and she will shine.

I don't ask for anything. I don't ask if she is free. Or if she would like to go for coffee. Or what she is doing later. Or if she has a boyfriend. I simply invite. A grand invitation. A luscious invitation. I tune into her desires and extend my hand, as it were, in invitation. Always by invitation—never by force, never by control—an invitation devoid of presumption or expectation.

I extend an invitation very early in the interaction, sometimes even as my opening line. I always say it with a smile, with delight, and without apology. If I get close to her and everything about her is nice—the way she smiles and the way she smells—then I invite her to join me. Where? When? How? Is it even possible? I have no idea. I haven't even thought that far ahead yet. All I know is that she and I should be together. And this is exactly what I say to her. I lean in close to her and smile, "I love your smile. Can you feel that in the air? You and I should be together…"

"No," she might say, "I have a boyfriend." If this is so, I will bow out gracefully, respectfully, for if she is in love with another, then she is not my girl, now is she? I want her full heart, her full attention, her full ebullient spirit, excited to be with me. Not with *him*.

I do not, however, apologize. I had no idea she had a boyfriend. How could I know? I did nothing wrong. I simply spoke my truth, expressing my desire for a pleasing woman whom I encountered, doing my job as a man. "Ah, I understand," I will say, "I meant no disrespect to you or to him. But of course I would be remiss if I did not say these things to you. Look at you in that dress… you, my dear, are absolutely lovely."

If she says she has a boyfriend but she signals to me with her eyes or body language (they often do) that she is not happy or not in love or not sure, ah then, that is a different story. My invitation stands. "I can't…" she says. Yes, well, I understand. And you're still invited.

"Come away, o human child, to the water and the wild" intoned the immortal Yeats. Because why not? What else is there? Why not escape into immeasurable, shimmering romance? Why not return for a while to the innocence and passion of our youth? What is the point of a life if we are not living? Look over there, my love. Can you see what I see? Over there… beyond the horizon… come away with me.

જીભ

Women are never offended by an honest invitation. I can't count the number of times a woman has stood before me and said, with her voice and her eyes, "I can't… but thank you. It is so *refreshing* to hear." Yes well, I hear you, sweet girl. I hear exactly what you are saying. You are thanking me for noticing you. You are thanking me for respecting you. You are thanking me for honoring your current relationship. You are thanking me for giving you the gift of desiring you. You are thanking me for presenting myself to you in all the ways that men do not. Yes, we both know that it can't happen between us, and that's okay. That's not the point anyway, now is it? The beauty of this moment is enough and will suffice. And what's more, you will never forget this moment, will you? That one time when a stranger expressed an honest desire for you—without presumption, without manipulation, without games, and with full respect. You will go forth from our little encounter floating a little off the ground, shining like an angel of glad tidings and great joy.

Because I am simply putting an invitation into the air and leaving it out there, because I am merely stating what I would *like* to happen, because I am not asking for anything, it is not possible to be rejected. Let me say that again: *I never experience a sense of rejection.*

A glorious invitation. Take it or leave it. Of course you are invited… *look at you*! It makes complete sense to my mind. What you do with the invitation is entirely up to you. The ball is in your court.

To live a life in the spirit of invitations is to live the life of a true lover. I have this notion that as long as I stay connected to what I desire in my life, and speak my truth and put invitations into this world, then the right ones will show up. *The ones you love are the ones who love you.* That is a law of the universe. If she accepts my invitation, then she is my girl. If she doesn't, well then, she never was. How perfect is that? We both win either way.

There is an alignment, a calmness, an elegance, about the whole thing. If I just stay on my journey, then one day, perhaps, I will look over and notice that someone lovely is walking beside me. I was alone before, and now, because of my spirit of invitation, she is walking beside me. Just like that. There is no need in me to go out and frenetically try to pick up girls or phone numbers. I know where I am going and I have no time to veer in the direction of any woman, no time to try to convince her of anything. If she is my girl, we will find each other in our travels, naturally and easily. Yes, there is a delicious calmness about the whole thing. That's the way it works.

ಬೋಲ

There are, I think, three levels of invitation. When a young man wants to invite a girl on a date, he asks her out: "Hey, would you like to get together on Thursday evening?" Now then, his whole plan for Thursday night is dependent upon her answer. She can, with a single word, determine how he is going to conduct that particular slice of his life. "Yes" will set him scurrying off in all directions at once, excited, nervous, and making plans. "No" will return him to his former state of equilibrium (albeit a little more subdued) to do whatever it is he would normally do on a nondescript Thursday evening. You could say that she is the arbiter of his fate for that particular Thursday evening. You could even say that he gives her that power.

If she says yes, he is excited and now must create a date he hopes she will like, something memorable, something better than all the dates she has had with all the other guys. He racks his brain. Where should he take her? What should he do? What will she like the most? Coffee? Dinner? Movie? Concert? Art gallery? Hot air balloon? Ah, who knows? It's all so confusing. If, on the other hand, she says no, then he will just stay home or hang out with his buddies or do whatever. Let's call this the *first level of invitations*.

As he gets a little older, experience or advice teaches him that it is better to already be doing something interesting and then to ask her to join him. "Hey, my friends and I are going to a concert on Thursday. Would you like to come with us?" He discovers that this is much better than just asking her out and then trying to dream up something to fill in the time slot. This is much better because it looks like he already has an interesting life and he is going to have fun on Thursday anyway, with or without her. You could say the only power he is giving her now is the power to enhance, with her presence, what he is already doing anyway. Yes, this is much better. Let's call this the *second level of invitations*.

Now then, is there perhaps a *third level of invitations*? Yes, my love, I believe there is. I've never heard anyone describe it like this before, but it makes complete sense to me, and aligns with my experience. The third level of invitations is this: inviting her into nothing... absolutely nothing.

An invitation into nothing. How truly powerful this is! I am not worrying about where to take her on a date or what memorable event I can invite her to. I am not trying to prove to her that I have a busy or interesting life. I have nothing special planned at all. I am offering her *nothing*. Which is to say, I am inviting her into the presence of us. Which is to say, I am inviting her into our own little world. Which is to say, I am inviting her into *everything*.

It doesn't really matter what it is we do at all because we, together, are the event. We, together, are the memorable occasion. We, together, are all that matters. In other words, I actually do have something special planned: the experience of me and her together.

There is even a sense, I suppose, of subconsciously down-playing and disqualifying myself. It's almost like some quaint part of me wants to strip everything away, down to the essence of just me and her, down to the simple ascetic beauty of "a jug of wine, a loaf of bread, and thou," as Khayyám so wonderfully put it. I want her to accept my invitation simply because we like each other, not because of the distractions I might offer or because I have something cool for us to do. Yes, my love, I have nothing spectacular to offer you… just me… and yes, you're still invited.

৪০৫৪

When a man meets a woman and he wants to ask her out on a date, he usually does it by… well, literally *asking*. He will say something like: "Would you like to get together sometime?" or "Are you free tomorrow evening?" or "Do you have any plans for this Thursday?" or "Would you like to have coffee with me?" or "It was nice talking to you. Can I call you sometime?" On the surface, these questions all seem innocuous and normal, a good thing to do. It's better than doing nothing, right? However, he is still, hat in hand, asking.

I don't ask for anything. I make statements. Big difference. With ease and delight, and a sparkle in my eye. I will say, "It was nice talking to you. I would love to see you again." Or "Cancel your plans, sweet girl! Let's get together tonight." Or "I'm going for a coffee right now, if you'd care to join me." All of this is presented as what it is, a pure and honest invitation. There is no hint of ordering her around or controlling or demanding. And no questions at all.

Only statements. Never questions. There seems to be little difference between saying, "Can I call you sometime?" and "I would love to call you." Each, at first glance, is pretty much saying the same thing to her. In fact, she won't even notice the difference. But the effect on the interaction is huge. Subtle but monumental. It speaks volumes to the heart of a woman, for it telegraphs to her that not only am inviting her to dance with me, but I am willing to lead the dance. Where are my desires as a man? Where is my masculine edge? Where is my love of women? Right there. Right there in front of you, my love.

ഇരു

The waitress with the pink apron and wispy waterfall braid is exceptionally pretty, and the four guys who just came in notice her as they are about to sit down. With all eyes fixed on her, they arrange themselves around their table, and when their chairs are sufficiently scuffled into place and they are comfortably planted, it begins. I know exactly how this will unfold.

She is turned away from them, whisking along among other tables, doing waitress-y things, and they take full advantage of this opportunity to stare at her (I must admit) superb body. They collude, euphoric at their good fortune, in a flurry of exaltation, with raised eyebrows and "Not bad!" nods all around. They nudge each other with their elbows. They whisper and duck behind upright menus. She's still not looking? Well then... they lean out from their menus, hanging off the table on all sides to get a better view, like teenage boys cruising Main Street in Dad's convertible on a Saturday night. They are all admiring her, desiring her. Surreptitiously, or so they think. She doesn't notice, or so they think.

Oh, but you do notice, don't you, lovely girl? Of course you do. Every pretty woman is keenly aware of the effect she has on a room. She doesn't even need to look over at them to know what is happening. She's seen it all before.

Having returned the other tables to a temporary equilibrium, she turns around to face our illustrious little group, straightens her apron, and approaches their table.

What happens now? No surprise here: in an instant, a synchronized hush descends upon them and they scurry together, averting their eyes downward, pretending to scan their menus, intent and serious, like little boys over marbles, like they barely noticed her at all. "Yeah, uh... I'll have a coffee and, uh..." They never really engage her at all. They barely look up.

Why is this? I've never understood it. If men love women as much as they say they do, why do they hide it? Why is that exuberance suppressed?

Most men will check out a woman's body when she is not looking, then laugh and high-five their buddies behind her back. I don't get it. That's juvenile and asinine and disrespectful. A real man will check out her body, make sure she sees him doing it, then laugh and share the experience with her! This is fundamental. How ridiculous is it to check out a woman behind her back, without her noticing! It's no fun if you don't get caught. In fact, what's the point if you don't get caught? That's the most important part!

Here you are before, me pretty waitress... I can already smell your perfume and hear your laughter, and it's all for me, all for me. For I, too, have noticed you, and when you come to my table you will know that you are seen. I will turn in my chair toward you, my whole body facing you, I will smile with my eyes and my whole being, I will behold you entire, imbibing every detail in an instant: the flounce of your

wispy, auburn braid, the curve of your waist, the distance
of your horizon, and my spirit will thrill at the sight, like
the discovery of a new and raucous morning, like a happy
sunrise, and I will spread, as it were, my blanket before
you and bask in your sunlight, calm, unhurried, serene,
for all is right with the world, all is good, all is good, and
I will exult in you, in the triumph of you, in your luster, in
your life-giving energy, in the glory of your feminine essence,
and I will focus on you like you are the only woman in the
world. For, in that moment, are you not? You will have my
full attention, my full presence... Of course you will... look
at you! How lovely you are!

  Oh... and I will have the Eggs Benedict.
                    — The Alabaster Girl, *page 66*

ঝ৻ঞ

A man sees a woman over there and he studies the situation, stands
back, watches her, and wonders what is the best thing to do. Then
when he has summoned enough courage, he approaches her and
says whatever he thinks might be best to say. His intentions are good.
His attraction is real. His approach is honest.

However, he has been conditioned by media or mother that he must
remain sexually neutral, that he must not offend her. He has learned
to hide his attraction, his desires, and certainly his sexuality, beneath
a politically correct neutrality. This sets the tone for the encounter.

His conversation is surface, breezy, and innocuous. He might be
pleasant and interesting. He might offer to buy her a drink. Oh, but
he has something... he has an agenda, a desired outcome, hidden,
buried, shunted into the shadows. He wants something from her:
a phone number, or a date with her, or a one-night-stand, or a relationship, or love and marriage. None of this is secret to her, even
though he thinks it might be.

He is afraid to just say it. He is in his head the whole time, trying to figure it out. He is not really listening to the things she says because he is trying to angle the whole conversation toward his subterranean goal. He's thinking: I have to somehow get her phone number or I've failed. And thus, he spends the entire time calculating, calibrating, inching toward his goal.

He measures his success in the interaction by her response, and how well it seems to align with his agenda. If she responds favorably, he feels good. If she doesn't, he starts to feel that old familiar twinge of rejection. His hidden objective, he realizes, just might not be obtainable. Once again, he has failed. He turns away, dejected. He walks away knowing what he's known all along: that he is not good enough.

None of those objectives are, within themselves, objectionable. People can want what they want. Desire is not a bad thing. *Needing* what they desire will create problems; *hiding* what they desire will create even more. And hiding it, of course, exacerbates the neediness. The mistake is to not express what we are really after. The hidden-ness of his agenda, his masking of intentions, his secrecy about his desired result, is what clouds the interaction.

When I meet a delightful girl, she knows exactly what I am all about within the first minute. She knows there is no way she can put me in the "let's just be friends" box. How does she know this? Because I tell her! I tell her with my body language, my touch, and especially my words.

I just say it straight. Of course I would love to explore her in all her glory! Of course I am going to say, "Wow, look at you!" Of course I am going to say, "Run away with me…" That's who I am. This is what I want. She, of course, can want something else entirely. That's completely up to her. I can't be rejected by her because I am not *asking* her for anything. I am just stating what I would like to happen. I am just speaking my truth. I'm just saying what I want.

A woman knows the difference between me and a guy who is on the make, trying to pick her up. And also the difference between me and a "nice guy" asking her out for a coffee and a subsequent string of frustrating dates.

A woman knows exactly what she is getting into with me. My intentions are always as clear as the sky. I am remarkably direct. If I like her, I will say it. If I want her in my bed, she will know it. That's how I see it, so that's how I say it. I am honest about my intentions, but respectful if she is not interested. I am direct, yes, but at the same time, enjoying the moment with her and the interaction itself.

I never try to convince a woman of anything. Convincing is trying to convert her. This is something I will not do. Oh, I can do it, of course; I can convince a woman of just about anything, but I want her to be with me by choice, on purpose, and excited. I don't want her *consent*; I want her joyful willingness.

If I desire her, I will let her know immediately, without presumption or demand, and with absolute ease and delight. The next step is completely up to her. In everything I say and do, the ball is always in her court. I ask for what I want, a simple invitation, and she can do whatever she wants with that invitation. She doesn't have to accept it or even acknowledge it in any way. There is no attempt to convince her of anything, ever.

I do not make assumptions about her, and I do not remain passive and hope that she will assume certain things about me. Instead, I tell her everything directly, everything I am thinking. I describe to her *in words* exactly how I would like it to be. I invite her to dance and I promise to lead that dance. I will be the man. She will be the woman.

Inferences are kept to an absolute minimum. I never leave anything to chance. I never assume that, by my actions alone, a woman will know what I am thinking. I don't imply. I don't allow her to infer. I just say it. As in, "You intrigue me… there's something about you… and I don't know what it is." As in, "You are an absolute delight to me… you're my kind of girl." As in, "I can tell by your eyes that you would be a great lover for me… and maybe you can't… but look what's going on between us right now."

When I describe exactly what I want to experience with her, I am essentially creating it. By naming it, I make it real. What was not there before, now is. Or more precisely, what was unseen before, is now seen. Expressing what is already there, giving life to an idea that wants to be born. If I smile at her and lean into her and lower my voice for her and her alone, and say, "Can you feel that in the air? That electric vibration between us?"… well now, if she didn't feel it before, she will certainly feel it now.

ଞୠଔ

Men think that being direct means to be a caveman, aggressive, forceful, macho. And because men don't want to be seen as overbearing louts, they do the opposite. They dial themselves way down, in the other direction. They think that the opposite of being aggressive is to hide their intentions, to come in under the radar, and to pretend they are not really interested. By doing this, they hope that women won't notice their true intentions and thus, they won't be offended.

But being direct is not about being overtly blunt. It is about being clear in our intentions. I don't have to put any force behind the words I say, because I already have the force of truth. No hidden agenda. No "let's just see how it goes." I already *know* how it is going to go. Everything is in the open. There is no hiding of any kind.

Manipulation? Only in the sense that we get to choose one set of words over another, as in any interaction in life. Being direct is the absence of manipulation. There is no need for deception, for women are willing participants. A woman is right there with me, complicit in her seduction. There is no need to convince her of anything. She is already convinced. In fact, being direct is the opposite of convincing. It is a way of non-convincing.

I express my interest to a woman clearly and directly. I speak my desire. I am delighted to make plans with her. I call her when I say I will call. If she doesn't answer, no problem, I will leave a message. But only once. If she doesn't respond to that, I will never contact her again. And why won't I? Well, it's not because of any hurt or malice or indignation. It's because the ball is in her court. I did my job. I expressed my clear desire. I let her know that I would love to see her. I rang bells, I decorated the trees, I wrote her name in the sky. It is now up to her. If she desires it, she will find me; and if she does not, well, is that not a beautiful clarification?

ॐ

He likes her.
I can tell.
He is wondering if we are together.
I can tell.
How's it going? he says.
I shake his hand and smile.
Oh hey, let me introduce you to my sister.
She gives me a look.
I wink at her.
I sit back.
His face brightens.
He raises his beer to her.
Your sister, huh? Cheers!
He starts to talk.
And talk.
She gives me a look.
I wink at her.
I laugh and laugh.
　　　　— The Alabaster Girl, *page 68*

ॐ

Honesty is the greatest aphrodisiac. Glorious, profound secret of the universe! Women always respond to an honest invitation, as long as it is imbued with respect, kindness, and empathy.

And how does a woman know that I am honest? Because I tell her. That's how. It's as simple as that. Women always believe what I say to them. Why? Because they can and they know they can. I do not misrepresent.

Yes, I will whisper little white lies to you, beautiful lies, all the lies you want to hear. But I will *never* deceive you. My lies are honest, my lies are sincere, my lies are truth, and you, my love, you get to decide.

Every woman I meet gets the sense that I will never play with her heart, that I will never deceive her. I look into her eyes and tell her that she can trust me, a phrase she has heard from men all her life, and in her heart, she knows she can. I tell her quietly that she will be safe with me in every way, and she feels the truth of this in the air. I tell her that I will never mislead her and she believes me immediately. And what's more, she will believe me for the rest of her days, a sacred trust between us.

By trust, I don't mean what you might think I mean. I don't mean I want her to learn that she can trust me *eventually*—by getting to know me, by warming up to me, by opening her heart to me, by my proving to her that I am honorable. No, I want her to trust me *immediately*, to trust me simply because I ask for it, to look into my eyes and to know that, yes, she can trust me. Is that asking a lot from her? Yes, it is. But anything less than that is just fast-talking, coaxing, convincing.

This is the highest thing that I love: that a woman trusts me completely. I desire her complete trust. I want her to trust that I am on her side, that I will not lie to her, that I would rather die than purposely hurt her heart.

I am a believer in life, in love, in beauty. Why look down when I can look up? Why ask small questions when I can ask great ones? I demand the highest standard of myself, and I demand the highest standard of the women in my life.

And no, it's not an ultimatum. There is no sense of "you better do it my way, or else." No, not at all. There is no sense of demanding or controlling. I have no interest in petty mind games. Instead, it is a simple, clear, bright, honest invitation to shine. I will show up fully delighted to be with you, and all I ask from you is the same.

When I invite you into my presence, my love, I am inviting you to show up in your full, rapturous beauty. Because that is the way I choose to see you, the only way I ever will see you. And by your beauty, I mean the full you, the authentic you, the feminine you, the trusting you, the shining you.

ഇൟ

What is it that I want from a woman? Everything. That's what I want. I want everything. I demand all yet I never take. I don't need her support. I don't need her help. I don't need her comfort. I don't need her understanding. I don't need her body. I need nothing from her. But I *want* it all. I want everything of her. I want all her talents. I want all the languages she speaks. I want her to gather everything up and bring it all here to me. I want her full surrender. I want her complete worship. I want her absolute devotion above all.

And by devotion, I don't mean quiet servitude. I mean that she would do *anything* for me. Yes, anything. I do not want a demure accompanist, a blind follower. I want a partner, an accomplice, and at times, a provocateur. A woman who is with me had better be prepared to hold her own. Inspire me, girl, make me proud to be with you.

When I have her absolute devotion, well then guess what, my love? Now she is my girl. Now I want her completely. Now I want her support. Now I want her help. Now I want all her understanding. Now I want her body. Now I can learn about her. Now I can love her mind. Now I can be a student of her body. Now I can give her everything, everything of me to her. Now, I can sit at her feet and look up to her face and be amazed.

I will cast a protective shield around her. I will destroy anything that would harm her. I will pry the stars from the sky with the tip of my knife for her. I will delight in presenting her to the world. I will be proud of her in public moments of us. She will never feel alone. She will never feel abandoned. She will be noticed, seen, found lovely, delighted in. She will be the queen, the beauty—*my beauty*—maximally beautiful in my presence, in my eyes, for this is the only way I will ever see her. Yes, she will stand before me in her true beauty, and I will worship her forever.

It is our little secret that no one else can share, for she is over there, flirting with all the men and I am over here adoring all the women, and I will look across the crowd and catch her eye, and we will both smile, for it is us against the world, my love, us against the world. And the people will never understand.

ß©CR

Some men, upon hearing me speak about beauty, think I am all about circuitous compliments and verbal floral arrangements. They think I represent a throwback to the type of effusive, back-of-the-hand-on-the-forehead, swooning dandy who falls forever at her feet. But ah, my love, I am the most direct man I know. I have no hidden desires. *Au contraire*, my love. My desires are spread out before you, back-lit and in focus. I never hide my desires, ever.

I compliment women all the time. Oh yes, I do. Ornate, lavish, curli-cued compliments. "But you can't do that!" men shout, "Beautiful women hear it all the time. You're making yourself too available! Women love the chase. She will see you as just another guy kissing her ass, breathlessly approving of her, needy and weak. Isn't complimenting a woman putting her on a pedestal? Isn't it bordering on worship? Surely it elevates her and diminishes you? It's far better to be a little dismissive of her or even knock her down a bit. That will set you apart from all the other guys, and she will want you. Complimenting her is just giving away your power." No it isn't. Not even close.

I don't understand the concept that a man can somehow "give away his power." To appreciate beauty in a woman? To call it like I see it? To speak my truth? How on earth is that giving away power? How can I possibly lose any power to a random girl *I just met*? She's just a girl! I may never see her again! How can I possibly fail? Yes, she is beautiful to me. What of it? No matter what her response is to anything I say or do, I'm still me.

Feeling a loss of power comes from the assumption that her opinion is a judgment made upon us by *all* women, not just her in particular. It's taking her words and treating it like she just told our fortunes, dictated our futures with all women forever. Loss of confidence equals loss of power equals loss of confidence.

The reason that compliments from a man can fall flat to a woman's ears is because she knows the *intention* behind his compliments. He has a hidden agenda, and she knows it. He is thinking, "Maybe if I compliment her, I will get something in return. Maybe she will like me more than all the other guys, or maybe she will give me her number, or maybe she will even sleep with me." In other words, his compliments have conditions attached. In other words, his compliments have nothing to do with *her* at all, and everything to do with *him*. In other words, his compliments are almost always entirely selfish. It is all about him, and not about her at all.

I have nothing to hide. I am a man. She is a woman. Is that not enough? Is that not reason enough for everything? I compliment her, yes, but not to get something in return. I am simply stating my truth. I'm simply expressing my appreciation for beauty. I am simply giving her the gift of desiring her. She can do whatever she wants with that information. It is not my responsibility. As always, the ball is in her court.

There is no presumption in my compliment. There is no manipulation. There is no hidden agenda. There is no neediness. There is no anticipation of rejection. There is no crushing feeling of failure just because she has a boyfriend. There is no "If you don't accept what I'm offering, then it's your loss." There is no trying to wrest a phone number from her. There is just me expressing who I am and that I like nice things and that in another time and place, we would be lovers, yes indeed, and that I am not afraid to walk across the room to tell her that very thing.

It's so simple, and men make it so hard. If a woman walks by, all I say is something like, "Hi, how are you today? You have a lovely smile. Stop and talk to me for a while." Never, ever—not once—have I ever seen a girl throw up the proverbial "bitch shield" around that kind of clarity.

When I look into a woman's eyes and say, "You're a real beauty, and I like that," it is a recognition, an affirmation, an invocation to the spirit of beauty I see in her, a desire to see her elegance and grace fully arrayed before the world, before me. I need nothing in return, for having experienced the vision of her, having bathed in her light, I have already received everything that is holy and pure between a man and a woman. I have encountered beauty. All is right with the world.

A little of the light is enough, just as wonderful as a lot of it. A little sip, when taken in full awareness, is as amazing as drinking the whole glass. A man who thinks in terms of failure—that a half a glass is more of a failure than a full glass—will have that agenda, and of course it has to be a secret agenda. Not just because it's unseemly, according to society, but because it's actually a power play and somewhere down deep he knows it.

Most people think that the very gauge of whether they care about something is how much they need it to happen. I think the opposite is true. I am open to all outcomes, but attached to none. Everything is possible; nothing is necessary. It doesn't mean I don't care. It means I *do* care. It means I have great desire, but no neediness. It means I have no hidden agenda. It means I am wonderfully attracted to her and would be delighted to see her again, but there is no desperation in me to try to force it in any way, and no sense of failure if, for whatever reason, it doesn't happen. It means I trust that if I put myself forth into the world as best I can, if I plant my stake into the ground right here where I stand, if I state exactly what it is that I want, then all outcomes are possible and all outcomes are good.

Of course, there is always the possibility of a great attraction turning into a great event (which takes two to tango) but I care most of all about telling the truth. A great attraction on her part is partly out of my control but stating my desire is entirely up to me. So if the first one doesn't happen but I fulfilled the other, well hey, at least I showed up in the world.

∞CR

Here is another subtle distinction, my love: *I compliment a woman in the context of all women*. What does this mean? Well, when I show appreciation for a woman's beauty, I am, in essence, showing appreciation for the beauty of *all* women. When I celebrate her, I am celebrating everything that women represent. I might say something like, "I love your hair, the way it frames your face... you are so strikingly beautiful right now... in this light... this is why I love women so much!"

But, you might object, a woman wants to feel special. She doesn't want to be compared to other women. Yes, yes, of course. I understand this. As often happens when I try to describe the way my mind differs from other men, the description pales in comparison to the execution. When I describe this concept in words or on the page, it falls flat and women tend to wrinkle their noses and shake their heads, unsure. However, when I actually *do* it, women—all women—respond in a wonderful way. Why? Because it makes them feel special indeed.

Here's the subtlety at play: This has nothing to do with *other women*. This has everything to do with *her*. When I compliment a woman in the context of all women, it doesn't mean that I am comparing her to other women. No, I am comparing her to the *essence* of women, the *essence* of beauty. I am celebrating the spirit of women that I see in her. I am complimenting her specifically, yes, but I am also complimenting the soul of women that she embodies. I am in love with all women, not *other* women. Can you see the distinction there, my love? I love women and the myriad of gifts they bring into the world. I love beauty. I love art. And this woman arrayed before me is a perfect example.

To elucidate this concept further, think about how most men will talk about an ex-girlfriend. If you ask a man you are dating what happened with his last relationship—why did it end?—his tendency is to be a little dismissive of his ex-girlfriend, or to mildly diminish her in some way. He might say something like, "Well, she had trust issues" or "She didn't really understand me" or "She was always jealous for no reason." In other words, his tendency is to downsize her importance to his life. Why? Because he feels that by doing so, he is implying to you that, in his mind, you are better than her, that you are not like her.

Not me. If you ask me about an ex-girlfriend, I will say, "Ah, she was so beautiful and her heart was so lovely and I miss her so much. What a wonderful girl in this world." And I will mean it. The difference here is that nothing is taken away from you, my love, nothing whatsoever. When I celebrate my previous girlfriend and the beauty she added to my life, I am, in essence, celebrating all women. I am celebrating *you*.

All the women of my life knew that I love and celebrate the essence of women, and yet there was not even the slightest hint in their minds that I would ever hurt them, or cheat on them, or chase other women behind their backs. My love of women has nothing to do with other women. It has everything to do with a hosanna of the female spirit.

ଅଣ

So... there's a party later tonight. You want to come?
No... I don't think so.
It will be great fun.
Where is it?
My apartment around the corner.
Well... maybe...
Some wine, some music, some dancing.
Who's going to be there?
I smile and wink.
Well, so far... just you and me.
— The Alabaster Girl, *page 72*

ଅଣ

There are two ways a man can show up in this world. The first man buys expensive champagne and pours it for a girl. He is trying to impress her and make himself more attractive in her eyes. He asks himself, "Does she like me? Does she like me?" She sees his attempts to impress, smells his neediness, happily drinks his champagne, and then goes home with someone else.

The second man buys expensive champagne and pours it for a girl. He is having fun tonight, living his life, on an adventure, with or without her. He asks himself, "Do I like her? Do I like her?" She senses this, feels the calmness of his spirit, happily drinks his champagne, and stays right there beside him, a hopeful escape from the sameness of her days and nights.

ஒஐ

A man tends to go through three evolutionary stages in his life when it comes to women. In the first stage, he is nice and accommodating. He buys dinners, movies, flowers. He picks up the check. He opens the door. He tries hard to be interesting and charming. And he discovers that his experiences with women are okay, but nothing ever seems to go anywhere.

In the second stage, he is tired of those lackluster results. He learns not to be so accommodating, not to supplicate, not to put women on a pedestal, not to compliment them too much. He backs off from buying them things and being too available. He makes her split the check. He lets her open her own door. And he discovers that his experiences with women are now more… interesting. It's a little better, but he is still not getting the type of experiences—or the type of women—he really wants. It's all kind of hit or miss.

In the third stage… guess what? None of this matters anymore. He does whatever the hell he wants. He buys women dinners, movies, flowers. He picks up the check. He opens the door and takes her by the hand. He compliments women highly, he celebrates them graciously, he moves among them easily. He kisses their cheeks whenever they're around. Supplication is no longer an issue. In fact, he never thinks about it again. The result? Women in his arms, women in his bed, women in his life.

Let's examine this. In both the first and the third stage, it seems he is putting women on "pedestals." So what makes the difference? The difference is the frame of reference, the motivation behind it all. The man in the first scenario is thinking only of himself and what he can get from her. The man in the third scenario is doing all the same things as the supplicating guy in the first scenario, but it comes from a different part of his being, from a different center of gravity. The difference is in his intention. And that is all the difference in the world.

Men are so guarded about putting a woman "on a pedestal." But appreciating a woman's beauty has nothing to do with putting her on a pedestal. When a nice guy puts a woman on a pedestal, he is trying to contain her, in a way. It is all about winning and conquering and controlling. It is all about him, not her. When a man who loves women puts a woman on a pedestal, it is a true elevation, an appreciation of her beauty, a recognition, an acknowledgment. It is all about her. A nice guy puts a woman on a pedestal. A true lover puts *women* on a pedestal.

ജ

Many men like to chase things. If a woman is too available, too excited, too so-called "easy," they get bored or the reward just isn't fulfilling. They like a challenge. I do not. I'm too lazy, I suppose. If I can't find a shortcut, an easy path, a way to clean the Augean stables in a single day, I'd rather not bother.

I don't want to chase anything in this whole wide world. What really endears a woman to my heart is when she is smitten by me and she shows it. It doesn't mean I want a girl to be all over me or hanging on my every word. I don't like a challenge, but I do like a mystery.

I show up one hundred percent, and I desire the same from her. I want her full attention, her aliveness, her presence, because I am surely going to give all those things to her. I never play that silly little parlor game of hard-to-get, and when a woman insists on playing it, I simply turn away. I have no time for this tedium. I lose all interest. Because where is she? I showed up. Where is she? I am here before her, with arms open wide, and I want her to be as excited by the possibilities as me.

The secret of all this is that there is no need to "chase" women, ever. It is completely unnecessary. When a man sets out on a journey of excellence, heading toward the life he desires, seeking relevance in his life no matter what the cost, he discovers that women always find him attractive, that there is a great abundance of women in this world, that there is no need whatsoever to play games, and that trivialities like phone numbers are automatic, falling all around him like snowflakes in a field.

ഇൽ

Many men need the support of "wingmen", the camaraderie, the fist-pumping assurances of their buddies. Not me. Men are never my wingmen. I enjoy the company of sincere men and good conversations, but never when there are lovely girls floating by all around us. I don't go out to hang out with guys. I go out for only one thing: to surround myself with female energy. I couldn't possibly imagine going to a pub or a bar or party with guys, only to talk about sports or cars or whatever. I mean, c'mon, where are all the girls?

I don't need a posse. I operate far better alone. I am like the lone gunslinger that rides into town on dusty horseback, orders a shot of whiskey in the saloon, beds the feisty town beauty (and her friend for good measure), then rides off into the sunset alone. It helps me not at all if men try to join the conversation, disrupting the little reverie I have with a girl.

Most men, bless their hearts, tend to get in my way when I am talking to women. Even well-meaning friends. My interactions with women are low-voiced, connected, lasered in. I talk to women with a certain cadence, a rhythm for her and I alone, a connection that is impossible if there is anyone else included. If another man enters the sphere, friend or otherwise, it is no longer her and I against the world. The magic is dispelled, our secret garden dissolves, the electricity dissipates.

It doesn't matter who it is. It could be a friend of hers, or even a friend of mine. I will welcome him, of course, be gracious, introduce him, and include him. "This is my friend," I will smile and say, then I will stand back and give him a chance to engage. I wouldn't dream of shouldering him away. He has every right to be there, to present his best self to her. And if I detect that she likes him, perfect. She is not my girl. If she doesn't, eventually he will leave and I will be right back in there with her and our little conspiracy. "Hello, my dear. How are you? Did you miss me?"

Which brings me to my next point: A lot of men think they need a wingman to stave off the blows of her overprotective girlfriends. Let's say a guy is out in a bar and sees two girls over there. They are immediately shunted into one of two categories in his mind: the one he likes and the "obstacle." The obstacle is now the "enemy," the potential "drag-away girl." He worries that if the obstacle is not entertained or is bored, she will grab his girl's arm and say, "Let's go." Thus, the need for the saving grace of a wingman. Someone to "lean into the pitch" or "jump on the grenade," to use the crude, but common, vernacular.

I don't need someone to occupy or entertain her girlfriend. I always engage her friend directly, in an open attempt to get her on my side, to make her my erstwhile "wingman." For I know that if I include her in my shenanigans, she is the best wingman I could possibly have. If I include her, she will *help* me with her friend. No obstacle there. Making sure the one I like can hear, I say, "So, tell me about your friend here… is she a good girl? Will she take care of me when I am old?" Smile, wink.

৪৩৫

Some men have this curious notion that they must somehow out-display, out-gun, or out-alpha other men. Not me. I don't compete with other men at all. I am not interested in playing the role of the alpha-male gorilla trying to attract the female. Let the other gorillas prance around and display personality and beat their chests. Instead, I am going on an adventure to the other side of the jungle to see what magic I can find. And I extend my hand to her in quiet invitation. I would love her to come—what a beauty!—but I am going anyway. Whether or not she comes with me, I am going anyway.

True lovers of women are highly gracious, highly respectful, of other men they meet. Their energy radiates outward to all. They smile and nod and shake hands firmly with other men. They are not "sneaky fuckers," to use the abrupt but delightfully accurate phrase coined by the late biologist, John Maynard Smith, after studying deer populations. They approach men, not their girlfriends behind their backs. They say things like, "It's nice to meet you, and your wife here is absolutely beautiful." It is as much a compliment to him as it is to her.

True lovers of women are planets. They know the score, they stand on their own two feet, they break off their own piece. They orbit around no one. Other men, naturally, are satellites.

ഇന്ദ

I have a boyfriend.
Of course you do! That means we will have to be extra careful during our secret trysts.
She laughs.
One boyfriend is more than enough for me.
Oh really? You look like the kind of girl who could use two boyfriends.
Two boyfriends? I don't think so.
Sure. One for movies and popcorn and cuddling... and one to drink champagne from your belly button...
— The Alabaster Girl, *page 75*

ഇന്ദ

I have spent a significant portion of my life in bed between two girls. And I am not talking about threesomes. I am talking about my girl (whom I love, love, love, adore!) on one side of me and her best friend (or not) on the other side. How perfect is this? What celestial bliss do I have after a night spent with women! Picture me, my love, resplendent in my element, surrounded by beauty, a cornucopia of breasts and lacy invitations on all sides, and so amazed by life and its multitudinous treasures—albeit hot and squished in the middle as they rustle and flail about in their sleep! To wake up to the manifestation of this is a gift to the heart, truly a sense of coming home, a sublime alignment in the way things are supposed to be. At least to me.

Oh, how I love my girl! *She* created this. *She* made this happen, not me. And this is exactly why she is my girl. She knows how much I love women and because she knows, she surrounds me with women, fills my home with women. I would never violate her trust or hurt her heart. How could I? Look what she has done for me! She has perfumed my life with beauty, and because of that, I adore her. How could I possibly lust after another woman or turn my face to others? Just because she brings other girls into our circle doesn't mean that it is open season, that I have been given *carte blanche* to romp around at will. Not at all. It means that she loves me and understands me and knows me oh, so well.

All of my relationships are like this. How? Because I *ask* for it. I describe clearly what I want. Inferences, as always, are kept to a minimum. I say to her, "My sweet girl… I adore women and I thrive on the energy of women. I love women and I want them around me all the time. Bring female energy around me, my angel… your sisters, your mother, your girlfriends, other girls. For I promise you this: You will never feel jealous. I will never take my eyes off you, for you are my *only* girl. And you will know it and feel it every moment of every day. I am not a king without my queen." And she looks at me, and she ponders for a second, and then she says okay.

Most women have expectations about how things should be, but because I ask for different things than other men, and because I say it right from the very beginning, and because I arrive into a woman's life as a completely new experience, all those usual expectations are never cast upon me. Here is the most important part: I am just describing how I want it to be with her. She has absolute autonomy and full choice.

Well, you might be thinking, she is only agreeing to tolerate it for a while. Ah, but she doesn't just tolerate it—she embraces it and *makes it happen*. This is why she is my girl. My girlfriend is always my co-conspirator. Never trust a woman who is not your biggest fan, who would not cover for you, who is not a willing accomplice to your sundry crimes.

She does all the work. Everything is up to her. She must choose the women in our sphere, for if she does not enjoy the energy and beauty of a girl then I can't either. I am not going to go out and collect women. I would never be so gauche, so crass as to gather other girls into a basket to present to her. The last thing I would do is tell her, "Hey, I met a girl... and you would really like her." That is volumes of disrespect. That is misaligned and misguided motives.

But no self-respecting woman would ever be willing to do this, some will say. Oh yes, they would. You would be amazed what a woman will do for a man who makes her feel like a queen. Okay, but these must be flash-in-the-pan, disposable girlfriends, some will say. No, no, not at all. These are women who were in my life for years.

Women give me everything. They give me women. They bring other women into my life. That's the way it is. This defines my entire experience. Most men do not understand this, but it is exactly the way my life flows. It is because I simply ask for it, because they understand me, because they feel loved.

How many women will accept this arrangement? All... if they feel loved enough. A woman will do anything for a man she loves and who loves her. As D.H. Lawrence said, "A woman unsatisfied must have luxuries. But a woman in love with a man would sleep on a board."

Even a woman who says she would never do that. Yes, she would. She might prance and stamp her feet, adamant, insisting that no, not her. Oh, but they all do. If given the chance, they all do.

Don't get me wrong. I am physically intimate with *my* girl—not with multiple girls. My fantasies are of her and her alone. Men think it would be great to have two girlfriends at once. Well, I've been there, and it is great for a time. And by a time, I mean a night or two. After that, it devolves into seething mind games and a requiem of utter destruction.

I should know: Years ago, in my unquenchable (and thoroughly naïve) youth, I lived with two excitable, nineteen-year-old beauties for several months. Two girls in my bed, two girls in the shower, two girls before me every time I turned around. Every guy's dream, right? Yes, well, never again! An unbelievable hornet's nest of favoritism accusations and petty jealousies. I was in love with one and accepted the other. And the other felt snubbed, left out, upset. I almost needed porters to handle all the extra baggage!

ৡেপ্ত

I am already on the subject, so here goes: Threesomes are quietly corrosive to a relationship unless there is harmony and balance, a clear understanding of roles, and a holding, loving carefulness. The secret of threesomes is this: It is all about *her*. You can never take your eyes off your girl. *She has to be the center of attention the whole time.* She has to feel praised, beautiful, desired. It is you and the other woman kneeling together before the throne of your queen.

In fact, the man has to get out of the way. A guy raised on a superfluity of porn, thinks it should be all about him: lying on his back with his arms behind his head while the girls go to town on him. But it doesn't work that way. His role is to circle around the periphery, let the experience unfold gently, like a conductor before his magnificent orchestra. Baton in hand, so to speak.

There is something about the tender touch, the emotional understanding and validation that women never get from men and maybe were never supposed to. Women know what women want. Most men don't.

The other woman knows her role. If she is smart, she will stay in her lane. She is your accomplice tonight, an adjunct, Santa's little helper. She is nothing more than that and she knows it and is okay with it. If your girl feels—*even for one second*—that you have turned your face away from her to the other, third-party girl, everything will come crashing down. She will become quiet and uncomfortable, infinitely insecure, with doubts flying around her head like bats: "She is younger," or "She is prettier," or "He desires her body more than mine."

Here is a secret of the universe: *Women don't care if you are faithful. They care if you are loyal.* And yes, I am fully aware I will get lambasted from all corners for that antediluvian comment, but that's okay, I will say it anyway. And no, I am not condoning mistresses in any way. I'm just telling it like it is. There is a vast difference between being faithful and being loyal.

A woman is okay with other women, as long as she feels like she is your goddess above all. She will do anything for you, as long as she feels like she is number one in your life. If you let her know—and it is true and she can feel it—that you will never turn your face away from her, that you will adore her above all the lilies of the field, that you will celebrate her and her alone and that you will always place her, sublime, on lofty heights for all to see, she will do *anything* for you.

೮ೱ೧೮

A humid evening in the heart of old Montreal, a festive night, the narrow cobble-stoned streets outside filled with people. The piano bar is embroidered with the city's artists and musicians, interweaving and interwoven—but my mind is elsewhere, on her.

The wine begins to touch me now, softly. I hold the glass out before me... thick and red, the color of lips I used to know.

And then, you ripple into view... an auburn-haired vision... a serendipitous sylph... a welcomed breath of fresh air.

Other men notice you too. I watch them and I can see their minds racing, trying to decide what to do, how to do. They do nothing, of course. One by one, they talk themselves out of doing anything... they will have another beer.

One man, however, stands tall, rearranges himself and smooths, then accosts you as you pass by. I see his mouth forming the words, "Can I buy you a drink?" and I see you gently smile and touch his arm and point to where your friends are waiting. "Thanks anyway," you say. And off you go.

He leans back against the bar, conflicted, watching you walk away, then looking down and slowly swirling the whiskey in his glass, glancing up at you again, then back to the whiskey swirl, back to you, back to the whiskey, sinking lower into a damp and miasmic mood, and turning away at last to stare obliquely into the crowd, over the crowd, through the crowd.

— The Alabaster Girl, *page 77*

෧෨

There is a dance that happens before words are exchanged. It is just as clear and just as direct as anything we might say in words. But it isn't necessary to say it in words, because the language of women is entirely sub-communicated. Very few men understand this.

Women are always radiating signals to the world of men, but because most men do not pick up on these signals, women receive little response. This is why women gravitate toward men who have taken the time to learn the language of women, the rhythm, the cadence, the intricacies of the unspoken word.

Sub-communication is not a method, a trick, something to pull out of your pocket in order to be seductive. It is a natural, ever-present, ethereal note below the noise. It is a color of the spectrum that most men will never learn to see, a language they will never learn to hear.

There is a subtext in everything I say to a woman. On the surface, it might seem that I am conversing with all the others nearby (and I am, with what I hope is great articulation and charm), but at the same time I am sub-communicating massively with her. Everything I say and do is loaded but spread face up, everything has a double meaning but clearly defined.

My interaction with women is all intrigue, mystery, conspiracy, a knowing, a constant communication, a steady hum. No one else even notices. They have no clue what's going on. But she does. Oh, yes she does. She notices and understands every little unspoken word I say, every seemingly casual gesture. She sees it all and she knows the meaning of it all. Even when I am seemingly addressing the others, she knows that everything I say is really directed to her. I am offering myself to her as a lover *sub rosa*, if she desires, and nobody else ever needs to know. It is ours alone, our secret garden. The others? Blithely ignorant of our little sub-communication, our conspiracy. But it's there all right, as clear as ringing bells. It is letting her know… I see you, yes… I desire you, yes… I know you, yes… and *you know I know.*

My sense of conspiracy with women is complete and explains all. It is always our little intrigue. Casanova relates a wonderful story: He was attending a play in Russia when he encountered the Parisian actress, Valville, who was renowned far and wide for her beauty. In the intermission, he hovered around the periphery and watched the scene unfold. He observed all the other men cascading around her, jockeying for position, trying to out-alpha each other, trying to be more funny, more interesting, more confident, more eligible, or just more loud than the others. He observed all this for awhile, from a distance, then had a servant discreetly slip a note into her hand that read, "Madam, I should like to begin an intrigue with you…"

Ah, that's the spirit! Zest for life and love! Call it like you see it. Casanova knew that no woman can resist the idea of an intrigue, a conspiracy. He *always* created conspiracies with the women in his life. This was his entire *modus operandi*. Nothing he ever did was overt or obvious or an attempt to wrest a prize away from other men.

Casanova's whole presentation was one of quietly leading and of women being quietly led. There was a rhythm in his overtures, a metaphorical rocking in and out toward them, a subtle but clear acknowledgment of their hidden desires. There was respect, empathy, and discretion. There was a knowing conviction, a masculine non-apology for his simple and honest invitation. It was the concept of the two of them against the world. He offered a secret affair, an intrigue, to every woman; and the reason women responded so favorably is that he, himself, was no secret to them at all.

৪০৫৪

Men have no clue about me and my love affair with women. Men don't even see what's going on. I operate beyond the pale. I circulate unseen, behind the scenes. If men only knew the level of two-way communication I have with women, all women, even *their* women, they would be sobered and shocked to their foundations.

This is why, I suppose, some men might perceive me as being indirect or even passive. For them, direct means being in your face, approaching, approaching, approaching, verbally explicit, and it would appear that I am doing nothing, saying nothing. But I've already shared hidden words, paragraphs, chapters, entire volumes with her. If only they knew, my love, if only they knew.

This conspiratorial intuition is so finely tuned in me that I can say things to a woman out loud and no one will even hear it. We could be sitting around a table with everyone in the group talking and laughing and sharing with each other, and she is sitting away from me, across the table somewhere. I've already planted the seed, of course: The moment she was first near to me, through introductions or happenstance, I let her know with my eyes and an imperceptible nod that I see her and I like what I see.

Now then, as the evening progresses, as the interactions around the table weave in and out, I am always keenly aware of everything that is happening, of everything that is being said. I can sense the undercurrent, the ebb and flow, the rhythm of the conversation, and I can sense the exact moment when I can say something to her that *no one else will even hear*. This guy beside me is telling a joke, these two are listening to it and laughing, this girl is distracted by the waitress, the girl on the other side of me is talking quietly to the girl beside her, the other guy over there is looking at his phone, and in that exact, perfect moment, with all bases covered, a magnificent portal opens in space-time, everything slows down to infinity, and I can smile and say to her across the table, with all the time in the world, "You know that I see you, girl. You know that I like you, don't you? And I know that you like me, too. You can feel that, right?" Out loud. In words. And no one but her even hears it, has a clue.

৪৩৯৫

She smells like the flowers of Colombia... the perfumed gardens of Medellín.

Four of us at the small, round table, enjoying a few moments of wit and wine. She sits to my left, beautiful, regal, poised. Her date sits across from me. His friend sits to my right. Conversation swirls among us... she is mine. I can tell. I have been in this situation too many times before not to recognize a connection.

She is talking to me now, telling me something, something about her work or life. I, of course, cut her off, mid-sentence, "Can I ask you a very important question?"

"How important?"

"Life or death."

She smiles. "Sure."

"Can you feel that in the air? You and I are going to get together. It is absolutely pure, and absolutely going to happen. You know it and I know it. I can see it in your eyes."

The two men at our table are oblivious, talking to each

other, animated. They can't hear us. This is our space. My
communication with women goes completely unnoticed by
other men, even men who are trying to listen. No matter.
Ours is a secret language.

She stops talking and looks down at the table, contem-
plating my words, my announcement, my imperative. Her
eyes flutter, a slight hesitation, then barely audible, "Yes."
— The Alabaster Girl, *page 80*

ॐ

In a group, you can always tell who a woman likes the most. How?
Watch who she looks at when the whole group is laughing. Even if
she tries to hide who she likes by not talking to him or not looking
at him too much, she will always glance at him when the whole
group laughs, especially if he is the one who made them all laugh.

This is a vital lesson I learned years ago when I was young and vaca-
tioning in Cancun. I had gone there with a good friend of mine and
all we wanted to do was meet girls and have fun. So as soon as we
winter-weary Canadians stepped off the plane into the blast furnace
that is Mexico and tossed our scant belongings through the door of
our hotel room, we headed straight for the beach.

Without hesitation, and in our let's-not-hold-back-because-we-are-
on-vacation exuberance, we walked right up and introduced ourselves
to the first girl we saw, a vivacious redhead in an equally vivacious
bikini. She might have been waiting for someone, but ah, we didn't
care. She was sitting at the beach bar, the kind with a low, over-
hanging grass-thatch roof, and with one of those silly little umbrella
drinks in front of her. She turned to us, friendly and receptive; so
far, this was very good.

We joked and laughed, and joked and laughed some more, but slowly
I began to notice, to my deepening chagrin, that she was directing
most of her conversation to my friend and not to me. For instance,

when she asked a question like "So how long are you guys staying?" she would direct the question to him, and not to me. My initial interpretation of this, of course, was that she liked him the most and ah, why not? My friend was, after all, good-looking and personable. I figured I might as well just sit in the back seat and enjoy the scenery.

Slowly, however, it dawned on me (and him, I think) that it was really *me* she was interested in, for I noticed that as she continued to talk to him, she would frequently glance at me. Simple and subtle, ridiculously easy to misinterpret or miss completely, but for the very first time, I intuited what is, I think, an immutable law of the universe. Let's be specific and call it, say: *The Theorem of Deflected Attention.*

The Theorem of Deflected Attention states that: *Whenever a girl is talking to N guys, where N >1, the guy she talks to the least is the one she is interested in the most.*

The amazing thing is that she wasn't doing this on purpose. It was a subconscious subtlety on her part, and what I have discovered over the years is that this law is always true; a woman in a conversation will subconsciously direct her attention away—at least initially—from the one she is interested in the most.

෩෪

I can't tell you how many women have said to me, "I dress up in my favorite dress, I go dancing with my girlfriends, I look around, I am open and friendly, I smile. I see guys looking at me, but they just stand around over there with their buddies and their beers. They never approach me until they are drunk. And then they are slurring and spitting on me as they talk. It's always the same."

Ah, my love… single women are in a difficult position. A woman doesn't want to be the one who leads, the one who approaches. She wants a man to notice her signals and take charge, take the lead. She puts signals into the world all the time and men don't act on them or even recognize them. She sees the men looking at her, she smiles and hopes they will come talk to her, but the men do not. So what can she do? Should she be the one to initiate? Should she approach the men? If men are not showing up and doing their job, should she?

The problem for women is that they lose no matter what happens. If a woman is single and wants to meet someone, and a man she is interested in doesn't approach her, she loses. If she takes the initiative and approaches him, she still loses. In the worst case, she will be seen as easy or desperate. In the best case, she will forever be the one who had to take the first step. Even if she ends up marrying the guy, some imperceptible measure of respect for him has been irrevocably lost. Because, well… where was he? Why did he not show up? Why did he not do his job as a man? Why did she have to lead the dance? Why must she support both sides of the equation? Oh, and here's another lovely side effect: guys are turned off because she is too forward.

The natural order of things is for women to signal their openness, and for men to straighten their ties, smooth back their hair, and respond. That's the way it works, or at least the way it is supposed to work. The problem is that the signals of women are, by their nature, so subtle and the minds of men so cluttered with societal static that, in this disconnected age, men have forgotten how to read the signals. In other words, the men are *not* approaching. Not anymore. Thus, we have the women standing around, frustrated and alone on one side of the room, and the men standing around, huddled, muddled, and murmuring on the other side.

But we can't blame the men. They have *tried* to approach and they have gotten slammed repeatedly. They tried it and it didn't work. This is because, not being able to read the signals of women and thus discern who is receptive or not, they approach *every* girl that seems pretty. And because there are plenty of women out there who are simply bitches about the whole thing ("Whatever made you think that *you* could come talk to *me*?") the men recoil, lick their wounds, and stay increasingly on the sidelines.

A single woman is broadcasting on an unused channel. But she is *always* broadcasting. It's there in the way she touches her neck. It's there in the way she adjusts her skirt, her hair, her jewelry. It's there in the way she tilts her head. It's there in the way she averts her eyes. It's there in the way she arches her back. It's even there in the way she pretends to not notice a man, or to even outright ignore him. Yes, women are constantly putting out whispered, subtle signals everywhere, hoping men will understand. But men do not understand. So women give up, and resort to virtual shouting, which only adds to the confusion and the noise.

The difference with me is that I have learned the language of women and I speak it fluently. And wow, there are signals everywhere! I see them all, my love, all the implied invitations, and I actively follow up on them. A woman might hold my gaze for a few seconds, then glance down and back up to me again. She might blink a little more rapidly than usual. She might sweep her hair back or casually play with it. She might soften her eyes when she looks at me. She might widen them briefly. She might glance at my mouth, she might stroke her arm softly, she might twirl the stem of her wine glass slowly, she might lean toward me slightly, she might align her body toward me; she might uncross her legs, only to cross them again. She might purse her lips ever so slightly, she might touch her teeth with her tongue, she might even bite her lower lip. I see it all. And it makes me smile and acknowledge her, thanking her for all of those beautiful things, for it truly is a breathtaking sight.

It takes time and infinite practice in the land of women to learn the signals, the language, and the rhythm of women. There is no other way. An intuition, an awareness of the way women communicate with men can only be learned by trial and error. No shortcuts here. But just being aware that this is happening all the time is the key for men. Now they will start to see it *everywhere*.

ജ്ഞ

Women complain that men shouldn't be so easily influenced by the way a woman looks, that inner beauty is far more important than any other aspect, that surely a woman's personality is the only element that will keep him enchanted for the long-term, and that men shouldn't be so shallow all the time. Yes, well, you can't see personality from across the room.

Men are almost entirely visual when it comes to their initial attraction to women. They need to see a peripheral curve or two. That's just the way it is. Men are mesmerized by the female form, and it is disheartening to men everywhere when women insist on covering it all up. "That's ridiculous!" women cry. "We shouldn't have to show cleavage to attract good men!" I'm with you, girl, but because of the natural, biological urges of those *same good men*, you just might be passed on by for a woman who will. Don't get angry with me (or them). Blame the Creator.

Helen Rubinstein said, "There are no ugly women in the world. Just lazy ones." There are little things that every woman can learn to do that will automatically make her more attractive to men. Flirting, for example. We all respond to flirting. It is nature's signal of possibilities. Flirting is like a ray of sunlight breaking through the clouds. Flirting warms the spirit, lights the path, paints a rainbow now and then across the sky. This is nothing new. Smart women have been dropping the proverbial "hanky" since the beginning of time. All the other women who think they shouldn't have to embrace such "sexist" conceits don't fully understand men. And they will continue to watch from the sidelines, frustrated and forlorn.

It's not hard. Glance at him, then look away when he catches your eye. Two seconds later, glance again and hold it a little longer. Then look down and away and half-smile. Done. Women sometimes think it is enough to glance at a man and then turn their back and wait. "Well, he should know." But men need more obvious signals.

While I'm at it, women say they are never sure if a guy likes them or not. "Oh, maybe he's just being friendly." Hint: men are not that subtle. If he makes an effort to be in your presence, he likes you!

Men *love* feminine girls. What does this mean, practically? Dresses, for one. Men *always* prefer the way a woman looks in a dress or skirt. There is something so alluring, so promising, so heart-stopping, in the sweep and swirl of a woman in a simple dress that a man has no choice but to become a poet or a painter or, failing all that, a priest.

Heels, a dress, and a summer night... men *never* forget these snapshot moments in time, my love. Heels accentuate and define the glories of a woman's legs: the arch of her calves, the firmness of her thighs, the hinted-at imagery of a heart-shaped ass. Oh joy! An overwhelming onslaught, a collision of crescents, a chorus of curves, and all before our eyes in triumphant *tromp l'oeil*. But heels are uncomfortable, you say. Yes, I imagine they are.

And (since I am on the subject), if women only knew the effect of red lipstick on men! "But we *do* know," say women, "and we don't like to wear it because we don't want to look like prostitutes." To which I can only answer: what kind of an alternative universe do you women occupy? Only in the minds of women does red lipstick look like the exclusive adornment of a harlot. Red is the color of movement, of hurtling desire. To men, it is a gift from above, from the goddess Aphrodite, a reminder that life is fundamentally worth living, a happy interlude from the dreck and drear of this cold and graying world.

I will always walk across a room just to thank a woman for wearing red lipstick. "Sorry to interrupt your conversation," I will say to her little group, "but your friend here is wearing lipstick and it is glorious to behold." Turning to her, I will say, "Thank you for wearing red lipstick, sweet girl. It is so rare to see these days, and so refreshingly feminine. You truly are a beauty. Never forget it." Then with my hands outstretched toward her, like I am unveiling an exquisite painting (and I am), I say to her friends, "Look at your gorgeous friend here and the ray of beauty she has brought into this world, and how the light in this room was created just for her and her lips of red." Then I bow out gracefully and carry on.

All of these little *conscious* gifts from women are wonders of the world. Even more wonderful are the little *unconscious* things that women broadcast, completely unaware. A lover of women, on the other hand, is magnificently aware, and he intercepts these signals and decodes them all.

There are women, for example, who kind of… *sashay* when they walk. The chassis of a woman like this swivels, in all directions, a circular figure-eight of the hips, up and down, forward and back, around and around—and not just side to side, on a horizontal plane. And it's not necessarily smooth or even—there's a kind of syncopation to it all, a noticeable, and sudden, drop and lift of each cheek, like a jazz drummer playing slightly "behind the beat." This is entirely unconscious, by the way. It's hard to describe it in words, but I can sure do it with my hands. These women are multi-orgasmic.

The French have a lovely word for the small of a woman's back: *ensellure*. This is, to me, the greatest curve of all. I suspect that entire novels have been written, entire mountains climbed, entire villages razed, because of the madness induced by the curvilinear sensuousness of the small of a woman's back.

And here's something… you can tell everything about a woman by the shape of her calves. A great pair of legs is usually an indication of a pretty good body all around. Shapely legs usually mean she takes great care of her health. It takes no more than a daily walk. Breasts and hair and other various things can be purchased. Calves never lie.

Also, color is a reliable informant. Color tells me a lot about a woman, her mood, and her unconscious desires. Specifically her shoes and nails. If she is wearing neutral heels (beige, ivory, white) or clear nail polish, she wants a little attention (the heels), but she is relatively content. If she is wearing red heels or red nail polish, she is open to romance and courtship and love. Dark heels or dark nails? She's feeling a little sexy tonight.

Generalizing again? Yes, of course I am. Let's continue. I can smell the perfume of a woman's period. Not always, but some of the time. And a woman who is ovulating, well… look out. I can spot her in a crowd immediately. She will play with her hair a little, run her fingers along her necklace, uncross her legs only to cross them again. If an ovulating woman is out with her girlfriends—girls night out—she will sit with them at their table or dance with them in a circle. But she will look away from the group frequently, for seemingly no reason at all, as if searching the room, looking at everything and nothing. Her eye contact is held a little longer, her center of gravity is a little lower, she is more in her body, in her hips. Hormones take over and all logic goes out the window—doubly so if it is a full moon.

It's a great sight. An ovulating woman is like a wildflower from a remote place, a little more ragged and disheveled and *plucked* than her friends, who are all arranged in rows in a carefully constructed garden. An ovulating woman is beauty personified. If only men knew what is possible with her on those great, dark, and sultry evenings. They hide it well but I see it all. It makes me smile.

∞⊂⊃

I like it when you are quiet and near.
I am with my writing and you are with your book.
Occasionally, you interrupt me to share with me something you just read, and that is a welcomed interlude, a reinforcement of the moment. Together apart, apart together.
A beauty unsurpassed, a beauty nonpareil.
I've just put into words something I've long understood: "A man is happiest with a girl who reads books."
— The Alabaster Girl, *page 83*

ഇന്ദ

Men are always trying to decipher and understand social group dynamics. It's simple. Women have a "girl's night out." Men do not. Oh sure, men might go out together to have some fun, but for the most part, when it comes to the opposite sex, it's every man for himself.

A "girl's night out" is virtually unassailable. A woman will rarely betray her pack, no matter how much she likes a guy she meets, and no matter how charming his rhetoric. There is an unwritten code of conduct: everyone connects with an interesting guy tonight or *none* of us do.

Women take care of their own—even sometimes to the chagrin of the one they are trying so fastidiously to "protect." If one of them is not being treated nice or having fun or feeling included, the whole pack turns inward, forms a circle, like musk oxen protecting the little ones in the center. Any attempt to isolate one of the herd at this point is fraught with danger and luck based at best.

Oh sure, they will let a guy talk to one of them if they can see she likes him and if he seems nice enough, but they have their eyes on the situation, and when it's time to go, *it's time to go*. They will descend upon the two of them, hovering around semi-patiently, holding out her purse to her, as he tries his best to continue to talk to her, and she tries her best to linger, to stretch it out long enough to give him her number. Then *whoosh*, she is gone.

Men, on the other hand, are only too happy to assist one of their own. One of their buddies likes a girl? And she wants to leave somewhere with him, but all the guys are miles away from their shared apartment and he has the only key anyway and he drove them all there and he is their ride back home and they have no cab fare? Oh well, don't worry about us. We'll be fine. Go and have fun!

So now then, knowing that a "girl's night out" is likely to result in a circling of the wagons if one of them does not feel included, I do my best to include them all. How? Well, most guys concentrate only on the girl they are interested in, even to the point of tuning out the others. This is where they fail. I expand and include them *all*, making sure they *all* feel pretty, making sure they *all* receive an equal amount of attention, adoration, and adulation. All, that is, except for their unofficial leader. She gets my *full* attention.

Every group has an unofficial leader in the ranks—from rebellious classrooms to skeptical corporate executive boards. All the members of the group secretly look up to this leader, even though they might not even realize that they do. No matter how strong and dominant of a teacher or CEO you imagine yourself to be, and no matter how much fealty you think you have managed to extract from the ones you are in charge of, the members of the group secretly follow this undercover leader, not *you*.

So the secret is to identify early on, then to focus on, then to win the heart and mind (no small feat) of the unofficial leader of the "girl's night out." My entire verbal dance is with this leader, letting her win most of the sparring points, making fun of myself right alongside her and winking and smiling at all the others as I do. If I manage to get her on my side, all is well, and I am given a shocking amount of latitude. The unofficial leader becomes my greatest ally. She does everything to help me from that point forward. Like I said before, I get my women through the tacit complicity of other women.

Here's something else that just occurred to me, my love: the greatest social gatherings are V-shaped. In other words, if a group of girls goes out with the desire to meet guys, they should not clamp tightly around the circumference of a table, or stand or dance together in a tight circle. A closed group is a closed group. A V-shaped group shares its energy outward and invites possibilities.

ഇരു

The secret to being mesmerizing to women is to listen to them and look deeply into their eyes. If a man can communicate to a woman— with his eyes alone—that he finds her truly beautiful, truly desirable, without the layer of "hey baby" and without a hidden agenda of any kind, just genuine appreciation, she will remember him for the rest of her days.

Eye contact is the eighth wonder of the world, the solution to all the problems of men. And it's the easiest thing in the world. All a man has to do is take enough time to memorize the color of her eyes. That extra second or so is amazing! That's all it takes. She will feel noticed. She will feel seen.

When they hear the phrase "eye contact," a lot of men, influenced by Hollywood syrup, think they have to stare longingly into a woman's eyes and into her soul, like a reverential lover, like a beamish beau, holding steady, like a laser. Squinty, smoky bedroom eyes, hold it… hold it… hold it… gaze… gaze… gaze…

Ease up on all that staring, cowboy! That's far too much of a force field, a death ray. Just relax, I tell them, and have fun. Hold eye contact with her for a few seconds, a firm connection, but glance away occasionally, not at other things, but almost like you are lost in thought, like you are contemplating the universe, because if you think about it, you are. This will give her a respite. But nothing is ever broken. Ease and delight. Ease and delight. Soften your gaze, put a little curiosity, a little whimsy, a little sparkle in your eyes, and you're good to go.

ഇരു

A lover of women looks in the eyes of every woman he meets, young and old, even the sixty-year-old waitress who is serving him eggs for breakfast. They are all his girls. It is his mission to make women feel beautiful again, to make them feel noticed and appreciated. It doesn't mean that he is going to try to steal her away from whatever man she is with. It just means that in his presence, she feels like a woman. He makes that waitress shine. He sees beauty in her and he makes her feel pretty and he makes her feel alive and he makes her feel inspired. He makes her feel like a girl once again.

They are all your girls. That's a very powerful frame of mind, because when you believe that, they will believe it too. When you consider it like this, there is no such thing as "picking up" a girl. She's already picked up. She's already your girl. Sure, she might be in a relationship, and yes, you respect that, but she's still your girl.

When I catch a woman's eye from across the way, I hold it for—if I were to guess—about three seconds, then I smile as I glance away. A beat or two more and I look at her again, sideways, out of the corner of my eye. An intrigue! And just like that, a connection is established. She knows exactly what I am saying to her.

From that moment on, oh, how I love to see her, to gaze upon her. From that moment on, she is my girl. From that moment on, I am her greatest defender, her biggest fan. I teach her everything she needs to know about me with my eyes. And my eyes alone. My eyes portray my intentions more clearly than anything else I will ever say or do. With my eyes, I express my clear desire for her. With my eyes, I describe the experience I want to have with her. With my eyes, I invite her to dance. From all the way over here to all the way over there.

It can't be helped, my love. How can I look away? My eyes are forever drawn to beauty and art. And the greatest manifestation of beauty and art in this entire world right now is standing right over there. It is because of *her* that there is mischief in the air and the proverbial sparkle in my eyes. It is because of *her* that my eyes shine. My eyes can't help but reflect everything she creates in me—all the curiosity, wonder, and intrigue that I feel. Her light shines through me, to the center of my being, illuminating my heart from without, like a stained glass window of vibrant, jewelled colors on a bright and sunny day.

ౠ

Some men think it is a good thing to just plow through a woman's resistance, to keep on talking, to overwhelm her with their presence or platitudes, as if they will somehow gain greater rapport with her by staying in her face. Mustn't allow any dead air! Keep talking! Keep talking! Be interesting! Be funny! Mustn't let her get bored.

A man will stand directly in front of a woman, clutching his beer high in front of his chest, like a shield, then proceed to peck in and out at the poor girl's face. "So uh… you live around here?" Peck. "What do you do?" Peck. "Can I buy you a drink?" Peck. It's too much. It's too confrontational. It forces her to lean backwards a little, away from him, a polite but definite recoil, but it also kind of traps her there, giving her little room to roll out and be free.

Or he will spy two women sitting down engaged in conversation, and he will walk over, try to say something cool, interrupting them with his plosive fast-talking. Then, without gauging their response in any way, he will reach out for a chair. Oh wow! Is this not the height of presumption? What an imposition! These girls might even find him semi-interesting, but there has been no clear invitation to join them. Here they were talking about their boyfriends or their projects or their work situations—and now, all of a sudden, here is this guy, camping out. And now they are stuck with him. And now they don't know what to do. They want to talk with each other alone but they don't want to be mean. So they smile and nod and answer his questions politely and smile and nod again.

Seduction requires space and lots of it. There should never be anything that limits her chance to participate or leave. I wouldn't dream of taking a chair and joining her or her little group. Without a clear invitation to join, this is completely presumptuous and invasive. I never lodge myself, lumpen, in a woman's space. I never stand directly in front of her, as if in opposition. I never invade her personal space or presume that I have some inherent right to engage her in protracted conversation. And I would never take the chair beside her without her implicit, gesturing, smiling invitation.

⁐⁑

You know what I am all about.
I am no mystery to you at all.
Most guys will hide their natural impulses because they really like you and want to give you a good impression.
The difference between me and them is that I don't hide my desires.
Yes, but I don't want to be just another one of your girls.
Of course not. I desire you, that much is true. I very much want you to stay. But if you go, I understand. Either way, you have my highest respect. I want to see you now and in the future. I can only promise you two things. One, I will never lie to you or play with your emotions. Two, I will take you higher up the slopes of Parnassus than you have ever been.
— The Alabaster Girl, *page 86*

⁐⁑

This is how most men fail. They hang around far too long. They try to work up some grand conversation. They try to get "in rapport" with her. What? What a waste of time! A woman knows if she likes a man within the first few seconds, so there is little to be gained by hanging around and trying to be more interesting. There is no amount of talking that will make her like him more. In fact, more often than not, it will only work against him.

Here's a scenario that is common all over the world. A man gets up his nerve to talk to a girl, and lo, she politely responds. So he sits down beside her and begins to talk and talk, trying to get into rapport with her, trying to be funny, trying to be a little cocky, asking her about various banalities, and she is being nice to him, so this continues for a full twenty minutes or so. He sees his buddies over there out of the corner of his eye, but ignores them so he doesn't break the force field. She's smiling and answering his questions and laughing occasionally, but after a time, she interrupts him and says, I'm sorry, I have to go… my girlfriends are waiting… it was nice to meet you. And he smiles and nods and mumbles that he, too, has to be somewhere, and hey yeah, it was nice, and maybe we will see each other again some time, and then she gets up to leave, and he gets up to leave, too, and he watches her as she goes, but not for too long, because that looks needy, and then he does an abrupt about-face, spinning on his sentry heel, and now, and only now, does he look over at his buddies, who have assembled at the bar, holding court, watching his little encounter with silent encouragement and assessing. He walks toward them, taking a swig from his now warm beer, smiling to them, but it's not a good smile really, it is kind of sheepish, because he doesn't know if it was a good thing or not, if he had a good time or not, if she was into him or not, and he just spent twenty damn minutes, and it seemed to go okay, right? But in truth, he has no clue whatsoever, and this always seems to happen to him, and once again he feels like a man trapped outside a woman's body.

Women have told me they know within thirty seconds of meeting a guy whether or not they would sleep with him. One girl told me she has what she calls a "hover test." Whenever she meets a man, she tries to imagine him hovering over her—as in a sexual position. If she can imagine him hovering over her, if she can get that picture in her mind, she is receptive to sleeping with him. That is, of course, if attraction is mutual and opportunity and circumstances align. But if she can't get that picture in her mind, she will *never* sleep with him. She just can't see him in that way. Other women have described it to me as "trying to get a mental image of kissing him," but it works just the same.

৪০৪

Someone might see me talking to a woman over there in the corner for ten minutes, see her laughing and responding to me, and think, "Wow, he's really having a great conversation with her. I wonder what they are talking about." They assume we are talking about the usual things: what-do-you-do, how-long-have-you-lived-here, how-many-brothers-and-sisters, any-pets? They also assume that I must be a brilliant and engaging conversationalist. But that is not necessarily the case.

It's simple. When I am talking to a cute girl that I just met, I just repeat the same few phrases over and over again. That's it. Smiling and winking and having enormous fun. "Are you my girl?" "Why do you love me so much?" "Do you have a lover? Every girl needs a lover." "Cancel your plans and run away with me!" Over and over.

I dispense with the chit-chat. There is plenty of time for small talk in the future, plenty of time to find out details like brothers and sisters, hobbies, pets, and where she went to school. Instead, who is this beauty before me? What do you love? What do you love? Tell me something interesting about you. Come spend the week with me.

৪০৪

The color of the voice is amazing, fascinating, a supreme part of the magic. Voice is vibration, and vibration, to a woman, is everything. Women respond to my voice, for I have mastered it. I play it for them like a fine instrument. My voice is a sound track, underscoring and augmenting the story of her and me. I say all kinds of things to her in all kinds of ways. I am conscious of my voice at all times, for I learned a long time ago that what I say doesn't matter nearly as much as the way I say it. My voice opens doors.

Men everywhere are desperate to find the magical opening line or excellent thing to say. If only they would toss all that aside and instead, study and practice and master their voices. They might have heard somewhere that it is good to lower the voice a little, to slow it down. Yes, but it is much better to infuse our voices with our love of women! To align our voices with the message of the words we are speaking. To enhance our voices with a little coloratura, with the sing-song quality of music, changing it up now and then, alternating between fast and slow, loud and soft, playing with the timbre, the pitch, the tone, the inflection, the cadence.

Men think they have to talk constantly to elicit a woman's interest. They rush out words to keep her attention, fearing the silences, or "dead air," as they say in radio. They are shooting wildly all over the place hoping to hit something. A real gunslinger pauses, takes his time, as the bullets whizz all around him, to really aim.

It is the pauses that make the music. To master delicate spaces in our phrasing creates a sense of suspension and commands attention. Profundity out of silence, one could say—a delightful contradiction. Chopin said this: "Simplicity is the final achievement. After one has played a vast quantity of notes and more notes, it is simplicity that emerges as the crowning reward of art." And after a lifetime of playing Chopin's nocturnes and mazurkas, the great pianist Artur Schnabel had this to say: "The notes I handle no better than many pianists. But the pauses between the notes—ah, that is where the art resides."

At times I speak high and bright, laughing, my voice diffusing into the air all around her, and at other times, I speak directly into her soul, laser-low, vibrating, to the center of her being. At times my voice is strong and commanding, and at other times I am quiet, calming, whispering softly into her neck. At all times my voice is elastic, a vibration, a vibration tuned to the exact frequency of her.

ଞଠ୪

Traditionally, a man and a woman will go through a series of distinct stages in their courtship together. There is a meeting stage, a getting-to-know-you stage, a story-telling stage, a comfort-building stage, a familiarity stage, a romance stage, an intimacy stage, a last-minute-resistance stage, and whatever else. There is something good and familiar in this. It is the normal progression of a man and a woman, a kind of escalation, higher and higher together.

Except... not with me. There are no stages with me. If I like a woman, if I feel an attraction to her, then all of these traditional stages are conflated into the first few minutes. There is no need to convince her of anything. She is still talking to me because she knows exactly where this is heading and wants it too. Everything has already been presented, dealt with, and transcended. She knows it, I know it, and she knows I know it.

We might elect to travel along the traditional courtship trajectory because it's fun. But everything is as clear to us as freshly cleaned glass. Pretenses and posturing simply fall away. Hesitation and games are swept aside like yesterday's dust. I have already said everything I need to say to her with my eyes, my voice, and my words. She will look at me and smile and say, "You're bad... you're trouble." And I will laugh and say, "Ah yes... and I see that you are still right here talking to me."

ഹോ

She's young and pretty and standing at the hotel bar with a little chi-chi drink in one hand and a cigarette in the other.

"Good evening," I say.

"I'm taken," she says without looking at me.

"I have no response to that."

I lean in beside her and try to get the attention of the bartender.

"I have a boyfriend."

"Yes, I understood you the first time. Does he make you happy?"

"Yes."

"Because you don't seem very happy."

"Well... I am."

The bartender is busy.

I turn to her.

"Are you asking me to invite you up to my room?" I say.

"What? No! Whatever gave you that idea?"

"You did. Just now."

"Don't be ridiculous. I can't."

"Of course not! I would expect no less. So, let's see... how about you come up to my room at, oh say... ten o'clock?"

"You can't be serious."

"Yeah, you're right. That's a little early. So how's this then? I'll put the champagne on ice at around ten, so when you get there at eleven, it should be perfectly delightful."

She finally breaks into laughter.

"No. Boyfriend, remember?"

"Ah, but forbidden fruit is sweetest."

"You're bad."

"You started it. Besides, it's a good thing that you have a boyfriend."

"Oh yeah? Why's that?"

"It gives you something to do when I'm not around."

She laughs again and turns toward me.

"What are you doing in this hotel anyway?" she says. "You here on business?"

"What kind of a question is that? Are you trying to turn this into a civilized conversation or something?"

"Just asking."

"No, I'm not here on business. What about you? What are you doing here?"

"I'm here in town for a little modelling gig."

"Yodelling? That's very interesting! A dying art, I'm sure."

She laughs and laughs.

"How old are you, anyway?" she says.

"I'm not sure... I was raised by wolves."

She laughs and hits me on the shoulder. A girl who is

interested in you will always touch you, and always touch you first.

I lift her chin with my finger, gently.

"You're too young for me, you little minx. Run along and play with your little friends."

"I'm not too young. Not at all."

I point to the front of her skirt.

"Whatcha got in there? Huh? You know how to use it?

"Of course!" she says, indignant.

"No, I don't think you do. I'm twice your age, girl. I've seen some amazing things in my life."

"That old, huh?"

"Yeah, I'm old and decrepit. So you see? You're safe with me. I can only cuddle."

She laughs. "Oh really?"

"Yeah, what about you? Do you like to cuddle?"

"Yes."

"So do I... doggy-style!"

She laughs and hits me again.

— The Alabaster Girl, *page 89*

కింజ

The only question on my mind when I first meet a woman I am attracted to is this: "Are you my girl?" That's it. In everything I say and do with her—all my winking, all my smiling, all my banter—I am only trying to ascertain that one thing. This is the essence of my interaction, the third level of curiosity. "Are you my girl? Are you my beautiful lover? If not, it is okay. Someone else will be. I will still adore you, I will still be excited to see you, I will still kiss your cheek and celebrate you whenever you are near, but my mind is elsewhere. For you are not my girl, my sweet, not my girl."

The thing is, I already know. How do I know? I know. I can immediately tell. I can see it in her eyes, in the way she moves, in her energy, whether or not she is my girl. The only question now is: does *she* know? So when I say to her, "Are you my girl?" I am really saying, "I already know you are my girl. Do you know it, too?"

The interesting thing about the way I interact with women, and my desire to focus only on the dynamic of us together, is that small talk is impossible. I am asking larger questions than most, and there is no time now for details. Details are a great subject for later. Much later.

Attraction is there or it is not. Attraction cannot be created. It can only be uncovered. It is not about creating something out of thin air. It is allowing to blossom what is already there.

This is why I never go on a date with a girl I just met. Dinners, coffees, movies? Nope. I only go on those kind of dates with women I am already sleeping with. Sounds a little abrupt, perhaps, but it's the truth.

Let me explain. Most of us go on dates to test the waters, to see if we like each other, to see if we are compatible, to see how it goes. I already *know* all this. Her signals, her responsiveness, her unspoken invitations have already told me everything about her and the way it will be. Everything has already been shared and accepted between us.

There are no secrets. I know everything about a woman from the moment I lay eyes on her. I have been, after all, a life-long student of women (and now, specifically, a student of her) and I have been an *excellent* student, with years of trial and error and volumes of practice.

Everything about her is exposed to me in an instant. And she recognizes this immediately. She can detect it instantly, from across any room, any crowd. She knows that I see her with different eyes than other men. She knows that I can hear her heartbeat from all the way over here. She knows there is no point in engaging in the usual tentative, frivolous games that people play. She can sense that I am on her side and she relaxes. She accepts. She concurs. She submits.

There is an instant knowing when I meet a girl who is *my* girl, a calm connection, a mutual empathy. I already know I like her. I already know she likes me. I can see it in her eyes that she is my girl. There is no possibility of failure.

Well… about the only thing that *can* cause it to fail is formidable: logistics. Logistics is the bane of my existence, messing things up for me time and again. How many missed rendezvous because a woman and I couldn't work out the logistics? Yet even that cannot change the fact that she is my girl. Logistics and circumstances might screw me over—and quite often—but *never* my judgment.

෨෬

Approach anxiety is the number one predicament of men, our biggest deflation of spirit. It ruins our day, our evening, our confidence. We all know well that heart-stopping twinge when we see a pretty girl and the ensuing internal battle, the almost (but not quite) convincing of ourselves to approach her.

Some men try to solve approach anxiety by treating it like a numbers game. They are machines; they approach, approach, approach. They are like salesmen, cold-calling prospects, picking up the phone and dialing numbers at random. Every woman is a potential target. They see a new girl over there and they spring into action, their arsenal of opening lines and howitzer questions armed and ready. Trying to solve approach anxiety in this way is trying to solve the wrong problem. The solution to approach anxiety? Stop approaching!

I rarely approach women uninvited. I never really have, I suppose. I don't need to. I am already in constant communication with them. I approach from afar, if that makes sense. I am always scanning a room, checking in with every woman, watching for their signals, letting them know that I am here. I let them know with my eyes and my smile that I see them, oh yes I do. Everything is already presented and laid out before them, like a map on a table.

The ones who are open to my approach-from-afar, or even mildly curious, will let me know. They will speak to me in a soundless, but loud and clear voice. I only go where I am invited. I never waste a moment of my time approaching women who are indifferent to my presence. And because I never go where I am not invited, I never fail. There. I said it.

Wait a minute. Is it always true that I never approach women? Well, not exactly. It's true that I rarely take more than a step or two toward a woman who hasn't invited me (I am too lazy!), but I *will* engage any woman in my immediate proximity. Girl standing in the line at the bank behind me? Girl at the table beside me in a restaurant? Girl standing next to me at the bar? Hello, lovely, what's your name, and why are you not my girl?

∞

A man puts too much pressure on himself. It makes no sense. He sees a woman who is attractive to him, say at a coffee shop or a lounge, and instantly a sea of thoughts floods his mind: "Wow, what a pretty girl… I would love to meet her… I want to approach her… should I approach her? If I do, what will I say? She certainly has a boyfriend… she really is amazing… she would never go for me… I should approach her, but I will run out of things to say… she won't be interested in me anyway… and everyone else in the room will see if she rejects me… which is almost certain… Ah, if only…"

It's like he is standing over here, staring bleakly down a one-way street, that universal and instantly recognizable corridor called Approach Anxiety Alley. At the end of the street is the pretty girl. And lining the street on both sides are rows of houses three stories high, and all the people are leaning on elbows out the windows between flower pots and watching the street below, bored.

He would love to meet her, yes, but in order to meet her, he will have to walk down that dismal street, all the way to where she is, to the very end, with every eye upon him, watching in silence. And once there, he must find a way to elicit her attraction. What if she is not receptive when he gets there? What if she rejects him, dismisses him outright? Ouch! And no matter what happens, he will have to walk back out the exact same way he went in. There is no other way out. And not only that, all eyes will be upon him again as he returns, for surely the bored people along the street will perk up and lean even further out of their windows with even more intense scrutiny, crossed arms, and heaving breath, watching his every plodding step.

This is why he hesitates. He imagines himself walking alone down this intense cul-de-sac of emotion, sweating and anxious, knowing that if it does not go well, he will have to return the same way he went in, his shame and embarrassment evident, with all those eyes upon him, contemptuous, derisive, laughing. If he does *not* get a favorable response from her, everyone will see him for what he really is: a loser, a guy who once again has proved to himself and everyone else that, despite all his hopes and good intentions, *he does not have what it takes.*

There you go… that's a lot of emotion and trauma that a man will invent. It is such an undertaking to him, such a journey, that he is convinced that in order to be successful, he must first pack an entire suitcase full of interesting stories, opening lines, confidence-boosting affirmations, tips and tricks, just to walk down that alley to talk to that girl. And that is too much work, too much thinking, too much trip-planning, too much of a journey. It is far easier to just stand over here and wish.

I prefer to travel light. I can't be bothered to pack a whole suitcase full of opening lines, conversation topics, or stories. I can't be bothered to hang around, to try to be interesting, to try to convince her of my worth.

Instead of walking down that long, lonely corridor and then back out again, I simply *swerve by*. I see a pretty girl, I swerve by, smile, wink. "Hello, pretty girl… I love your yellow dress. You look absolutely radiant." And then I am gone. I don't wait for a response. I don't need to. That transaction is complete.

I plant seeds, my love. I never stick around. My job as a man is to plant the seed. If she is receptive, she will respond. I swerve by, say something strong, a high compliment, and then I am gone. I never hang around.

Swerving by is all it takes to plant a seed. I never try to get into "rapport" with a woman I just met, or try for some deep conversation. There is plenty of time for all that later. "So what brings you to this place?" or "So how many brothers and sisters do you have?" Ah, that's far too much talking. I just swerve by, say something strong and direct, and then keep on going. I slide right on by. It allows her to breathe, to realize that she is not going to be stuck with me all evening if she doesn't want to be.

So how do I get things like phone numbers or future plans with women? Simple. When you are planting seeds wherever you go, beauty springs up all around you. There is no need to chase it down. This is a secret of all men who have women in their life. They *never* chase. While other men are out there harvesting phone numbers, true lovers of women put their energy into the world to everyone around, an equal radiance for all. They let their presence be known. They smile and wink at all the girls. And women are universally and forever drawn in.

"You," I say, "are absolutely beautiful… why are we not together?" If she likes me, she will either stop me right then in my tracks with a question or a smile or… she will find me again. That's the way it works. Women will respond if given a chance to respond. A simple appreciation of the beauty of women gathers far more phone numbers than any protracted cold approach. If she likes me, a phone number will materialize out of thin air, almost as an afterthought. No need to ask.

The great thing about swerving by is that you can never be rejected. You are not asking for anything. You are simply planting seeds. And no opening lines to memorize, no stories to inflate, no worry about running out of things to say. Approach anxiety? Ah, best leave that to others.

§

Why should I respond to you?
Maybe you shouldn't.
Maybe you should run away from me right now.
Maybe I will only break your heart.
Maybe you need a nice guy who will buy you flowers.
Like that guy over there.
He is perfect for you.
He will buy you nice flowers.
All I can promise you is hours of exquisite pleasure.
You need more than that.
      — The Alabaster Girl, *page 92*

§

A lot of men are excited by phone numbers. They collect them like they have meaning and value in and of themselves. To me, they are just so much paper and ink. I know women who will go out of their way to be especially kind to men who try to ask them out, even if they are not interested or it's not possible. Sometimes, a woman will give her phone number to a man just because she doesn't want to be seen as yet another woman who is rejecting him. Why? Because these women are nice, that's why. Because they know what it's like to feel rejected.

Phone numbers by themselves mean nothing. Voice mail, dead messages going nowhere forever. A phone number is never an end in itself. It is simply the means to the next logical step. I never ask for a phone number. If it is obvious we are going to get together, a phone number will magically appear between us, a logical connector for making that happen. A phone number is a *fait accompli*, a natural means to an end.

If a girl gives me her number, I tell her exactly what I am going to do with it. I smile and wink and say, "Well, you crazy girl… you just gave me your number and I am going to honor that by calling you tomorrow at seven o'clock. Wait by the phone! Catch it on the first ring!" If I am specific about when I will call, she will always answer. She will not, as they say, "flake." Why? Because I told her exactly what I am going to do with her number and when I am going to call. Because she invited me to lead and I led.

℠)ℓ•

I am always on a woman's side. In every sense of the word. Physically, mentally, spiritually, and metaphorically, I am on her side, shoulder to shoulder, aligned with her, on the same plane. Everything I say and do with a woman is just like that. It is our little conspiracy. It is her and I against the world. Her and I against mediocrity. I am right there beside her, for she is my girl, and we are looking out there together, arrayed against the world.

I never stand directly in front of a woman I am talking to—especially one I just met. My approach is oblique, discreet, from the side (my right side, if possible, for I am left-handed. Always keep the gunhand free!) and never directly in her face. I dance-step in lightly, on the balls of my feet, placing my hand gently on the small of her back and smiling, "Well hello… and who are you?" Then I rock back out again, just a half-step or so, a simple weight transfer from one foot to the other. My outside foot is always, in a manner of speaking, heading out the door. Because I know that sometimes a woman needs a moment of hesitation, a little time to assess, to decide if she is receptive… then a little more time, then a little more time… until she knows.

If she smiles or responds, I rock right back in again, lightly on my feet, but closer to her than ever, shoulders touching, my voice low but bright. "You're very pretty… why are you not my girl?" And again, a rock-step back out, leaning away from her, but holding steady eye contact and smiling, my hand still on the small of her back.

If she continues to smile or again responds (it doesn't matter what she says, only that she responds), I am right back in again, even closer, smiling warmly, voice vibrating in her ear, lower, brighter. "So what do you think… you wanna run away with me?" Repeat, repeat, dance in, dance out. Until there is a clear receptivity on her part, a turning toward, an open stance, a silent but unmistakable invitation to yes, please proceed. In a sense, I have just "approached" this lovely girl three or four or more times in the space of a few minutes. And each time, I was clearly invited.

Everything I do is just like that: rhythmic, syncopated, small bursts of energy, and never a constant onslaught. I might talk in close to her neck one moment, then completely turn my back on her the next—even to look at a wall! I break it off completely and constantly, but only for about five seconds or so. Metaphorically, I am keeping her at arm's length for a moment, then sweeping her back in. At all times, I am giving her all kinds of space, allowing her the room to breathe and move and leave.

At all times, my hands are fluid, always in motion, every flourish in perfect synch with her. It's almost like I am painting an invisible picture, a vista, a horizon of possibilities. It doesn't matter what we are talking about. I could just be asking her name. It doesn't matter because underneath the conversation is the beautiful subtext of her and I together. I stand close to her, beside her, I look at her, into her eyes, then turn my head to look out there in front of us, to the painting I am creating with my hand in the air. Can you see what I see, my love? Out there. Away. Her eyes will follow my gesture and lo, now she can see it too.

This is an important distinction. I am always talking out *there*, gesturing out *there*, like an artful conductor. One hand on her back and the other hand in the air before us, like Picasso in broad strokes on glass. I do it this way because, well, I see it this way. I see an image out there, a pellucid dream, a vision of beauty before me, and all I am doing is pointing to it and describing it as I go. I include her in this ridiculous, sublime, projected image that I see ever before me, and it aligns her and me on the same side, in a way. Oh, beauty seeker, treasure hunter that I am! How can I not share with her the desire that I feel, writ large out there on an astral plane? How can I not invite her, with all the kinesics of my being, to experience the journey along with me?

This is how it all begins, a metaphor of how it will always be between us. The two of us aligned shoulder to shoulder with my hand ever so lightly on the small of her back, my other hand stretched out before us in the air, gesturing out before us, out there, out there toward a myriad of painted possibilities, out there toward that magnificent horizon. Can you see it, my love?

ღჯოლ

I touch women often. Constantly, actually. Right from the moment I first see her. Sometimes before we have even said a word to each other. But she doesn't even notice. This is because my touch is subtle, gentle, feather-soft, like a whisper on her side, her arm, her hand. A mere tap, the softest brush, no pressure whatsoever, cloth only, and paying no attention to it at all. Like a magician, pointing over there with this hand and imperceptibly pulling something from behind her ear with the other. She doesn't even notice.

It's not a trick or something contrived. There is no hidden intention behind my touch. It is simply a natural extension of the gestures of a man who loves the essence of women. I connect to her subtly with my fingertips, my shoulder, my elbow, anything. It almost can't be helped. It is so innate that I do it all the time, subconsciously.

When do I touch a woman? Whenever she is in range, to be honest. When I am talking to a woman, connecting with her, listening to her, and interrupting her like I am wont to do, it is always accompanied with an occasional soft tap somewhere on her body. Even sitting across a voluminous table from her, I will still reach across—stretch right out—to touch her hand or arm.

Men, to their credit, are cautiously sincere; they do not want to come across as gauche or disrespectful by stepping over physical bounds or invading personal space. This I understand, of course, but sometimes prudence tips over into paranoia.

A man will go on a date with a woman and deliberately go out of his way *not* to touch her. He will reach way around her to open the door for her. "Here, let me get that for you." Reach. He will sit right beside her in a restaurant and share the menu with her, but heaven forbid his shoulder should ever brush hers. Mustn't offend her, you see.

Think about the way women interact with men. Women touch men all the time when they are talking to them, and men never really notice that they do. A small, quiet touch on the hand or the arm, "It was nice to meet you… but I'm running late. I have to go." Touch. "That is sweet of you to ask… but I have a boyfriend." Touch. Yes, women touch men softly and respectfully all the time and men never do it in return.

This is another thing that sets true lovers of women apart from other men. They touch women all the time, in the same way that women touch men. Their touch is easy and light, a natural anchor to the blossoming conversation. If you observe a man who loves women moving around a room, you will see exactly what I mean. He is smiling, winking, entertaining, tapping elbows, kissing hands, his fingertips brushing lightly on shoulders, waists, lower backs, including, inviting. And not one woman is offended. In fact, they don't even notice.

But on a subconscious level, the effect is powerful, exponential. It is a sub-communicated signal to her, almost imperceptible, ever so brief, but long-lasting. It is masculinity signaling to femininity. It is a resetting of the balance, a realignment of the polarity between a man and a woman.

Women are never offended by an honest and respectful touch. They understand implicitly that this is just who this man is. This is the way he celebrates life and women. This is his style. Other men, with agendas hidden in their fingertips, are not allowed to touch. Other men will have to work for it, to jump through hoops, to prove certain things about themselves and their intentions. A true lover of women gets a free pass; his touch is always understood and welcomed.

This is why true lovers of women are *never* relegated to the dreaded "friend zone." It simply doesn't happen. It *can't* happen. By the simple expedient of touching her, he shatters that possibility forever. He signals to her that she is in the presence of a man. She can now only see him as a man. She may not be attracted to him in any way, and they may never get together in any kind of romantic or physical sense, but make no mistake, she will never see him as just another emasculated male. She will never consider him and think, "He's a nice guy, but..." No, not with him, for he is in his body, he is not holding back whatsoever, he is unafraid to connect with her and everyone else around him.

Ah, I must be extremely careful here, my love. There is a subtlety at play here that is phenomenally easy to misunderstand. Some might read into my words that I am advocating grabbing women or pawing them or caressing their hands or—the most despicable blasphemy of all—groping them. Make no mistake, there is a fine line between a respectful, engaging touch and a creepy guy with wandering hands. It is a tap, not a stroke; a touch, not a massage. Women will recoil from a sticky, lingering, disrespectful touch, and understandably so, for this is a breaking of the covenant of respect between men and women, a violation of her personal space.

Let me make an important distinction: The rampant sexual abuse of women everywhere is finally being held up to the light, a much-needed and long-overdue exposition. An unsettling majority of the women I have known in my life have been violated in some way. So let me be clear about one thing, my love: There is not the slightest hint of tolerance or sanction or excuse for intrusive behavior in anything I am saying here. I *despise* men who prey on women, who violate personal boundaries, who disregard the notion of clear consent, who disrespect a woman's right to own her sexuality.

All great lovers have great empathy. It is the essence of their lover-ness. This is the secret of a man who loves women: his touch is *always* imbued with respect, honor, and empathy. First and foremost. There is never anything blatant or sexual or intrusive in his touch in any way. It is merely a manifestation of his natural aliveness, an automatic extension of his delight-filled way of communicating. Light, simple, and without intent, his touch does not linger or stray. It simply connects with her—one human being connecting with another—in the way we used to connect.

ℰ⌘ℛ

She is standing behind me as I order my simple coffee. I turn around and smile.

Hey... I've seen you around here before. You look especially lovely today.

Thank you.

You live around here, too?

Yeah.

See that building over there? Across the street? I live there on the ninth floor. You should come visit me.

What do you mean come visit you?

I mean come visit me! I think you would make an excellent girlfriend for me.

Uh, okay... I don't even know you.

That is true... and you're still invited.

So is that how you usually ask girls on a date?

Hey, as it so happens, I met the love of my life in this very coffee shop.

Really!

Yeah. It's still pretty new... I just met her here today.

She laughs.

Why should I come visit you?

Well, the thing is... I never seem to leave my apartment these days. I'm writing right now, day and night, and I'm so focused that I rarely go anywhere. Just down here for an occasional coffee.

Writing? What are you writing?

Well, let's see... are you familiar with erotic fiction?

She laughs.

Just kidding! Come visit me!

I can't just... come visit you. Who are you anyway?

Oh, just some guy who likes a girl he met in a coffee shop...

And you want me to come visit you? Just like that?

Yes, of course! Look at you. That's exactly what I want. I think we would be fantastic together.

But I don't get it... what would we do?

Ah, now that's a good question. Hmm... I haven't thought that far ahead yet. I have no idea, to be honest. I don't even have a TV.

She laughs.

You're crazy.

And you... are still invited.

Just like that, huh?

Just like that.

You want me to come visit you...

Yes, come visit me.

She laughs.

You're crazy.

Come tonight!

Bring me some soup!

— The Alabaster Girl, *page 94*

සංශ

The highest gift a man can give to a woman is respect. All she needs is to feel comfortable, and to feel comfortable, she needs to know that a man respects her. This is why a woman will artificially and arbitrarily put a time frame on how soon she will sleep with a man she is attracted to. It might be a cliché that a woman has a "three dates" formula, but it is more or less accurate. Men blame women for doing this because they think women are just being petty, perpetually dating them, and taking advantage of them for free dinners and drinks and movies. But it is not that at all. Women do this because if a man will wait that long—three dates—if he is willing to invest that amount of time with her, there is less chance that he is just going to give her the "wink and the gun," then run off and high-five all his friends.

I share the secret of women, my love: they love men, desire them, desire sex as much as any man, and yet sometimes must disguise it. Because of society, friends, family, career, they must hide it. Thus, when a woman says that old-fashioned but universal phrase to a man, "You won't respect me in the morning," what she is really saying is this: "I already like you, I want to be intimate with you, I want it very much, but I am so afraid that if I open up to you, you will leave me alone and exposed, and you will tell all your friends, and people will find out, and I don't want that because I am a nice girl." And she *is* a nice girl.

Women think about sex constantly. Even the ones who say they don't. I know the heart of women, and women are dirty, dirty, dirty. Which ones? *All* of them. No, not my girl, a man objects. Not my special snowflake, my little sunbeam… she is innocent and special and would never do something like that. Think again, muchacho.

The remarkable thing is that as soon as women are aware that you know all about their naughty little thoughts, they stop pretending. Their sexual energy comes to the surface whenever you are around, and they laugh about it with you. Around other men, they act innocent, but not around you. You are forever included in their secret club.

Oh, the things that women will do if they know for certain that they are safe and that no one will ever find out! Men would be shocked if they knew the truth. But in our society, women have to worry about their reputation and appearing too easy. Men do not. This is a concern that looms large on the horizon for most women. A woman will feel devastated if people judge her unfairly. And people will do just that. And no, it is not fair.

For men, the opposite is true. A man's reputation is a great thing, if he is not afraid of it. It is his wingman, as they say, the best one he can have. His illustrious and well-meaning buddies, having different agendas, different motives, different attitudes, and different levels of consciousness, are not.

How does a woman know that I respect her? After all, she doesn't even know me. Here's how: *I tell her*. Just like that. I look in her eyes, smile kindly, and say, "There are three things you need to know about me. Number one: I will never lie to you, never misrepresent. This is my clear promise to you. Yes, my invitation to you is a strong one, but it is also an honest one. Number two: You will always be comfortable. What's more, I will take it upon myself to personally ensure that you get home safely. The choice, my dear, is yours. I only desire what you desire. I can only be excited if you're excited. As for number three, I am absolutely discreet. What happens between you and me is *only* between you and me. Forever. No one will ever know about it. Unless, of course… you *want* them to know. In that case, tell the whole world!" This is pretty much what I say to a woman, and she believes all this immediately because, well… because it's true.

℘ℭ

A lot of guys will go on a date, get a tepid kiss on the cheek at the end of the night, then lie to all their buddies the next day about how easy she was. A true lover of women will *lie the other way*. When asked by his friends, "Who was that girl we saw you with last night? She was cute, what happened? Did she go home with you?" he simply says, "Yes, she is wonderful. We had a great time. I really like her!" "Yeah, but what happened? Did you sleep with her?" "No, we just talked all night and it was good." That, to me, is true respect. It's none of their business.

Why do men brag about their exploits? I've never understood this. I never kiss and tell. *Ever*. Why? Respect. That's why. A man usually doesn't need to worry about his reputation, but women do not have this luxury.

A key that opens all the locks is called a master key, but a lock that can be opened with just about any key is called a broken lock. Men are celebrated and women are judged. An unfair double standard, to be sure, but that's the way it is. Maybe she doesn't care about any of this, but I will always err on the side of caution. It is just part of the social contract I have with women. Out of respect for her and her reputation, a true lover of women *never* kisses and tells.

Besides, it has been my happy experience that when a woman truly believes that her friends, her family, and her co-workers will *never find out*, well, let's just say that she will open herself in ways that most men have never dreamed.

Discretion is incredible. Doors will open that would otherwise remain tightly closed. Oh blissful discretion! Why is it so hard for a man to grasp that if a woman knows he is *always* discreet, that no one will ever know, then she will open herself up to him completely? Sometimes I shake my head.

Not that I care if people know, of course. It's actually a good thing, but it will never come from me. I let *her* say it, if she is so inclined. If she tells others about our time together, then great! The proper response to a girl who looks up at you and whispers, "Wow, that was

amazing!" is to smile and say, "Don't tell me! Tell all your friends!"
A reputation is like scratches on a guitar; the first two or three stand
out and alarm us, but a myriad of marks only add to its charm.

I am asked all the time how many lovers I have had. Why on earth
would I ever tell anyone that? What do I have to gain? The admiration, the envy of men? I absolutely do not care what men think of
me. A tally, a score, a number? Does it really matter? Quantity does
not make a man a lover. The number of women I have been with
over the years is irrelevant. Not to me. To you. I remember them all.

I have nothing to show. I have nothing to hide. I am ashamed of
nothing. My reputation is not something I feel compelled to defend, inflate, or advertise. A lot of wannabe swordsmen like to boast
about how legendary they are, parading around, chests out, strutting.
Their shiny swords, studded with glass jewels, are purely ceremonial,
in faux-gilt scabbards, and displayed proudly at their sides on the
parade ground for all to see. Rank amateurs, who got lucky a few
times and like to brag about it. True lovers of women don't care at
all what others think. Theirs are swords unsheathed—a little worn
perhaps, a few nicks here and there, but well-sharpened, well-oiled,
well-trusted, and ever ready to spring into the fray!

ഇൻ

*You are so lovely as you bring me burnt popcorn in a por-
celain bowl. You smile, embarrassed, but not really, for it's
fun and funny for both of us. You wanted to share a little
treat with me, you said, and you ran off to the kitchen happily. And it is a treat. Burnt popcorn will do nicely.*

*We sit enraptured and quiet for a while in the gorgeous
ambiance (Patsy Cline) of your apartment with the burnt
popcorn in the porcelain bowl, and then you say, "Do you
remember when we first met? When I gave my number to
you in the store? Did you notice how everyone at the other
sales counters was intensely watching us?"*

"No," I say, but I kind of do. I was there with a friend that day, and we had been wandering, for no particular reason, through the first floor of Saks Fifth Avenue, with its immense array of cosmetics and perfume counters as far as the eye can see. We were day-dreaming and wandering and enjoying New York, and we happened to drift past a beautiful girl selling perfume.

"Would you like to try our new fragrance?" she called to us as we passed, waving a little white card in the air.

"No, thank you, we're just wandering through."

"It's very nice…"

"I'm sure it is." I turned toward her briefly, my smile thanking and dismissing her at the same time. We kept on walking.

She sang out then, loud and clear, "You know… a gentleman never walks away… especially when I'm talking!"

Ah, mischief is in the air! I stopped then and turned back toward this smiling girl of mischief waving her little perfume card through the air like a fan.

"What did you say?" I asked.

"I was only joking," she laughed.

"Yes, but what did you say?"

"I said, 'A gentleman never walks away, especially when I'm talking.' But I was only joking."

"Fantastic! You are trouble, aren't you? I love it. Come out with us tonight. This is our last night in the city. We're catching a plane tomorrow. Cancel your plans, trouble-maker, and come celebrate with us tonight."

"Tonight?"

"Yes, tonight. Join us."

That smile again, all mischief. She looked at me sideways, a little askew, and then with great intent she said, "Are you asking me out?"

To which I laughed, looked her up and down, and said, "Of course I'm asking you out… look at you! Come out with me tonight!"

A dramatic, staged pause, then she nodded. "All right, I

will. Let me give you my number." And she retreated behind her counter to discreetly write down her number. But it was not discreet for—as she reminded me on this popcorn night two months later—we were the center of attention, the talk of the floor, her co-workers buzzing together at all the other counters, pretending to be busy but straining to see.

And she did come out with me that night and it was wonderful. And, as promised, I left on a plane the very next day.

And now here I am with her again, in her home, eating burnt popcorn from a porcelain bowl.

"Yeah, what was that all about?" I say. "Why was everyone there so curious?"

"They were amazed to see me give my number out to a guy. After you left, they all gathered around and asked me about it, and the whole department was talking about it."

"About what?"

"About me giving my number to you."

"I don't understand... why?"

"Well, because in the entire time I have worked there— nine months at the time—I have never given my number out to any man. I get hit on every single day—we all do— by all kinds of guys, sometimes rich, sometimes famous, even royalty once or twice, and I have never once accepted. My friends at work think I'm crazy, shaking their heads, because I never accept. So, naturally, when I gave you my number, they were amazed."

"But wait a minute..." I say, my handful of burnt popcorn paused in midair, "Why did you give it to me? What was different?"

"Because when I said to you, 'Are you asking me out?'—do you remember I said that?—you said, 'Of course I'm asking you out... look at you!'"

"That's it? Because of that?"

"Yes. Every single time a man asks me for my number or asks me to join him somewhere, I always look at him and say, 'Are you asking me out?' And the answer—at least here

in New York—is always the same. He will say something like, 'Uh, well... I just thought... that, um, perhaps we could get a coffee or something... you know... hang out... see how it goes.' You know what I mean? It's as if when I say 'Are you asking me out?' they can't admit to it. They seem to back away slightly and say, 'I didn't really mean anything by it...' Why can't a man just admit that he thought it would be nice to ask me out? So that's why. No man ever says to me, 'Yes, you better believe I am asking you out!' But you did. Only you."

— The Alabaster Girl, *page 96*

೭೦೧೪

Men constantly worry about things they cannot change. They tend to invent all kinds of problems concerning all kinds of things and this is completely unnecessary and all in their heads. Their height, for example, or their age.

Age is a relative thing, is it not? An older man might feel that his age is a hindrance to him, when in truth, it is the opposite. As in everything else he worries about in his interactions with women—all of his perceived inadequacies and shortcomings—age is rarely an issue for her if it is not an issue for him.

When a man is attracted to a younger woman and he tries to deflect the "age question"—whether by humor or avoidance, or worse, by flat-out lying—he is essentially playing just another tedious and recognizable social game. And once she detects that he is playing games, she thinks to herself, "So this is how it is going to be..." and she resigns herself to playing games as well, a role she knows well.

A man's perspective describes to the world how he sees himself and ultimately determines how others will see him. A man who embraces his age and the joy of his considerable life experience, holding everything up to the light—mountains climbed, oceans crossed, realms conquered, and the wonders he's seen—will find women of *all* ages interested in him. If he is unfazed by the age difference, she will be, too. If he tries to hide it or avoid it, well then… if it's a problem for him, it will be a problem for her.

Groucho Marx said it best, "You're only as old as the woman you feel!" The older I get, the more younger women are interested in me. In fact, the first thing out of my mouth when talking to a twenty-one-year-old is my age.

And the age of women, my love? Ah, I have never had a preference between younger women and older women. I happen to revel in the spirit of *all* interesting, beautiful, and feminine women, no matter what their age. A spectacular woman is a spectacular woman.

୧୦୧୨

Women, when asked, will say the number one thing they find attractive in a man is a sense of humor. When men hear this, they think they need to learn a bunch of jokes or stand-up routines, or learn to be quick on their feet, dropping witticisms at will. And how many guys will make fun of other men in her presence, but never themselves? Volumes of men do this. They think, "I can't knock myself down in front of her. That will make me look bad. But if I make indirect, slightly condescending comments about other guys—or even about *her*—that will raise my value in her eyes." Oh men, if you only knew! You are condescending upward!

I have no need to diminish other men. Let them give their best effort. Let them break off their own chunk. They have every right to occupy their space on earth. And as for women, well, I *do* make fun of women all the time, my love. But never in a put-down kind of way. Always teasing, but never derisive. I don't subscribe at all to the concept of psychological one-upmanship, knocking a woman down a little in order to put her off balance or to elevate my status in her eyes.

Here's the secret: what women really mean by a sense of humor in a man is the *capacity to laugh at himself*. Exactly that and only that. Because who does this, my love? Swashbucklers, princes, *bon viveurs*, irascible lovers of life. Their humor is self-deprecating humor, and self-deprecating humor is the *ultimate* display of confidence, an essential component in the aspect of charm.

Every great lover in all of history has had a delightful sense of self-deprecating humor: an enormous capacity to laugh at himself, a spirit of teasing, relaxed fun, a sense of mischief in his heart, and a "just kidding" kind of energy. In fact, I would go so far as to suggest that it is *not possible* to be truly loved by women if you do not have it.

A man who can make fun of himself is a man at peace with himself, completely and unapologetically being himself, never shy of being put on the spot, with nothing to prove and no fear of ridicule. Cary Grant, when asked the secret to his success with women, said, "I tell them I can't get it up." There you go. Beautiful.

So yes, my love, I do make fun of women all the time. But I also make fun of *myself*. That's the key. I never take myself, her, or the situation seriously. I am having enormous fun, with or without her. Self-deprecating humor is wonderful. It's irrepressible. It's mischievous. Everything I say to her is said with a smile and a wink, like an inside secret we both share.

Ɛ☯Ↄ

I smile and wink at women constantly. Which ones? All of them. Because, why not? There is mischief in the air, is there not? I also smile and wink at any man who happens to catch me smiling and winking at all the women. For he is now included in the fun, a collusion, a brother, a welcomed spirit.

I used to tell men, "It's easy to be charming to women. All you have to do is smile and wink at them when you are talking to them." Ah, but as most things are with me, it is much more subtle than that. One day I realized that, even though I have been saying this for years, it isn't what I do at all. I don't smile and wink at *her* when I am talking to her… I smile and wink at *her friend*. A subtle but monumental distinction. When I say something ridiculous like, "You're kind of cute. You would make a good girlfriend for me," I am smiling and laughing with her, but sideways winking at her friend. Or my friend. Or anyone else around who happens to be listening. It makes all the difference in the world.

Ah, mischief! As little boys, we used to tease and pull the pigtails of the little girls. I still tease women, in the same spirit, laughing and joking with them, and rarely giving them a straight answer. I tell little white lies to women all the time. What's important is to let them *catch* me in the lie, then laughing with her at myself for getting caught. There is no fun in lying to a woman if she doesn't catch me in the lie. That's just plain deception.

ഇൽ

How many men on a first date act stiff, subdued, and constrained? I am not talking about nervousness; I am talking about purposeful stoicism. Like a man is afraid to have fun with a woman, like he must show some kind of manly strength to her, to prove to her that he is an *arriviste* in the world of adults, that he has a lot to offer, and is thus a pretty good catch, don't you see? He sits up straight and correct. He orders the wine with calculated aplomb. His baleen smile is relentless, fixed in place, but devoid of mirth. She might really like him, alas, but wading through this evening is going to be slow-going and laborious, a slogging chore.

How tedious and uninteresting this is for women! For anyone. Where is the sense of wonder and delight at the beauty of this girl before him and the beauty of their time together? Men have forgotten how to be natural, spontaneous, and relaxed. They are too worried about the impression they are making. They are too restrained, too concerned about the outcome, too swathed in doubt and guesswork. They beat themselves up and perspire if they say something stupid. Who cares?

Fun. We have forgotten how to have fun. We *unlearn* fun. Every interaction with women should be infused with fun. This includes the way we meet, the way we date, the way we are together in bed, and the way we are together in relationship. If it isn't fun, then what's the point? If it isn't fun, it needs to be left behind. Because… why not? We are treasure hunters, adventurers, raconteurs, are we not?

The spirit of fun is part of what makes a man truly compelling. It is a necessary facet of charisma. Sure, it is good for a man to learn to smile more readily, to look others in the eye, to firm up his handshake, to find his own personal style, to overhaul his wardrobe, to get in shape. These are important things, to be sure, but he should never lose that little boy in him, curious and in love with the world.

It is interesting that the traits we had as children are the traits we need to reclaim now. We squander our childhood gifts: our sense of wonder, of adventure, of learning, of curiosity. We forget what it was like to be fascinated by little things, our sense of awe for the world around us, and the downright amazement we had as children on those summer vacations that lasted forever and ever.

&つ♡β

I have a boyfriend.
Great! I have a girlfriend!
You have a girlfriend? So, what's your girlfriend's name?
Wait! What day is it today?
Friday.
I smile and wink.
Friday? Well then, my girlfriend's name is Maria…
You're impossible.
                    — The Alabaster Girl, *page 100*

ಬಂದ

Oh to be audacious and unrestrained! How wonderful it is, when interacting with a woman, to let go of everything we think we know, to turn up the volume, to push the envelope a little, to come to life, to blurt out what we are experiencing in the moment, to describe to her exactly what we want, to gesture a little more, to smile with our eyes, to hold her gaze just a little longer, to add a little more aliveness to everything we say and everything we do.

How many of us spend our lives holding back? How many of us, at a social gathering, think of something funny to say but we don't say it because, well… what if they don't think it's funny? We bite our tongues. We hold back. We are afraid to simply blurt out what's on our minds. We have forgotten the simple joy of being spontaneous and fun. Once again, as we've always done, we shrink back and play small.

When we pretend to be cool and confident, we are attempting to contain and control the situation. It is better to be unabashed, audacious, wide open, living in the moment, going with the flow, lowering our center of gravity, and shooting from the hip. I am not afraid to say something light-hearted but shocking and then to own it, even in the face of any challenge from her. To be spontaneous, funny, adventurous, outrageous—if nothing else, at least I am amusing myself! *Anything* but boring.

It is a well-known phenomenon that women are more attracted to married men. We know why, we assert. It is because a married man is unavailable and thus presents a perception of challenge. Or we might conclude that it is because a married man has already been vouched for—some other woman has already examined him and found him worthy. Perhaps. Perhaps. I would suggest that a married man is more attractive to women because *he is simply being himself.* He doesn't care. He says whatever he pleases. He has nothing to prove. He is more relaxed and less worried about impressing her than other men. He is just being himself, which is to say, more real, with bright-hued playfulness.

The solution for a man is to simply blurt exactly what he is thinking. Just name whatever is going on in the moment with her. If he is nervous, say it. If she seems nervous, say it. If she appears to be uninterested, say it. If he likes her, say it. If he think she likes him, say it. If he wants to see her again, say it. If he wants her in his bed, say it. And even if he runs out of things to say, well then, say that. "Uh… I just ran out of things to say… tell me something interesting about *you*."

Blurting whatever comes to mind and naming everything that is going on in the interaction allows us to get out of our heads and into our bodies. Trying to think too much doesn't help. It is far better to just flow, to lower our center of gravity, to stay focused on our bodies and to say whatever we are experiencing in the moment. To describe everything that is happening is part of the celestial dance with her, the creation of the moment.

ℰℂℛ

I am never serious, my love. And by serious, I mean heavy. I refuse to let my energy slip into "let's have a talk" mode. This does not mean that I avoid having a serious conversation with a woman, or that I am always flippant or frivolous or dismissive. No, far from it. I am never *uncaring*. If she is having trouble with her boss or she is stressed because of a project or she doesn't even know why, I am right there with her, unflinching and unbowed. Maybe I don't understand and maybe I never will understand, but I will do my best to be curious about the way she is feeling—with no hint of blame or frustration. A willingness to listen will suffice, and I will listen to her for hours.

But I do not allow *heavy*. Serious is good; heavy is not. Serious is necessary at times. Heavy is *invented drama*. And I will not spend even one minute in the presence of drama. I have neither the time nor the inclination. I refuse to try to correct the behavior of dramatic women.

Let me be clear about what I mean by drama. There are times when a woman is sad or hurt or angry, and in those times of dark clouds and thunder, I will sit with her and hold her hand. I will listen to her for hours. I am the greatest listener in the world. I will put my arms around her and wait with her in the storm, for there is nothing to solve here. This is not drama. This is only a storm. And this, too, shall pass.

Every woman gets upset for reasons that no one can identify—least of all her. This is no mystery to anyone. Upcoming deadlines, upcoming birthdays, upcoming hormonal surges. Who knows why? That's just the natural cycle of human nature. And that's fine. No, what I am talking about are the women who fester all day long in a woe-is-me, you-don't understand-me mood, poisoning the air with their disrespect and captious remarks, and forever rolling their eyes.

Ease and delight! These are the words I live by, my creed, my mantra. I love life. I am fascinated and curious all day, every day, and if I ever find myself in the presence of a woman who persists in trying to sideswipe my wide-eyed, wondrous mood, with aloofness, games, or drama, well then, she is simply removed, edited from my life. I will cast her out of the garden like an avenging angel with a flaming sword at the gates. Don't believe me? Then test the edges, my love, test the edges.

Fortunately, I know enough about the heart of women to avoid stepping on that particular land mine in the first place. The women I am drawn to possess the same ridiculous love of life and bountiful enthusiasm as me. Oh sure, problems assault them from every angle, just like anyone, but they are resilient enough to bounce back, find their smile, count their blessings, and give thanks again for little things.

ഇൻരു

Women are great at *pretending* to be offended. It's just the way it is. It is something natural and common and the way it has always been, a simple, effective, subconscious screening mechanism. She is simply testing a man's ability to take a punch, to see if he will stand up to her or if he will bow down like all the others, a known entity. Sometimes, she isn't even aware she is doing it.

A man will say or do something to a woman that he thinks is interesting or funny when, without warning, she becomes a little cold or distant. He is flabbergasted; he has no clue what he said or did, and he immediately switches into *explanation* mode, which is to say, *defensive* mode, which is to say, *supplication* mode. Her mood switches to negative and her energy darkens, for no real reason, and men, foolish men, follow on to the darkness.

Thirty seconds ago, he was having fun, telling jokes and stories to this pretty girl before him, and now his energy has completely downshifted and everything is heavy. His lighthearted banter, his story, his smile, everything, is stopped mid-stream, like he was floating happily on a raft on a perfectly sunny day when it thudded suddenly against a rock, and now he has to flail and paddle furiously to extricate himself. He winces, his face blanches, and his tone becomes apologetic. He starts explaining and fast-talking and defending, trying desperately to recover. No, I didn't mean it like that, he says. I was just joking, he says. I was just trying to be funny, he says. His explanations and apologies drag out and flap around and everything gets wrapped around the axle.

Ah, why does a man feel compelled to explain himself, to defend himself, to a woman he just met? It's like King Henry IV waiting three days in the snow, barefoot and penitent, before the Pope would let him through the gates. I never explain or defend myself to a woman I just met. I don't respond at all to her faux indignation. If I did nothing offensive, then I do not apologize. I owe her nothing.

I never allow myself to feel under siege, under threat. I refuse to let my energy be dissipated and dashed upon a rock. I never do anything I don't want to do, just to please a woman. There is no respect in any of that, there is no strength in that at all. If I apologize when I have caused no real offense, then I deserve her disdain.

So how do I respond to a woman who is pretending to be offended? Simple. *I agree and make it worse.* Whenever a woman challenges me with anything, anything at all, I agree with her and make it worse. I keep the level of my energy exactly where it is. I smile a big smile. I wink. I agree with her. I make it worse.

She says to me, "I saw you talking to that other girl over there. You probably said the same things to her." My answer: "Of course I did. Did you look at her? How could I not?" Smile. Wink. She says to me, "You travel all the time so you probably have girlfriends in every city." My answer: "Ah, yes, it's true... but I don't have a girlfriend here in London yet... so your timing is perfect!" Smile. Wink.

When I agree with her and make it worse, I am effectively saying, "Yes, I'm on your side." She has nothing more to push against. She can't argue her point any further with me because, well... I already agree with her. She can't show me the error of my ways because I already know it. In fact, it's worse! Once again, I am making fun of her, of me, and of the whole situation. I did nothing to cause real offense and we both know it.

ॐ

So... what do you do?
What do I do?
I lean in close to her.
I give women pleasure...
That's what I do.
                    — The Alabaster Girl, *page 103*

ଞଦ୍ଧ

Some men accuse women of being flaky, of being master manipulators, of carelessly toying with hearts and minds. They think that women are malicious, but women are not malicious or conniving or uncaring. Women are intuitive by nature, guided by rhythm and flow, whereas men are bound by structure, the concrete, the black-or-white, the my-word-is-my-bond, the either-here-or-there.

A man will meet a girl and make plans with her. Then something gets in the way of those plans on her side. She calls and cancels, or she doesn't call, or she doesn't respond to his flurry of messages, or she just doesn't show up. No matter what she does or doesn't do, he gets angry at her for "disrespecting" him.

I've never understood this. She is not my girlfriend or my wife. *She's a girl I just met.* And yet she somehow *owes* me something? Now I'm going to be *angry* at her? I'm going to teach her a *lesson*? I'm going to *demand* to be treated a certain way? It makes no sense to me. It comes across as petulant and needy.

What kind of man is not bothered by a girl who doesn't call or show up when she said she would? A man who has options, that's who. A man who doesn't really notice such trivialities, because he is busy with larger, more interesting things. A man who is not dependent upon her in any way whatsoever for his enjoyment of life.

There is nothing on this earth that a woman can say or do to me that will affect my mood in any way. I am not afraid of her hollow-point words. I move through life at full speed. I have no time to pause to correct the behavior of a woman I just met. I'm nice to her and she's a bitch? No problem. She ignores me? That's okay too. She's overly critical or unkind or judgmental of me? Doesn't matter to me in the slightest. She's just a girl! How can she possibly affect *me* in any way?

If a girl says to me, "I'm so sorry. I know I said I would come see you last night, but I was really busy and I wasn't feeling well and I'm sorry I didn't call to let you know and…" I will laugh and wink and point to my cheek, "Where's my kiss?" I will pat my knee and say, "Come here… have a seat… I'll tell you a bedtime story!"

⁓

There are all kinds of sightings in the wild of the proverbial bitch, a woman who, for a variety of reasons—insecurities, jealousies, pettiness—will roll her eyes and turn her back on a man who is just trying to be genuine and nice. "Can't you see we're talking here? Go away. Leave us alone." She is dismissive and mean, flicking him off her shoulder like so much lint. Ah, what then? say the men. How should we respond?

How should you respond? What? *How should you respond?* I don't understand the question. Why hang around that negativity for even one second? Why try to go where your energy is blocked? It's like trying to ride a bicycle with the brakes on. Say nothing more and leave. Let others attempt to "educate" her or teach her a lesson. Consider the favor she has done for you, self-selecting herself away from your life. *Bitchy women must be left behind.* It's as simple as that. Cut bait and run. Always move toward beauty in life, and only beauty. And this, kind sir, is not beauty.

It's like watching news all day on television. Does that reflect how you want your life to look? No, not at all. Then why would you spend even one minute of your time watching it? Where you look is where your life goes. Head toward the light and only the light.

I love beauty. I love women. I have great faith in women. Throughout the years, no matter how many times I have banged my head against a wall in my understanding, I have never lost my unfettered delight and profound adoration for women. And yet… never do I believe for a minute that women are all peaches and cream. There are as many bitchy, conniving, and petty women out there as there are bitchy, conniving, and petty men. That's just the way it goes.

So yes, I have experienced the kind of darkness that only a woman can unleash into this world, a wrath that is not hers alone, but that of *all* women, a collective. Some women are like ancient gods—they punish for generations. So why, oh why, do I still love women so much? Why do I still have such unfettered enthusiasm and curiosity and adoration for women? I just choose to see things in a certain way, I guess. No matter what manner of dismal, jaded, angry, vindictive, and petty women I have encountered in my life, I never lose sight of the wonderment of the female spirit.

Women make me believe in women. I have known countless women of renowned sincerity, beauty, and grace, women who forever reinforce my faith in women in general. The secret of truly beautiful women is sweetness. These women would never, ever be rude to a man who was simply trying to approach them. They would never act superior, never be dismissive, never turn their backs or roll their eyes, never mock him, never cast him down to the ground for pettiness or sport.

I move toward beauty in all its forms, art in all its forms. And oh yes, I have seen great beauty. I have seen true grace. I have seen a lovely empathy. Impress me, my love, for I have been remarkably impressed in my life. Yes, there are a few life-choking weeds in the garden, but from where I am standing, I sure see a lot of flowers. And it is impossible to be cynical in the midst of flowers.

five

The Way of Men

The years go by, the minutes slide
I clench my fist to slow the tide

Fervent forests and undulant hills, clattering by, churning by, repeating, repeating, repeating, like the background of an old cartoon with the characters running and running and the background comically repeating and there again we see the same cloud, the same rock, the same cloud, the same rock. Shall we learn and move on? Shall we ascend and transcend? Or shall we only repeat?

What do you think of the so-called Seduction Community? she said.

Oh, I don't know... I think it's run its course.

Was it a good thing or a bad thing?

Well, it was a circling of the wagons for men. It arose as a response to a very real need. The core of it was wonderful: a desire to reconnect with women. But from its inception, it took the path of a quick fix. Except for a few excellent voices, the emphasis was solely on tips and tricks.

On how to get women into bed...

Yes, and for this, it received a lot of well-deserved criticism. But the need was real, the response was real, and there was a kind of, well... *honesty* in the seed that gave rise to this "movement"—if you want to call it that—an honesty that still needs to be extracted and distilled.

So the motivation was sincere, but the overall execution was not?

The interesting thing to me about the whole thing is that the loud denunciation it received was based on the assumption that men were learning how to manipulate women. But this is wrong. The Seduction Community doesn't manipulate women. Women are too smart for that. It manipulates *men*. Promises of instant attraction and same-night "lays."

Something it didn't deliver?

Of course not... ridiculous Pied Piper promises of swooning, nubile women falling everywhere at your feet.

Does the ragged, rushing blur outside the window ever stop? Is there nothing more? It's flying by forever out there, yet slow-motion in here, the same drawling dream over and over again... slow-rocking... from side to side and up and down... oh yes, oh yes, this is how we spend our days...

So where can men turn for answers today? she said.

There are no answers for men. The dating and relationship advice that is available out there is flawed. Men have nowhere to turn. Women have all the resources, or so it seems. They have women's magazines, devoted to the microscopic examination of men and their motives. They have *chick-lit*, they have romantic comedies, they have bosom-heaving romance novels, they have talk shows, and they have their girlfriends. When a woman is having trouble in her relationship, she will spend countless hours discussing every detail with every one of her girlfriends, one at a time, and then, when she gets to the last girl-friend, she goes right back to the first one and begins the discussion all over again.

That's true.

Men? What do men have when it comes to relationship advice? Each other. Over a beer. While watching the game. Usually, it goes something like this: "Yeah, that sucks... ah well, don't worry about it. Plenty of fish in the sea..." And they drink the beer and they watch the game and they drink the beer.

ഇറങ

One hundred and fifty years ago, Thoreau wrote, "The mass of men live lives of quiet desperation." This is as true today as it was back then. How many men stand on a balcony and wonder what happened? How many men cast blame? Why has the world not provided a man with what he wanted? He wanted adventure and he got two weeks' vacation. He wanted a mission and he got a lawn that needs mowing. He wanted a purpose and he got a cubicle. He wanted a mighty steed and he got a minivan. He wanted a castle and he got a mortgage. He wanted a battle to fight and he got televised sports. He wanted wisdom and he got talking heads on TV. He wanted treasure and he got endless debt. He wanted every part of his life to be wonderful, and here he is… standing on a balcony, in bleak, ruminating hesitation.

Generation after generation, fathers handed down wisdom to their sons: this is how you be a man, this is how you wield an ax, this is how you treat a woman. Open the door for a lady, son. Take charge. You need a good woman to stay home and raise your kids and clean your house and cook your food.

This model of handing down the wisdom of the ages worked well, right up until about sixty years ago. Men were masculine, women were feminine. That's the way it was. But then when they tried to hand this wisdom down to us—these same navigational charts on how to be a man and how to treat a woman—our ships hit rocks and ran aground.

We're better off than our fathers, but we're not better men. We were never taught how to stand on this earth as men. We had no instruction. We live in a world where either we had no fathers to tell us how to be men, or if we did, none of the information they gave us has any application today. We've lost the masculine wisdom of ancient and forgotten times.

"What is the surest way to fulfill the dreams of my life?" a young man once asked me. "Hang around your heroes," I answered. Role models are rare. We had no real teachers, no mentors, no heroes, no champions to look up to, no men that we admired, no men that we worshiped. "Where are the real men?" women ask, and the answer is lost in the wind.

The simple truth is that men need direction. A direction in life. They need to be pointing toward something constantly. Women sit down to pee. They look around the room and, well, it goes where it goes. Men need something to aim at.

A controversial statement, my love? Oh yes, absolutely. But don't get me wrong. I understand, of course, that everybody—male or female—is much better off with a mission, which means doing something with their hearts fully engaged, a sense of travel with purpose. We all like to know that we are doing something worthwhile and heroic—that's why women had to bust out of the '50s housewife thing in the first place. But men slowly and quietly *die* inside without something to aim at.

8003

Women are a kaleidoscope of infinite patterns and colors. We never really know women—we only imagine them. We can never inhabit the minds of women. We can never occupy their experience. We can share moments in time with them, collective experiences, but the way they remember those moments will always be different from the way we remember them. Their sunset is not our sunset. Their walk along the beach is not our walk along the beach. Their stolen goodnight kiss under a dim porch light is not our stolen goodnight kiss under a dim porch light. Women store these experiences in different places in the heart than we do. Though we share the immense volume of our history with women, their history is not our history, their remembrance is not our remembrance.

Men are surrounded by women from the day they are born, and yet they don't have a clue. Women remain spectacularly inaccessible to them. Who are these creatures called women that inhabit the earth? It is like men are sharing the planet with aliens from another galaxy, or at least foreigners from a distant land, like Madagascar or Samoa. They inhabit the same world but way over there somewhere, across a vast and stormy sea.

Men have no clue, but they sure make a lot of assumptions. They imagine all kinds of things about the world of women, about the minds of women. A lot of men believe that women never think for themselves, that they let society, friends, family, and the media think for them, that a woman lets her friends pick her boyfriend.

Men are either happy or sad, angry or benign, on or off. Women are all of these things too, of course, but *all at the same time*. To men, women seem to flow somehow, wet and damp in their emotions and in their logic, a constant tide, continuously shifting, up and down, fickle, saturated, subterranean, and prone to seep out or erupt at any moment and drench everything in sight. These are the assumptions men make.

Men want answers. Men want closure. Women want to feel the depth of their experiences, the profundity of their emotions, far more than they ever want answers or closure. This baffles men, because they suppose themselves to be focused, logical, direct, concrete.

Men are trying to solve women. They think they need to work the system somehow, need to play the game, need to figure out the angles. Confusion and guesswork abounds, a kind of mystical alchemy. A hazy smoke is in the air.

Men have no idea how to approach today's woman, let alone date her or have a relationship with her. Women seem to them to be completely in control, standing on a stage, looking down upon the audience of men and arbitrarily handing out an uneven distribution of prizes and punishments. "What's the play?" the men ask, but no one knows.

80C3

You probably have girls everywhere.
Me? No...
See? You're bad.

Me? No...
The world is full of girls. Everywhere are girls.
Yes, so why are you here with me?
I don't know.
You intrigue me.
I don't want to be one of many.
Ah, but you are the fairest of all the maidens.
When I am with you, I forget all the rest.
You are the sun. They are only stars.
They disappear from view when you are around.
                    — The Alabaster Girl, *page 107*

ಬಃಞಿ

Imagine what goes on in the mind of the typical man in Western
society today. He is increasingly apprehensive and unsure, completely
masking his fundamental desires for the sake of political correctness
and, quite frankly, for his own sanity. It seems to him that women
have all the power—the power to validate him or invalidate him—
with one swift flick of the wrist. A man's approval from a woman
can take many forms: a smile, a number, a date, sex. If a woman
grants him any of those favors, he feels like a man. If she does not,
then his worth as a man disappears. Thus the relentless chasing after,
and trying to conquer, the women of the world.

The dating and relationship landscape has changed so much and is
so unfamiliar that it feels like an epic struggle or battle. Too many
men today believe that it is "us" over here and "them" over there.
They view women as some kind of enemy, a force to be conquered
or overcome. They don't see them as, well... girls. Just girls. That's
all they are. Their dreams are just as lofty and their insecurities are
just as dream-killing as our own.

The men are over here, arrayed on a hill, staring across an abyss of
silence at the women over there in their walled and imposing fortress. How to get past the walls? Men gather together, rallying in the

trenches and drawing up elaborate strategies and ingenious plans to find a way to effectively breach those walls. They encourage each other with their battle cries and their propaganda. They build siege engines. Attack, my brothers! With everything you have! And when they attack, they are met with a rainstorm of arrows and boiling oil. And that hurts. So they retreat and lick their wounds.

An indirect assault perhaps? They send out scouts, spies, trying to intercept and short-circuit female communications; they work feverishly through the night trying to break the codes. Then they share these codes on Internet forums, in men's magazines, in secret meetings. And the women look down from the walls and see it all.

Some men become double agents, disguising themselves. They act like they are not the enemy, that their intentions are not to gain access to the fortress of women at all. Don't worry about me, I'm just a friend, a nice guy. I am content to just hang around outside your walls. I have no interest in actually entering—I'll just wander around outside here... as long as you don't mind, of course.

And they discover that she does *not* seem to mind. They are *not* attacked by the flaming arrows and the boiling oil. So maybe that is the answer... always remain nice, friendly, accommodating. Pose no threat. A sensitive, modern man. A nice guy. See? My intentions are benign; I only want to be friends with you. But this man's intentions are not benign, for this is a secret and desperate attempt to dig under the foundations, to tunnel beneath her walls. He hopes that if she is lulled into a false sense of safety, then when she isn't looking, he can somehow burrow his way in.

The only goal is to get past her defenses, by any means. He has no real desire to know her in any way, for she is interchangeable. This is all about him. Through his conquests, a man feels he can reassert his authority and exact revenge for all the rejection he's had in his life. He craves validation, and he will only feel validated by conquering her. By getting into her panties. By wearing down her resolve until she eventually gives in. And when the relentless persistence, the onslaught, does finally wear her down and she gives in because it is, frankly, easier, he congratulates himself on his prowess and adds another name to his list.

Is it war? Is this rather a harsh way of describing it? Perhaps, but not to a lot of men. They really do feel like they have seen combat. Their war stories about their battles with women are legion. And these wounded, gun-shy men are the ones you meet today, my love.

But there is a better way. It is much simpler than that. For there are men who ride up to the walls of women, solitary, approaching the gates directly, honestly, and openly, with a hand in the air. I am not your enemy. I am not going to hurt you. I am not going to attack you. I am not a spy. I am on your side. I come in peace. I am a man, presented before you. Let me in. And women open the gates and let him in, for he is a friend to women and not their enemy.

₧₧

Too many men are waiting for women to play fair, to stop rejecting them so much, to be *nice* to them for once. Yes well, it's time for men to stop waiting. There is no time to waste. Women have their own work to do, and we can't wait for them to do it.

Nor am I suggesting that women must wait and remain passive while men get their act together. The shift has to happen together, in reasoned discourse, with a willingness to understand. The women have to come into their true feminine essence and the men have to come into their true masculine essence at the same time. The tide rises all the boats.

The problem is if the men show their authentic, vulnerable side, and the women do not, then the men will be seen as needy and weak. Conversely, if the women show their authentic, vulnerable side, and the men do not, then the women will get taken advantage of.

Therefore, any change has to be simultaneous; otherwise there is an imbalance. One side gets hurt and has no choice but to raise the shields again. The result is a kind of Cold War between the sexes, with neither side willing to reduce their stockpile of weapons because they just might get hurt.

Some men are so tone-deaf when it comes to the intentions of women that they interpret every little kindness as an invitation to hit on them. A woman shows appreciation and men think she is pursuing them or trying to pick them up, but she isn't, and because women don't like to hurt people's feelings, they learn to stop showing their expansive appreciation for men… and there you go, less charm in the world. Sad.

I am not blaming men, my love, but I am also not letting them off the hook. They have the power to cast off these heavy chains. All they have to do is choose new a new and interesting world-view, to look for the beauty, the treasure, the mystery in everything… but they don't. They just can't believe it is as simple as consciously adopting a new set of beliefs.

ഇൽ

It is all in our perspective. If we look hard enough, every woman we meet will have some aspect that is less than ideal. But why concentrate on that? By concentrating on her wonderful qualities, we get to see her in a certain light, and a woman will *always* reflect what we see in her. The way we choose to see the world is the way the road is paved before us. It is our steps that create our path. And if we observe closely, we will see that the way people react to us is a perfect reflection of the way we see the world.

A cab driver picks up a young man at the airport. The young man says to the driver, "Wow, this is my first time visiting this city. Tell me, what are the women like?" The cab driver says, "Well, what are the women like where you are from?" "Oh, don't get me started," the young man replies. "The women in my city are terrible. They are bitter and stuck up. And none of them are pretty. I go out and all I see is bitches everywhere I look." The cab driver says, "Yeah, I hear you, man. Well, sorry to tell you but it's the same here. No pretty girls, and they're all bitter and miserable and mean."

The next day, the cab driver picks up another young man at the airport. The young man says, "Wow, this is my first time visiting this city. Tell me, what are the women like here?" The driver says, "Well, what are the women like where you are from?" "Ah," says the young man, "they are amazing! The women in my city are so fantastic! They are gorgeous and fun-loving and open and wondrously sexy!" "Excellent!" says the cab driver. "You are going to love this city! The women here are the same. There are so many beautiful and sexy women here, it will make your head spin!"

ΒΟΩ

A pretty woman in an elevator.
A happy surprise.
I smile at her.
She smiles at me.
And off we go.
Suddenly...
A weird little jolt.
A tiny shudder.
The slightest hesitation.
Just enough to notice.
Just enough to feel it in the pit of your stomach.
We look at each other.
We both pretend we are scared.
Because it is fun.
She whispers.
What was that?
I wink at her.
I don't know.

But if this elevator gets stuck.
We could be trapped in here for days...
And then I would have to eat you.
— The Alabaster Girl, *page 109*

༈ ༀ ༈

Some men feel that women have become too powerful and that men need to be forcibly restored to their "rightful" place. Everywhere are battle cries and faces being painted. War on women! War on feminists! Take back the power! But this is dangerous, deplorable, and unnecessary thinking.

To hell with the misogynists of the world! Misogyny is a sin against beauty and as such should be struck down with every bit of righteous indignation we can muster. It is true that men have lost some measure of power. *But we can't blame the women.* Women didn't wrest the power from men, gaining the upper hand in some kind of epic, global gender struggle. What actually happened was that men abandoned their posts; women simply stepped into the breach.

Women do not deserve the anger, suspicion, and oppression of small-minded and bitter men. Women deserve truly masculine men, heroes, champions, men who know how to really see them, who don't put up with their bullshit, who put them in their place from time to time, who know how to evoke their inner beauty, who see them as true equals, and who know how to speak to their dreams.

Men are not evil either, my love. They are sincere but misguided. They do not deserve the bitchiness and mistrust of women. They deserve truly feminine women who see their true potential and inspire them to ever greater things.

Women complain they can never find a good man but they're out there *everywhere*. Men are sincere and want to be excellent with women. They, too, want redemption and connection in their lives.

They desire with all their hearts to have a better experience with women, to be real, to have a loving relationship with a good woman, but the lock is so small, they don't know where to put the key.

൦൦൙

All over the world, women are strong and the men are not. Women are strong *because* the men are not. Women are holding up both sides of the relationship, carrying both sides of the load. *Someone* has to do it.

Modern man is afraid of his masculine beauty. He is devoid of passion or purpose. He has no edge. He is tepid. He is soft. This is why when a woman encounters a man of balanced and joyful masculinity, the natural order is restored and she can relax and become a *girl* again.

Strong words? Yes. An attack on men? No. Men will hear what they want to hear in these words. Some will feel attacked; others will feel inspired. I wish someone had said strong words like this to me when I was young and pathetic and blaming others. This is not the time for baby-sitting and hand-holding. This is a call to action, a call for men to step up as leaders. Those who do not heed the call will be summarily cast aside and left behind. Change your own diaper.

There is a reclamation that needs to happen, but not at the expense of women. Women are not the enemy. The enemy is *mediocrity*. We need the fortitude to retrieve the wisdom of the masculine from ancient and forgotten traditions, and at the same time the grace to recognize the necessity and equal power of the female spirit.

The crucial thing to remember is that all of our redemption efforts as men will fail without empathy. Empathy for women and for the way they are experiencing this world. Empathy opens heaven's storehouse. Empathy is not understanding, because sometimes we don't understand. Empathy is the *willingness* to understand. Empathy is the vital ingredient that sets real men apart from Neanderthals and jerks. Without empathy, we are lewd and aggressive. Without empathy, we are brutish.

ಐೱಐ

Imagine a man strolling down a sidewalk in the sun, slow and serene. He is not in a hurry. He is calm, solid, like a rock in the middle of a stream, as the people, heads down, flow around him. Watch him as he lifts his face to the warmth of the sun, how he pauses to breathe deeply, absorbing the smells and the sights and the sounds. It appears he has nowhere to be and nothing in particular needs his attention. He is not doing anything. He is just… being. Just him and his thoughts. Just him and the smells of the shops and restaurants that he passes. Just him and the sound of traffic. Just him and the strangers around him, behind him, beside him, toward him. See how happy he is?

And then… he sees her. She, too, is ambling along the sidewalk on this fine, long day, moving toward him, stopping occasionally to look in shop windows. She is a beauty. A beauty in a crimson dress.

Time slows down. He is instantly transfixed… you can see it on his face, in the halt of his steps. He stops and draws in a sharp breath. He looks to the side, to the left, to the right, then looks at her again. There is something so beautiful about her… oh, how he wants to know! His mind flails, awash in the confluence of potentials. She is getting closer, oblivious to him so far, absorbed in her little reverie, window shopping. She, like him, is obviously not in a hurry. She pauses at a store window. Is she going in? No, she's not. And now… now she is even closer.

Here's the question: what will he do? We can imagine what he *wants* to do. He wants to walk right up to her, confident, sure, and say something charming. He wants to smile and ask her name. He wants to ask her to join him for coffee around the corner. And if she joins him for coffee, he wants her to sit with him, on that perfect, sunny day, enthralled by his easy manner and compelling conversation as he regales her with his stories and fun and witty repartee. He wants her to be so intrigued by him and their impromptu coffee date that she offers him her phone number, without him needing to ask. And then he wants to call her that very night. And the next night. And the next. He wants to tell her she is beautiful to him, and that he can't wait to see her again. We can imagine that he wants to do all those things. This is his impulse. This is his fundamental desire. This is his age-old longing.

But—and here is where our perfect, sunny day screeches and sparks—he can't. For alongside all those desires that he holds in one hand, in the other he holds a wilting bouquet of fears. He can't just walk up to her, say something to her... because *what if?* What if he says hello and she just smiles a thin-lipped smile and keeps on going past? What if she averts her eyes, shakes her head—not interested—and ducks around him? What if she just ignores him completely? Or what if she *does* stop to say hello and he stalls out, drawing a blank, looking foolish and feeble because he has nothing interesting to say? What if he *does* manage to engage her in some semblance of conversation that doesn't wither away into hems and haws, and he *does* ask her to join him for coffee around the corner, but then ah! sorry, she has a boyfriend? Or what if she *doesn't* have a boyfriend and she *does* agree to join him for coffee around the corner and, well, maybe she really isn't interested; she's just bored and has nothing better to do? Besides, what was he thinking? What if he isn't even her type? What if he is too short for her or he is not in shape enough for her or he isn't good-looking enough for her? What if he says something nice to her, compliments her on her crimson dress and her lovely smile, and she views it as supplication, sees him as needy and clingy and too available? No, no, no, he can't compliment her. Wouldn't that kill it dead? What if he just acts nonchalant and only mildly interested? What if he is just natural and real and doesn't play any of those games? What if, wonder of wonders, she seems to *really like him* and she does ask him to call her and she does give him her number, well, then what is he supposed to do with that? Call her right away? Wait three days? A week? He has no idea. What if he does manage to get up enough courage to call her, then what? How should he act? How should he sound? Upbeat, fun, and carefree, or suave, assured, and direct? Or should he just be himself? And for that matter, what does it mean to just be himself anyway? Why on earth would she ever be interested in him just being himself?

And there you have it. All in the first few seconds. Our dreamed-up gentleman's heart is sincere; his desire is honest and real. He wants to do, to move, to act. And yet… he doesn't. He doesn't because he can't.

She is almost upon him now, but it doesn't matter because in those brief, eternal moments, he allows all those desires in one hand and all those fears in the other hand to fall from his fingers and seep away together into the ground where they can't disturb him anymore. She passes by and all he manages to put together is a weak smile and a nod in her direction and, well… she may or may not have noticed; he can't really tell.

ഇറ

Why do I keep coming over here to see you?
Because you love me so much?
I need more than just this.
Yes, you do.
But I can't resist coming to see you.
I smile and wink.
Come over here and give me a kiss and I'll forgive you…
— The Alabaster Girl, *page 111*

ഇറ

Why does a man hesitate when he sees a pretty girl? What stops his natural forward momentum? Why so tepid, so tentative? What causes him to catch himself, to pause with that oh-so-familiar sinking feeling in his stomach? Why is it this way and not another way? Fear of rejection, we answer—an over-arching and oppressive feeling in his heart that he is not good enough for her and oh, she will surely see it.

This is not new to him. This is not new to anyone. There are volumes of public discourse on the subject of our fundamental fear of rejection and how to correct it. It is a universal fear, ingrained in all of us. Even the most confident men, those used to the company of women, still feel a twinge of hesitation whenever they encounter a woman who takes their breath away.

A man's fear of rejection is, at base, the fear that he is not good enough. And, of course, he can drum up all kinds of supporting evidence and arguments—that he is not tall enough, rich enough, good looking enough, funny enough, articulate enough, interesting enough—but they all add up to the same thought: he simply isn't good enough. For her. For anyone. Thus, the stultifying fear of rejection. Thus, the hesitation and doubt. Thus, the underlying theme of his entire life.

It has been said that we are born with only one fear: the fear of falling. If this is so, then somewhere along the line, all other fears are learned. When we were four years old, if someone asked us if we could draw, well, of course we could draw! We would jump up and say, "I am the best drawer in the world!" We believed it with all our hearts, and because we believed it with all our hearts, we were right. But then we looked over at another kid's drawing one day and for the first time ever, our heart sank, and we felt that maybe we couldn't really draw after all. Picasso said it well, "We are all artists. The trick is to remember it when we are older."

There is a light that is received into the heart of a child from a welcoming face—be it mother, father, teacher, classmates, or another child kicking a ball around at the end of the street—an inviting, smiling, take-my-hand sense of inclusion. And oh, the first time that face turns away, the first time that inviting light disappears, the child's heart breaks. An exclusion. A turning away.

This is how it all began for the typical man (and woman, of course)—
the doubt, the fear, the comparing himself to others, the deep feeling
of inadequacy, and the sense that maybe, just maybe, he simply isn't
good enough. Women rejecting him feels natural because he has
been rejecting himself for most of his life. He listens to that dismal
self-talk. He gets into his head, he tries to figure things out logically,
he tries to think his way through things, he tries to steel himself, to
muster any semblance of courage in the face of the inevitable rejection he just knows he is about to face at every turn. Everything is
a struggle. Even in relationship, his fear of rejection simmers just
beneath the surface, manifesting in acts of jealousy or attempts to
control or petty arguments about nothing.

A man wears his fear of rejection like a blanket; he's always worn it.
He hates it, he *deplores* it, because he knows how much it weighs
him down, how much it holds him back, how much it restricts him.
It is heavy and damp and rough. Ah well, he wears it nonetheless,
for he is accustomed to its weight and the penumbra it casts upon
his daily life. It keeps him safe. It keeps him warm. In a weird way,
it actually gives him comfort. It gives him an excuse.

He is so comfortable, in fact, wrapped up in his miserable security
blanket, that he gives in to an equally debilitating, hesitation-induc-
ing fear: *the fear of success*. For what shall he do if a girl actually likes
him? Then what? Then he will have to cast his blanket away. Then
he will have to be dynamic and interesting and charming and ah, it
is easier to do nothing, easier not to try, and yeah well, I'm not tall
enough anyway, and she probably has a boyfriend, and also I've got
this blanket, see…

                    ഇന

Sometimes, in spite of his fear, he manages to brace himself and
approach her anyway. He draws in a breath, squares his shoulders,
and goes to her. He has no idea what he is going to say. Maybe just
ask for directions or something.

What happens then? Well, he approaches her with his fear of rejection evident. He wears it on his face, in his body language, in his voice, in his words and actions. He doesn't really believe in himself. Without her saying a single word to him or even noticing him at all, he already believes he is not good enough for her. That is his starting point. "In my heart, I know I am not good enough for her… but I will try anyway… I guess." She doesn't have to reject him. He's already rejected himself.

"Thanks for asking but I'm sorry, I can't. It was sweet of you to ask." No matter how politely and kindly she lets him know she is not interested, he takes it personally. No matter what she says or how she says it, he is sent into paroxysms of self-examination. He beats himself up for once again saying the wrong thing, even though he has no idea what that "wrong thing" might be. "I blew it again! Why? What did I do wrong? I ran out of things to say! I am so boring! I didn't engage her on an emotional level! I should have been more serious! Or maybe I was too serious? I should have been more funny! Or maybe I'm not tall enough. Or rich enough. Or good-looking enough. Or interesting enough. Or… ah, whatever…"

Who knows what is going on with a woman? She could be feeling sad, or not fresh today, or she just broke up with her boyfriend, or she's frustrated with her career or her life. Who knows? Maybe she is happily married. Maybe she just got engaged to her sweetheart last night. Maybe she is just not interested, but she is nice and doesn't want to let him down. It doesn't matter. No matter what she says or how she says it, a man will take it as a personal rejection anyway. It's as if she has somehow invalidated his very existence, his soul, his worth as a man. He takes it to heart. He feels it right here. And it hurts.

Why do men take it personally? How is it possible that a random girl he just met can affect him so much? What right does she have to live rent-free in his head, affecting the rest of his day? *She's just a girl!* A girl he may never see again! It's like getting stung to death by only one bee!

She is innocent. This isn't about her. This was never about her. It has nothing to do with her at all. This isn't even about women in general. It is about us and who we are as men, our relationship to the earth, our sense of purpose, and our gratefulness to God for our brief moment in history. There is no such thing as rejection from a woman... there are only the stories we tell ourselves.

We think we are not good enough, but our problem is not that we are not good enough. We *are* good enough. As good as any there has ever been. Our problem is that we dial ourselves down, we hide our light under a bushel. We put on our masks and hope no one will ever discover just how scared and inadequate we really are.

This is how most men live their lives, my love. It is safer to stand aside and wish. A never-ending stream of beautiful, laughing, vibrant women flows by (it never really ends) and the men stand off to the side, watching and wishing, letting what could possibly be the most fulfilling romantic encounter they have ever experienced quietly pass them by. And yet, a wave, a nod, a hello, a smile, are that's all that's ever been needed to kindle a fire that lasts a lifetime.

∞⟡∞

Every man has a default set of unexamined assumptions—they're right there in his front pocket, wadded up and covered in lint—and he pulls them out every time he sees an interesting girl. A familiar chorus-rush of thoughts runs through his mind. Things like, "Wow, she is so pretty... she must have a boyfriend for sure." Or "She sure is dressed nice... she probably doesn't want someone as broke-ass as me." Or "She is in amazing shape and I... well, I really need to hit the gym." Or even "She looks busy and, ah... she probably doesn't want to be disturbed. I will wait for a better moment." Yes, these are the stories men tell themselves throughout their years.

We make up all kinds of answers to a myriad of unasked questions, and all in our heads. We invent an entire story about a girl we have never met. This is ridiculous, of course; none of these assumptions are based on any kind of evidence whatsoever. Our assumptions have nothing to do with her at all. They belong to us entirely, to us and us alone. We have no evidence that any of it is true.

The remarkable thing is that we never just… well, switch to a better set of assumptions. Is it that easy? Of course! *Anything* could be true about that girl over there. It *could* be true that she is lonely. It *could* be true that she came here tonight because she doesn't want to be home alone again. It *could* be true that she will be delighted to meet us. It *could* be true that she will be nervous if we approach her and say hello. It *could* be true that the encounter will be natural and fun and delightful. Yet we choose "truths" about her that make us hesitate? It makes no sense.

It is better to err on the side of possibilities. It is better to respond to an invitation that isn't there than to ignore one that is. A woman might resent a man for testing her resistance, but she will *despise* him for not doing so.

The only question I ever ask myself is this: Which perspective serves me best? If I am going to invent assumptions about a pretty girl, I might as well pick some good ones. If I am going to make up an entire story about her, I might as well give it a happy ending!

∞CB

In the little resort town of Sopot, way up here on the Baltic Sea, the sailboats heave and jostle, racing hard, sling-shotting around the buoys like champion cutting horses. I am on the Grand Pier, sitting in a beautiful, open-sided lounge, and watching the dance of the sunlit boats… and watching the dance of her.

This is as lovely a scene as any I have ever seen. The curves of a woman are proof that God is love. And the small of a woman's back is the greatest curve of all. The way a *skirt drapes down over and away from her body, water-falling into thin air, precarious, a shelf, a precipice.*

My table is next and when she arrives beside me to take my order, I don't just turn my head to her. I turn my whole body to her, aligning with her completely, my whole attention on her. I look up to her beautiful eyes. I greet her with a smile.

Then I say, "Can I ask you a hypothetical question?"

"Sure... I guess."

"What is your name?"

"Marta."

"Okay, Marta, here is my hypothetical question... I don't live here in Poland. That is obvious, of course. I am leaving this beautiful resort town in five days. And I may never see you again. And yet... if I said to you... that there is something extraordinary about you... and that I would love to spend every minute of the next five days with you... what would you say?"

She raises her eyebrows, stops moving, looks down to the tray she is slowly turning around in her hands, then looks back up to me, smiling and bemused. She is taken aback, which is good.

"Now then, I didn't actually say any of that to you—purely hypothetical, remember? But if I did? You and me... lovers for the next five days... and then never see each other again. What would you say?"

She laughs. "I would say no." But her body responds. I see it. Her back arches slightly, she stands a little straighter, an almost imperceptible shift, but I see it. She transforms before me, from waitress in Poland to woman desired, woman invited, woman in all her splendor.

"Wow... look at you now..." I say.

"What?" she says quietly.

I laugh and sit back, winking at her, "Such a ridiculous proposal, huh? From a complete stranger! Well, I didn't actually say it. I was just, you know, curious, just wondering *how you would respond if I did."*

She crosses one leg behind the other, rocking back and forth, the slightest of movements, the way all women do when they are intrigued. She shakes her head at me slowly. She smiles and smiles.

"I would say no," she repeats.

I look at her, saying nothing.

"Actually..." she says, looking out to the sea, "actually... to that I would probably say... yes."

And with that, she spins on her heels like a sentry and whisks away to busy herself with sundry tasks behind the bar.

I shift my gaze outward, out to where she had looked a moment before, out there upon the glory of the sun-kissed Baltic and the glory of the desperate, jaunty, jousting sailboats. And I gaze back in upon you, too, pretty Marta, soft and radiant, glancing and smiling at me and shaking your head.

Life is good.

— The Alabaster Girl, *page 113*

෨෬

Imagine a young man talking to a girl. It is going well. She is smiling and receptive. She gives him her phone number. He takes it with what he hopes is non-neediness. He folds it with what he hopes is nonchalance. He puts it in his pocket with what he hopes is aplomb. He says to her, "Okay, yeah, um... I'll, uh... I'll give you a call." Then he turns around and walks away calmly, like it's no big deal. But the moment he is out of her range, relief and fist-pumping exhilaration spill out of him like an overflowing vessel, for she is pretty and he likes her. His friends gather around. "So how did it go?" "I got her number!" "Excellent!" High-fives all around.

He goes home that night and what does he do? He takes her number out of his pocket and he places it carefully on the night-stand beside his bed. He runs through everything again in his mind, everything that he said, everything that he did, and he smiles to himself, for she is pretty and he likes her.

In the morning, ah, there is her number on the night-stand, right where he left it. Again he relives in his mind the experience with her the evening before, then he goes forth to his day, exalting, exuberant, smiling at strangers. And when he arrives back home, there it is still! The glorious number of the glorious girl. Yes, she is pretty and he likes her.

Now then, what does he want to do? He wants, with all his heart, to call her. Ah, but he can't! He can't because, well, because it is only the next day and surely that will seem too needy, too available, too soon. So he waits. Every part of his being desires, yearns, aches to call her, to hear her voice, to present himself as poised and interesting and magnanimous on the phone. Instead, he wanders over and looks in the fridge.

The next day, same thing. He sees her number on his night-stand in the morning and in the evening. He wants to call her. He almost does. But he talks himself out of it again. Can't do it just yet. Too soon, too soon.

Finally—interminably!—the evening of the third day arrives and he feels the time is right. Three days have passed, enough time that he will appear busy and non-needy and casual. He prepares himself for the call. His stomach is in knots. He is heart-sick afraid that he might somehow mess it up.

He rehearses what he is going to say. In fact, he rehearses two scripts, one script for if she answers, and another for if he gets her voice mail. He practices over and over: "Hey… what's up? How's it going? Yeah, I thought I would just, you know, give you a call…" He clears his throat and practices some more. He reminds himself that he should smile when he talks to her because he read somewhere that it will cause his voice to sound more assured and inviting. But no matter what, he must remain casual and relaxed, even a little aloof.

So he calls. She hears the phone ring, sees the strange number, and wonders who it might be. Then she remembers... ah, three days ago, I gave my number to that guy... hmm, this might be him. She decides to answer or, because she, too, is human and burdened at times with hesitation and insecurity, she might not.

Let's suppose she decides to answer. Now imagine what is going on with her in this moment. She might be thinking, "I like him and I am excited that he is finally calling me." But her underlying impulse, her subconscious thought is, "He waited the traditional three days. He is playing the usual game... well, I know my role." So she hides her excitement, too. She acts casual, too. She remains a little distant, too.

This is how it begins. With both of them playing the same old tired game, tentative, holding back, reserved, unwilling to be the first to open up. Who knows if they will go forward together? Maybe they won't. Maybe they will. Maybe they will go on a date, maybe they will start to see each other, maybe they will even get married. But their whole relationship was founded on a ridiculous game of *artificial unavailability*.

This game of holding back, of trying to wrest psychological control, of trying to occupy the mind of the other by force, injects a mild, anesthetizing poison into our interactions and relationships that never seems to go away. We think we are being non-needy and mysterious, but artificial unavailability is not mystery. It's evasion.

A man's mystery comes from having a compelling vision of what he wants and then speaking it clearly to the world. Right from the moment he meets the girl who is pretty to him. Mystery comes from his sense that he is caught up in something good and right and necessary. "You gave me your number and I am going to call you because I like you." Mystery is a constant theme in the storybook of his life, the book of picaresque adventure he is writing in every day. And now she's a part of it too.

∞ℭ

Here's another scenario: A guy meets a girl who likes him and she agrees to go on a date with him. So he takes her somewhere typical, say, to a nice lounge for a glass of wine. The whole time, he is trying to be interesting and charming. He is telling stories and telling jokes, and it seems to be working well. She is having a great time and laughing at his stories. He is kind and courteous. He opens the door for her. And at the end of the date, he is not sure what else he is supposed to do, so he thanks her for the great evening and asks her if she would like to get together again. She likes him, she enjoyed her time with him and it was fun, so she says yes, of course, call me. Thus ends the *first date*.

He calls her and they make plans again, usually something different than before—a play perhaps. They go to the play, they are a little more comfortable around each other, and again, they both have fun with each other on this second date. Once again, he is exceptionally kind and considerate. It is going well in his mind. He likes her and she likes him. So they make plans to get together again a third time. So ends the *second date*.

The *third date* is likely an arrangement to meet in one of their homes… they agree to watch a "movie" together, with "movie" in quotation marks because it is, of course, a respectable euphemism, an unspoken excuse for a move toward physical intimacy. There are all kinds of variations on this, I know, but I think we can agree that this is a typical modern dating progression.

So she enters his home, he takes her coat from her and hangs it up, and she gingerly sits down on one end of the couch. She is happy to be here, but a little self-conscious. She comments on the art on his wall; he walks around explaining it all. He offers her a drink. He dims the lights just a little. He goes to his movie collection and holds up various titles, and they laugh and joke and finally agree on one. The mood is light, genial, friendly.

Ah, but here is where it gets a little confusing and awkward for both of them. He starts the movie and sits down. *On the other end of the couch.* "Can I get you anything else?" "No, I'm fine." "Do you have enough wine?" "Yes, I'm good for now." The movie begins. They turn to watch. And there they sit. And sit. On opposite ends of the couch.

He appears calm, he appears to concentrate on the movie, but the questions are frantic in his mind: What now? How to make a move? How do I escalate? She is sitting over there... what do I do next? How do I bridge the gap? What should I do? Should I try to kiss her? Should I move closer to her? Should I use the old yawn-and-stretch trick? How do I shift from the role of the great guy I was on our previous dates to the role of her lover on *this* date? How do I become passionate with her now? I don't know. I don't know. I don't want to make her uncomfortable. I don't want to blow it. I don't want her to leave.

This has been a steady, progressive journey toward intimacy—something they both want—and yet... somewhere on that journey, the typical man gets lost. Remember, she is here *because she likes him.* She came to watch a "movie" at his house, but that was just an excuse to get closer to him, to get more intimate with him. Yet here she is on this end of the couch and there he is, all the way over there.

This three-foot physical gap between them is a perfect metaphor for the gap of intimacy between them, a psychological gap that is getting bigger by the minute. In fact, it is too big to close now. Thus, they continue to sit in frustration.

How did this happen? Well, here's how: even though he has been funny and even though he has been kind and even though he has been courteous on the previous dates, *he never once let her know that he desires her in any way*. He never once let her know that he is a man and he sees her as a woman. Everything he said and did in his earlier interactions with her were done in the context of "friend." This set the tone for the whole experience.

Men are confused about the "flakiness" of women. Why did it start so strong with her and then attenuate into nothingness? It's because we never give her a chance to desire us by letting her know that we desire her, that's why. Because we never let her know that, yes, I am charming and nice, respectful and accommodating, but I am something more. I am a man and I desire you and I will do all kinds of wonderful things to you if given the time and place.

This is not his fault. He has been taught his entire life that women will be offended, scared away, by any hint of a sexual overture; and because of this, he has learned to completely hide his desires from her. He uses neutral, non-threatening, noncommittal phrases like, "hang out sometime" and "see how it goes" and "I dunno... what movie would you like to see?" When he opens the door for her, he reaches way around her, careful not to touch her in any way. He sits across from her at the restaurant and tells pleasant and innocuous stories about his life. He never once gets close to her, never once ventures, with full respect, into her personal space.

And now he wants to somehow turn it on here? He never once expressed his masculine desire for her in any way, and now he wants to "escalate," to transform himself into a paragon of passion? He has been wearing his "just-a-friend" costume for the last two dates, and now he wants to suddenly convert into her lover? Like the cover of some dreamy, sordid romance novel? Can't happen!

ॐ

Most men are afraid to own their desires, my love, to be proud of their masculine beauty, to put a stake in the ground and stand resolutely beside it. This is one of the deepest poverties of our time. They shamble around, averting their eyes, picking at their fingernails, apologizing for their desires as men. A generation of closet heterosexuals.

A man will be talking to a woman and enjoying it, so he asks her if she would like to get together sometime. And she, because she is nice and because she is kind, says, "Oh, that is sweet of you to ask… but I have a boyfriend." And what does he do? He flinches! "Oh, I'm sorry… I didn't know… I just thought… uh, well… I didn't mean anything by it… I just thought that maybe… uh, okay, it was nice to meet you." Flinch.

Apologizing because he found her attractive? Apologizing for asking her out? Apologizing because she has a boyfriend? What the hell? How on earth is this possible? Of course he meant something by it! Wow and wow!

Well intentioned? Just trying to be respectful? Yes well, stand aside then. Women "flake" because a man is uncomfortable with his desires. I get away with everything with women because I have no hidden shame, I delight in my desires, and I share that delight with her. I *never* apologize for the fact that I am a man and she is a woman and yes, I see you there and yes, I am looking at you and yes, I love women. I never hide it ever.

Ours is the most deliberately indecisive and uncommitted generation of men. The voices of men today have little impact. They speak with an apologetic, interrogative inflection, with question marks at the end of all their statements. They repeat safe, neutral phrases to women like, "Would you like to hang out sometime?" and "Let's just see how it goes"—abject phrases, by the way, *that should utterly die.*

Men are afraid to own their own minds anymore, vacillating along with even the tiniest shift in the prevailing breeze, and yet they are hoping and wishing that women will somehow—magically! miraculously!—decide to join them in their lukewarm bathwater of mediocrity. From Tennyson: "How dull it is to pause, to make an end. To rust unburnish'd, not to shine in use! As tho' to breathe were life!"

This is what is missing in the hearts of men today. Conviction, courage, commitment—all have given way to an anonymous, vague energy. There was a time when we were willing to *die* to defend our honor. Where is our virtual sword today? Where are the gauntlets we used to throw to the ground? Where are the lines we used to draw in the sand? Where are the broncos we used to break?

Mediocrity is at war with excellence. We must pick a side because we can't fight for both. I might speak volumes of airy and florid words, but at least I say them with *conviction*. With all my faults, at least I am committed to commitment. I might be extreme, but hey, at least I *am* extreme.

৪০৫৪

I stop her as she is walking by.

That dress, I say… is a success.

She turns to me. I hold eye contact, saying nothing for an extra beat.

Thank you.

Who are you here with?

My friends.

I'm going to say something strong to you…

I lean in closer.

Of all the women in here—and I've talked to a few—you're the one.

The one what?

My girl.

Your girl? How can you tell?

I can see it immediately.

Oh yeah?

Yeah. I can't take my eyes off you. Do you want to leave

this place?

With you?

Yes.

I have a boyfriend.

That's not what I asked.

She laughs.

That's true.

Is that a no?

Yes, that's a no.

Another time and place, and all that, huh?

Perhaps.

Are you in love with your boyfriend?

Yes... no... sometimes.

Well, if you change your mind... I'll be right here.

You don't even know me. Maybe I'm a little crazy.

Yes, maybe you are.

Ah, she says, shaking her head. You and I would have a lot of fun.

That is certain.

Not tonight. I can't.

I understand...but it's great, isn't it?

What's great?

This... you and me. You can feel it, can't you? In the air? The electricity... the hum... the vibration... between us. Of course you can... look at you... you understand precisely what I am saying...

She nods her head slowly.

You would let me do anything I want to you, wouldn't you?

What do you mean by anything?

I mean... anything!

Her friends arrive suddenly, nod suspiciously to me, corral her firmly, and whisk her away. She looks over her shoulder at me, a brief glance, a half-pause, a half-smile, a small shake of her head, and then she is gone.

Oh, how I love women!

— The Alabaster Girl, *page 116*

∞○∞

But we are nervous, men say. Of course we are nervous! We are moving out of our comfort zone. This is marvelous, don't you see? Nothing wonderful is ever accomplished without the willingness to look foolish or risk failure.

What's so great about comfort? Comfort is what we've had our whole life. *Disdain comfort!* We should always be willing to be nervous, to scare ourselves a little, because nervous energy is the pulse of life. Celebrate nervousness, for it is the life-blood of reckless abandon, of great adventure, of desire manifested into action!

To be nervous and *embrace* it is amazing. Instead of using nervousness as an excuse to shrink back, a man can use it as rocket fuel to propel him forward. "Uh… I was standing over there, and I saw you over here, and uh, I'm a little nervous, but I had to come over and say hello. What's your name?" This will set him apart from all the other men in the world who are living their lives as spectators.

Besides, it is universally endearing to women when a man is a little nervous and doesn't try to hide it. How many times have I heard this from women? Sure, he might be stumbling over his words a little, but here he is, showing up, leading the dance, speaking his truth. That's more than most men can say.

What's more, a woman can be a little intimidated by a man who comes across as too smooth, too polished, too rehearsed. Why? Because she, too, is a little nervous, a little insecure, and it's nice to know that he, like her, has a vulnerable side, a human side, and isn't trying to hide it. Women don't relate to us because we are cool or perfect or living brilliant lives. They relate to us because we, like them, are scratching our heads every day, trying to figure it all out.

Vulnerability is not weakness. Vulnerability is not wallowing, pathetic, or needy. Vulnerability is authentic. Vulnerability is as masculine as anything else. It takes real strength to feel nervous, to be curious about it, to express it, and then to step forward anyway. This is the very *pinnacle* of masculinity.

Our body language will naturally follow suit. Men think they need to learn to stand up straighter, to throw their shoulders back, to cock their heads just so. There are all kinds of books on how to adjust our posture and body language but all of that is, for the most part, unnecessary. Our body language is an automatic expression of how we see the world. If a man sees the world with curiosity and wonder in his eyes, his body language will display it. If he loves women and life and is not afraid to show it, he will stand tall, his back will be straight, his chin will be up. If he feels nervous inside but chooses to show up anyway, well hey, he might look nervous... but he will also look *alive*.

∞

We always think it is only us. We think that everyone else is confident and funny and dynamic, and we are not. We might be at a party and over there in a corner we spy a clique of guys and girls talking and laughing, pearly teeth a-flashing, all fashionable and chic. The girls—look at them!—are so amazingly pretty and poised, and the guys... the guys are all so confident and cool and relaxed. Oh, how we wish in our heart of hearts that we could be just like them, so free-flowing and easy and beautiful and cool.

What we universally fail to realize is that they are all just as nervous and insecure as we are! Every one of them is in their heads, trying hard not to screw it up. The guys are mentally face-palming themselves, thinking, "Ah... why did I just say that? What a stupid thing to say. What an idiot I am!" And the girls are thinking, "Does he like me? No, he probably likes her. Or... maybe *her*? Ah, I knew it! I should have worn my other skirt, this one makes me look fat, or my red dress, why didn't I wear my red dress? And why, oh why, did I eat those stupid onions in the salad? I hope he doesn't come too close!" And yet… the only thing we can see from our vantage point over here are easy smiles and graceful grace.

Men can't imagine that a beautiful woman could ever be insecure or shy or lonely. "That can't be right," they say. "Look how perfect she is! She is *gorgeous!* Look at *her* compared to *me*. How in the world could she possibly be nervous or insecure? It makes no sense whatsoever." They can't grasp the notion that sometimes a pretty girl is quiet and only giving one-word answers to their questions because she doesn't think she has anything interesting to say. Men can't understand this at all. If I mention this to men, some look at me like I am crazy for even suggesting it, shaking their heads and chuckling, while others will nod in feigned agreement, then go quiet, pondering, looking up and to the right. I keep on saying it. They keep on nodding. But none of them understand it. The concept is too foreign for men. It's like trying to explain heaven to bears.

All of us have the feeling that we are faking it. We feel like frauds in almost everything we do. We go to our workplace and think, "I have no idea what I'm doing. How can they not see it? How can they not see through my ridiculous charade, that I'm faking the whole thing?" We project a film of us for others to see, expertly edited. Look over there, we say… don't look at the real me over here.

If we could see ourselves the way that others see us, *we would be amazed*. What a profound thought! Robert Burns said it like this: "O wad some power the giftie gie us, to see oursels as ithers see us." If we could see ourselves through the eyes of others—the way we look when we walk into a room, for example—we would think, "Oh, wow… that's not so bad!"

This is why when we get compliments from others, we have a hard time accepting them. "Oh, they're just trying to be nice," we think. The secret is to always stay connected to that part of us that others see and comment on, because the way others see us, *their* version of us—not our own myopic, dystopian version—*is* the real us.

ഌരു

Our patterns of hesitation and doubt recur throughout our lives. A man who is struggling to recover from the destruction of his relationship is terrified of the notion of trying to navigate the dating waters again. Suddenly he is an amateur, thrust back into singledom. He might be powerful in business, accomplished in many fields, experienced in his art, confident and sure… but not about this. He thrashes about in the dark, hopelessly lost. He has forgotten how to be single, how to date. Where shall he turn? Where shall he go? To a bar? To a club? To the Internet? What to do? What to do?

The Internet seems reasonable, but… what of our need for community? Our need to gather together? Our need to catch a woman's eye from across a room? Our need to wink and smile? Our need to be dashing and to sweep her off her feet? Ah, in this age of connectivity, it all seems so disconnected, so confusing.

There was a time when we met in churches and town squares, when we married the girl next door. Now we meet online. This is where we meet. This is where we gather. If we venture out at all, it's to loud and expensive bars, flashing all around us like a badly cut movie trailer.

Lasers and strobes, signs and wonders. Clubs are the new churches. On back-lit and black-lit dance floors, the believers, faithful, reverent, and transfixed, gather together to worship. DJs are the choristers of our day, spinning rapturous, celestial, thumping hymns on their turn-table pipe organs. Bartenders are today's priests, and the penitent line up to await their small cup of liquid absolution, forgiveness for their sins of mediocrity this week. Bless me, Father, for I am partying!

ഌരു

Traditional dating advice has failed men completely. Magazine articles and books and talk shows devoted to the concepts of dating and relationships are flawed. We all know this. They don't work. Most of the articles about the subject perpetuate the epidemic of manipulation and games. "How To Get Her Panties Off In Three Easy Moves!" "How To Get That Man To Commit To You Forever!" We've always had pundits who give "dating advice," who try to teach us how to have more "meaningful" relationships. It's time to recognize it all for what it is: bullshit.

Because of this morass of misinformation and dating advice that simply doesn't work, men are thrashing about, desperate for any type of vision, any ray of hope. Witness the popularity of the "Seduction Community," the Pickup Artist movement, seeping from the pores of the earth, appearing out of nowhere, simultaneously, in every city of the world, erupting from the people themselves, from the ranks of the common man, like the French Revolution. Men are trying all kinds of tactics and tricks, playing all sorts of ridiculous games, and it feels terrible, for it is not who we are at all.

There is a great deal of instruction out there on how to "pick up women," but virtually no instruction on how to create real intimacy, real chemistry or real passion, let alone how to maintain a relationship. Men are being taught specific things to do and to say, or even ways to mimic charm and charisma. And this is good, of course. Men want and need practical advice, things that make sense to them and that they can apply to their life immediately and every day. Even women would agree that it is not a bad thing for a man to learn how to be more fun, more articulate, and better dressed.

But what is missing from most of the instruction is the *soul* of charm and charisma. In other words, *why* certain things work. They are learning how to do more, but not how to be more.

ഇന്ദ

It's easy to say that we should all stop playing games, should be more authentic, should not be afraid to show the real us. But the problem is that the real us is the *vulnerable* us. And once we expose that part of us, all bets are off. In today's dating culture, if you state your desire for her too enthusiastically, you lose. A man really would like to say to a woman who delights him, "There's something about you... I would love to see you again!" But he can't. We've become too cautious, too afraid, too detached.

I have no choice," a man will say, "I have to learn these tricks. I have to play games because women are playing games too. I have to hide my intentions, otherwise I will appear too needy, too attentive, too nice. I've tried that and it doesn't work. I'm so tired of being the nice guy that never gets a woman. Women don't want nice guys at all. They always ends up telling me, after a date or two, that I'm a great guy but they're not sure what they want right now."

Oh, my fellow man! I feel your pain. I have been there and I know exactly what it's like. Ours is a spectacularly aimless generation, devoid of battles, inflamed with pestilent desires, porn-addled, unfulfilled, and forlorn. Ah, but look here, says the next fly-by-night guru. Come sample my wares...

There is a next level of interaction between men and women that wants to be created on this earth. We have hit the boundaries of what it is possible to explore. Like the early adventurers, crafting rickety canoes and rafts with tenuous sails, we have ventured out into the unknown sea and gone as far as these early vessels could take us. To explore further, to discover new lands, to be true treasure hunters, we need faster and better ships.

ༀ☙

I see her out of the corner of my eye, coming toward me, straight like an arrow through the crowd. Tall and sure, impeccably arranged, shoulder-length blonde hair, her Prada handbag held aloft in front of her like a bulldozer blade. A typical glamour girl, marvelously chic, in a bouncy, white dress that is too short in all directions and gold, strappy shoes and typical glamour girl makeup painted carefully over all her insecurities.

Every pretty girl is constantly aware of the effect she has on a room. She knows the way her dress floats on a cushion of air about her body as she moves. She knows the syncopated rhythm of her heels as they click-clack on the floor. She knows—without looking around in the slightest—that all the men are staring at her, that they are elbowing their daydreaming buddies and pointing to her. She knows, as well, that the women in the room are equally attentive, that they are all envious, and that they are rolling their eyes at their girlfriends as if to say, "Who does she think she is?" She knows all this because she has seen it all her life. Her senses have become so highly tuned to the dynamic of a room that she knows it all.

This girl definitely knows her impact. She is used to high attention, to being the spectacle, the greatest show on earth, the kind of event that a whole room turns to watch. This room, for example.

And here she comes toward me. I am just sitting quietly with a glass of water, relaxing, killing time, waiting for a friend. I am not sure why she is heading directly toward me but I, too, have gained a little clarity in my travels; there is no question she is laser-guided, on some kind of a mission involving me. So I sit back and ready myself for an encounter that will likely be far more interesting for her than for me.

Suddenly, delightfully, she is upon me with a little smirk. "Excuse me... do you know a girl named Jessica?" She raises one eyebrow in mock accusation.

This I love. I pretended not to notice her approaching, but now I turn to face her and smile as innocently and sweetly as I can, saying nothing.

"I thought so. Jessica told me all about you. She says that you tried to, oh, how did she put it?" She pretends to search for words. "What was the phrase she used? Oh yeah, pick... her... up."

She is pleased with her challenge; that last phrase amplified and precise as a snare drum: rat-a-tat-tat, pick-her-up.
She plants her elbow on the bar and leans in close to me,
her smile warm and mischievous, her breath on my face,
her hauteur admirable and complete, daring me to explain,
to defend. And I, of course, do not.

"What is your name?"

"My name? Michelle."

"Okay, Michelle, here is probably what happened with
your friend. I have an evil twin."

"An evil twin?"

"Yeah, he goes out and gives me a bad name—"

"I'm sure."

"—while I sit at home alone with my knitting and watch
animal documentaries."

She starts to laugh, then catches herself.

I glance down to her body and smile, "You know what?
You're kind of cute. Did anyone ever tell you that?"

"Are you for real? Kind of cute? Is that the line you used
on Jessica?"

"Hmm, I can't remember. Let's see... Jessica... Jessica...
can you be more specific? I know a lot of Jessicas."

"Whatever."

"And I tried to pick her up, did I? Really? Was I good? Did
I succeed? Did she fall madly in love with me? Oh, wait a
sec, yes!" I laugh and snap my fingers. "Now I remember
her! Yeah, that Jessica, she was a wild one in bed."

"Uh, no. Jessica did not sleep with you. You wish!"

"She didn't?" I feign confusion.

"No, of course not!"

"Hmm, I must be thinking of a different Jessica." I shrug
and turn away from her, picking up my water glass, pretending to examine it intensely. "There were so many of
them, you know..."

She laughs suddenly, then frowns again, tightens her
grip on her sword, and re-enters the fray.

She thrusts: "You're fake!"

I parry: "You're cute!"

"You're too old for her. She is only twenty-two, you know."

"Is that a fact? Well, I like younger girls... their stories are shorter."

This makes her almost laugh again, but she shakes her head and narrows her eyes. "Jessica was too smart for you. She saw right through your little games."

"Well, did it ever occur to you that I was really trying to use her to get to you... that you were the real object of my affection?"

"Ha, not a chance. We've never met. You've never even seen me before. And besides, your amateurish moves would never work on me."

"No? I think my amateur moves would work extremely well on someone like you." I continue my inspection of the water glass, pretending to half ignore her. "Truth is, I haven't even tried with you... yet. You're not even my type."

"Oh, get over yourself! It didn't work on her and it definitely wouldn't work on me. What makes you think a random and clearly inferior guy like you could get someone like me?"

At this, I stop pretending to look down at my glass. I smile broadly and turn fully toward her. "I'll tell you why..." I say and lean in close to her, placing my fingers lightly on her waist. "Because I've known a thousand girls just like you. They're everywhere."

She moves closer. "I am not like the thousand girls you pretend to have known. I am not like anybody you've ever known."

"No?"

Her face is almost touching mine.

"I crush guys like you," she whispers.

"Yes, I believe you do."

We look at each other, unmoving, my left hand ever so slightly on her waist, my right hand twisting the water glass slowly on the bar.

Suddenly, she straightens up. "All right, wise guy, you think you're good? Try it. Say something right now that will make me want to stay here and continue this little conversation with you. Go ahead."

Ah, there is mischief in the air and I love it.

"Go ahead what?"

"Try to seduce me."

I laugh. "You want me to... what?"

"Seduce me."

"Seduce you?"

"Yes."

"Right here?"

"Right here."

"All right..."

Her eyes are shining, electric blue, crackling and smoldering at the same time. She is having as much fun as I.

I stand up and put my arms around her, pulling her close, an exaggerated gesture, sweeping and epic, like the maudlin cover of a romance novel, and she laughs at the parody and does not resist. I hold her close for a long time, not saying anything, just looking at her with over-the-top, dreamy, bedroom eyes. I reach one hand up and lightly caress away a wisp of her hair from her cheek. I smell her neck.

And then, softly, my lips almost brushing hers, "Um... did you... um... what did you say your name was again?"

"What? It's Michelle!" She pushes me away.

"Okay, okay, let me start over." I pull her close again and she is laughing and rolling her eyes, but she is right there with me.

I whisper, "Michelle... did you..."

"Did I what?" she breathes, and her breath is jasmine on my face.

"Did you walk all the way over here... from across the entire room... just to talk to me about your friend Jessica?

"What?"

"Did you?"

"Yes, that was why I—"

"And not to talk about you?"

"No, of course not."

"You walked all the way over here?"

"Yes."

"To talk to me?"

"Yes."

"Then I've already seduced you!"

I laugh and abruptly sit back down, swinging my body out and away from her, breaking all contact. I prop myself with my back to the bar and look over at a pretty waitress who is fussing away empty glasses from a nearby table. I smile and wink at the waitress when she looks up.

"What? You're such an asshole!"

I laugh and continue to look at the waitress. *"Yeah, well, you're the one who came over here to me, scrubbed all clean and shiny. And besides, you're kind of pretty. I don't really have a choice, now do I?"*

For a few seconds she can't form any words. *"Amateur!"* she finally sputters. *"There are plenty of guys that are better than you."*

"There are?" I look at her, acting incredulous.

"All the things you say, the way you try to act so smooth, the way you talk to girls. Please! You can't be serious."

"I can't?"

"Women can see guys like you coming a mile away."

"They can?"

"Ah," she says and waves her hand, *"I am so done with this conversation."*

"You are?"

She turns to leave. *"This is absurd."*

"It is?"

She crashes off through the crowd, like a medieval horseman trampling enemy archers underfoot. And then over her shoulder, *"You're an ass."*

"I am?" I say to myself, smiling again at the pretty waitress.

I will not be her dupe. I refuse to let a woman like that decipher me, to put me in a comfortable little box of her design. She encounters something she thinks she has seen many times before, gets a little curious, and decides to poke it with a stick. What she really wants is to be able to say, "Aha, just as I thought—he is like all other men. He simply pretends to be something he is not. But in reality he is just a guy, and like all guys, he is unable to resist me, is easily controlled, malleable, and under my spell. Buy me a drink, little lap dog."

Women like her are used to being in control. They demand a pedestal and are comfortable nowhere else. And men everywhere are only too happy to comply. The irony is that I put women on a pedestal all the time. I celebrate them and tell them they are beautiful all the time, but only on my terms, and only when they deserve it. I will never give an inch to these vapid (but oh so delightful!) glamour girls.

I sit and think about what just transpired. I kind of liked her. Her and her scent of jasmine.

I lean on the bar and sip my drink and ponder. I think about how this scene would play out if this were a Hollywood movie, a romantic comedy, perhaps. How the dapper hero would continue to sit with his drink, looking coolly askance at the crowd, winking at the pretty waitress.

Then, of course, after a minute or two the heroine would sweep back into the scene, her cheeks rosy and her eyes flashing. She would say something witty and challenging and apropos and our hero, ever dashing, would fire back something equally witty, and they would then continue on together through the rest of the movie, the plot entertaining and rollicking, their badinage rife with sexual tension and disdain and desire. And, of course, at a pivotal moment in the movie they would fall into each other's arms, and the audience would secretly cheer.

I stare down at my drink, thinking of Michelle and her jasmine smell and how life isn't a predictable and popular

*romantic comedy with a cool hero who always gets the girl.
Things like that only happen in the movies, right? Will she
come back and talk to me again? No, of course she won't.
    And then she does.*
        — The Alabaster Girl, *page 118*

જીભ્ર

A young man decides he wants to become a pickup artist. So he
shines his shoes and coifs his hair. He learns a few opening lines,
canned routines, and jejune, memorized stories. He learns he needs
to act aloof and indifferent. He learns he should pretend to be unaf-
fected by her beauty. He learns to hide his true self under a layer of
false confidence and bravado. He shotgun-approaches every girl he
sees, slinging his lines left and right, talking as fast as he can in a
desperate effort to keep the conversation going.

Well, guess what? If he keeps at it long enough and doesn't get discouraged, he will one day manage to "pick up" a girl. Some girl will
eventually smile at him or give him a phone number or go home
with him. "Oh, wow!" he will think, "That actually worked!"

Pickup artists are like gunfighters with no one to shoot. Because
here's what really happens: She looks at him and thinks, "Ah, I see
he is playing the usual game. He is trying to act cool. He is trying
to act indifferent. But I can see on his face that he doesn't really
believe the things he is saying. He is nervous and pretending not to
be. But… I kind of like him. He's cute. He smells nice. And… he's
the only guy talking to me this evening. Ah, why not? I'm a little
horny right now… maybe I *will* go home with him."

So there you have it, my love. The dirty little secret of the whole
pickup artist industry is that it's not the things they are teaching that
work. It doesn't matter at all what they are teaching. What matters
is the fact that the guys who are trying to learn these things are, for
the first time in their lives, *interacting with women.* The only good

thing about a guy aspiring to be a pickup artist is that it gets him out of his mother's basement and into the land of women.

୨୦୧

It is ridiculous for men to try to hide their desires from women. They think they can fool women but they cannot. Women know. A woman can unravel a man's carefully woven nets before his very eyes, dropping the pieces to the floor all around him. One woman told me, "I can see a man's entire belief system on his face the moment he walks up to me."

Women have been reading faces their whole lives. Men have not. When little boys play together with toys, the toys are the focus of play. When little girls play together with toys, the inter-relation between the playmates is the focus of play. Little boys look at objects. Little girls look at faces. Give a little boy a doll and he will smash it. Give a little girl a toy truck and she will give it a personality, a name. Little boys want to be King of the Hill, and they focus only on the summit, fighting their way to the top. For little girls, the desire to be on top of the hill is equally strong, but they will always check in with the others first, scanning faces, seeking consensus, taking turns, sharing the summit.

This is the difference between men and women. In fact, this pretty much explains everything. Men head toward things and goals in their lives that are external to themselves, at the risk of alienating relationships. Women desire the same great things and goals in their lives, but only in the context of relationships. I will even dare to stick my head above the parapet to say this: The fulfillment of men is attainment. The fulfillment of women is relationship.

୨୦୧

Women have far more experience in dating and relationships than do men. How can this be, we ask? Surely it must be fairly even?

Consider this: When a man is single and wants to be "less" single, he will put himself forth into the world, going places and doing things to actively seek out women. He might go out with his friends to a bar or to a party or a gallery opening or whatever. But in general, he puts his attention on places and activities that are conducive to meeting woman. He ventures *forth* into the land of women.

When a woman is single and wants to be "less" single, she opens herself to the world. She might go out with her girlfriends or to a party or a gallery opening or whatever. But in general, she puts her attention on places and activities that are conducive to meeting a man. She puts out signals to the world that she is open and receptive.

Let's imagine them both at an art gallery. They might be looking at the art, of course, but they are far more interested in solving their loneliness. He sees her in the crowd and smiles at her. She smiles in return! So he summons his courage and approaches her, for better or worse. He is nervous but he moves toward her. He takes an active role by making that move. In other words, men generally play the "game" of courtship *actively*.

Now she notices that, yes, he is approaching her, for better or worse. She is nervous but she waits to receive him. She takes on a receptive role by remaining open to possibilities with him. In other words, women generally play the "game" of courtship *passively*.

Now let's imagine they hit it off and it is a positive experience for both of them. They like each other. They go on a date. They start to see each other all the time. They fall in love with each other. At some point along their courtship trajectory, they commit to each other. By commit, I mean that they agree, whether implicitly or explicitly, that they will no longer see others. Wonderful so far.

They are now exclusive to each other. And because they are exclusive to each other, *he stops approaching other women*. He is no longer actively moving toward other women. In other words, he has taken himself out of the "game." She, on the other hand, *never stops getting approached by men*. Even though she is no longer receptive to advances and she gives out no signals to other men, it doesn't matter. She is still approached by men. She could be wearing a wedding ring and some men will still constantly approach. In other words, she is never really out of the "game."

Thus, women have far more experience than men. Men remove themselves from the game periodically. Women are *always* in the game. This is why when a long-term, exclusive relationship ends, the man is completely lost. He no longer knows what to do. He feels he has lost his mojo. Women are more resilient. They tend to pick right up where they left off.

෨෬

The lounge is empty and we make our way to the bar.

"I guess the reason I wanted to talk to you is… well, I've never really had a girlfriend," he says. "I go on dates from time to time, but nothing ever seems to stick."

Thus begins our conversation. I nod my head and listen. He tells me of business ventures and schemes and plans. He tells me of hobbies and sports and things he loves. He tells me of college crushes, furtive one-night-stands and "the one" who got away.

"I want a girlfriend more than anything, but the women I meet are just so… I dunno…" he says.

Time passes, thirty minutes, forty minutes, an hour. I cannot say for sure. I look at him. I listen. Thirty-six years old, MBA from Harvard, plum apartment right around the corner here in Miami Beach. He seems agreeable enough—an elegant demeanor, a calm and introspective inquisitiveness. I find myself wondering, along with him, why he imagines he has such a difficult time with women.

He continues, "I dated this one woman recently from my gym who turned out to be…"

I notice two girls, out of the corner of my eye, standing near us and alone.

"...I dunno. Maybe I should just go out more and..."

I smile and nod at the girls without turning away from him.

"...but it's frustrating because women are only looking for..."

They smile and raise their glasses to me.

"...I even took an improv class to learn how to..."

I wave them over.

"Hello, lovely girls," *I say when they arrive, and introduce around. And now we are talking to girls. And now the evening has infinitely brightened. And now we are laughing and joking. And now we are having fun. Everything is as it should be in this world. For we are talking to girls!*

Fifteen minutes into this and I have to pee. "Be right back." *I say,* "Gotta go shake hands with an old friend." *And off I go.*

Now what's this I see when I return? My hapless companion leaning against the bar on one carefully planted elbow... with his back to the girls. He is near them still—no one else is around—but cold-shifted away, squinting down the length of the empty bar, a bland, dispassionate perusal of... nothing at all.

The girls welcome me back with smiling eyes, but I raise the universal index finger that means, "Just a moment," *and descend upon him.*

"Hey, what gives?" *I say.*

"What do you mean?"

"Well, let's see... when I left a few minutes ago, there were two lovely girls in front of you, who are now directly behind you. How is this possible?"

He shrugs.

"Two interesting and fun girls who, a few minutes ago, were very much enjoying your company and mine, who were sharing ridiculous questions and ribald jokes with us, who were dancing sexily to the music a little bit. For us, mind you, for us. You saw that, right? And now here you are, with your back to them? You're ignoring them? Explain."

"I dunno. I'm not attracted to them. They're not pretty."

What? What? This from a guy who, just a few minutes before, had flipped over all his female frustration cards onto the table before me like a losing poker hand—See the crap I am always dealt? What the hell am I supposed to do with this?—who had bemoaned his loneliness and his desperation for a girlfriend. And there you go.

Will you never understand, men? You make it so easy for guys like me. I am not physically attracted to these two lively and lovely girls either. But that's not the point. Not the point at all. They are interesting. They are fun. Above all, they are women.

I stand directly in front of him, this man of Miami. I stand close, my face to his face, commanding his attention. "Listen to me, my friend. I am going to say something to you and I want you to pay attention. Look in my eyes. You asked for my advice and here it is: If you only smile and "turn it on" and "buy drinks" for women you are physically attracted to, and you ignore all the rest like they don't exist just because you think they cannot benefit you in some way, well then, quite frankly, you lose. You lose at women. You lose at life. Charm is not something you can turn on and off whenever you think it suits you. Charm is not what you do. It is what you are. I am not necessarily attracted to these two either. But they are women. They are lovely. They deserve our entire attention. They are dancing for us. For us. Do you understand? This is why I have women in my life and you do not."

— The Alabaster Girl, *page 120*

§೧೮

Imagine a guy with a small group of his friends gathered in a home waiting for the evening to begin. He knows everyone well. He's been here before and it's a comfortable place and familiar. They are all going out tonight and they are just waiting for one last friend to arrive.

So here's this guy, among friends, relaxed and at ease and doing and saying the things that all guys have done and said through all of time. His stories expand and fly in all directions. His jokes land. He is in his body, not in his head, fully authentic, fully outrageous. Not once does he bite his tongue, thinking, "Should I say that? What if they don't think it's funny?" He is fun and funny, engaged and engaging, being himself completely.

That is, until the last friend arrives, and then he isn't. Because imagine this twist: the late-arriving friend happens to have a pretty girl with him, something no one expected. "Hi guys," he says, "this is Stephanie. She just moved here and works with me in my office. She doesn't really know anyone here in the city, so she asked if she could join us tonight… you know, to make some new friends. I hope you don't mind."

This girl is pretty. This girl is wonderfully arranged. This girl has the eyes and the smile. Now, normally a situation like this should be very good for our hypothetical guy. He is, after all, in a perfect environment, in an excellent state of ease and comfort in this home, in a great mood, holding court amongst peers, confident and full of fun.

Ah, but something remarkable happens to our illustrious friend. Something changes, in the very air, it seems. The center of gravity in the room shifts for him, the energy dissipates. All of his excellent stories and jokes are abandoned mid-sentence, hanging in the air, useless, trailing off, in more ways than one.

As she is introduced around, and eventually to him, he downshifts. He subdues. He becomes more serious. A girl is here, a pretty girl, so now he dons his "cool" persona, that oh-so-familiar, paper-thin mask. Whereas before he was fun and brilliantly expressive, now he appears cool, aloof, not needy, like he has all the options in the world, like she is just another girl, no big deal. He shakes her hand, nods sideways to her, looks away to the other guys, and coughs. "Nice to meet you… so uh, guys, where should we, uh… go tonight?"

He is quiet now, serious, looking around and taking a chair along the wall. He shrinks, outgunned and utterly alone, at least in his mind. He is in his head now, trying desperately to think of something to say, something to do. He can feel his personality drain from his body like yesterday's dishwater, but he has no idea how to stop it. He spirals down, into the chair, into the floor, into an abyss, quieter and quieter, wanting to disappear. She is so pretty!

How can this be? How can he radiate such unfettered and raucous masculine joy one minute, then sink into the floor the next? What has changed? How did the arrival of this girl cause his mood to change? How did he *allow* his mood to change?

The remarkable thing is this: the very thing she would have been attracted to the most in him, *he just suppressed!* He killed it. He shifted himself from abundance to redundance. He transformed himself from the role of the observed to the observer. All he had to do was smile at her, include her, wave her into the group, and continue right where he left off with his dirty jokes and good-natured ribbing and ridiculous stories. All he had to do was not dial himself down in the presence of *a girl*, not hold himself back in any way. But no… the very thing that would have captured her attention the most is the very thing he just suppressed.

We always have an impact on every room. We might think we can just hang around in the background, remaining quiet and therefore unnoticed. But we always have an impact. Always.

৪০৪

Our problems are entirely self-contained. Our problems are with the stories we tell ourselves. We think we are not good enough. *A lie!* For we are more than good enough.

Embrace it all. Every part of a man should be fully presented to the world. No part of him should ever be hidden. This is his authenticity.

Even his faults are authentic. The good and the bad together—this is him being fully him. To hide nothing, to be various, surprising, extreme! There is glory in this. Even his moments of anger should be fully expressed, fully explored.

Anger is a wonderful tool, if not abused. I am not talking about rage, a senseless loss of control, indiscriminate hacking and slashing. I am talking about measured, composed anger. Honest anger has beauty, restraint, poise, elegance, and is the opposite of hostility.

We are all broken in some way. We all have faults and insecurities. We think we have to be cool. But we do not have to be cool. We have to be *authentic*. Authenticity means to embrace equally all of our strength, power, courage, passion, mistakes, failures, and insecurities. To present that whole self to the world instead of our practiced varnish of cool. Nobody connects because they are cool. They connect because they are real. Real is rare.

Our authenticity is the part of us that is led by our heart, our intuition, the part of us that aspires to excellence and to making this world better. We already have everything we need. We are whole, entire, complete. We just need the courage to believe it.

Authenticity is the essence of attractiveness. To find his authentic self is the only real task of a man, a never-ending journey and the only one that matters. It is all about searching for his truth and learning to express it to the world. It is all about not being afraid to want what he wants and to ask for what he wants. It is all about searching for what has heart and meaning to him, for what he wants his life to look like, and for ways to project himself forever onto the world's stage.

To find our true identity, our authenticity, we have to push the envelope, to step out of our comfort zones. It isn't always comfortable to speak our truth. But it is right. As Hemingway put it, "When you start to live outside yourself, it's all dangerous."

ಬಂಯ

Once upon a time, we had rituals. And our rituals had meaning, marking the occasions of our lives, times of recognition, of celebration. We used to honor the transition from boys to men. In virtually all societies throughout history, there has been a rite of passage from boys to men.

Inherent in this ritual was a clear separation, a symbolic putting away of childish things, a stepping away from the old, followed by a symbolic gesture of transformation, followed, in turn, by a stepping into the new. It was a conscious, mindful turning away from the past, never to return.

The Lakota Sioux had their Vision Quest, where they would send a boy out alone into the wilderness on an intense, personal, and spiritual journey, for days. "Go!" he was told. "Stand in the wind... and speak your name." And he would go. He would go out alone for days, scared, hungry, excited, exhausted... searching for the totems and the meaning of his life, searching for the why. And when he returned, sometimes weeks later, he was smiled upon and told, "Now you understand and now you have been given a name and now you can stand over here with the men."

Girls have a natural rite of passage. At the first hint of blood, they look to their mothers, and they are scared, worried, excited, and exhilarated all at once, because now they are women, and now they are shy and now they are proud. And yes, I understand, my love, that this rite, too, is usually scrubbed down into just a pragmatic trip to the pharmacy to pick up the necessary products, the significance underplayed, no guidance given and no sense of celebration. But at least they have something.

Us men? Where is our ritual? Where is our ceremony? When did we ever go off alone into a wilderness to discover our passion, our totems, our meaning? Our generation didn't get it. We never received our rite of passage. There is no real delineation between the time when we were boys and the time when we are men. We were boys playing with toys then, and we are boys playing with toys now. The difference is, we are no longer having any fun.

Oh sure, there are all kinds of mythopoetic men's movements, with ersatz ceremonies and retroactive rites of passage. Lots of men wander away from suburbia for the weekend and gather together in forests and yurts. Let's be primal! they cry out. Let's sit around in a circle! Let's beat some drums! Let's grunt and chant and hold hands and cry! As Betty Friedan so wonderfully expressed it: "Killing bears when there are no bears to kill."

The problem with modern men's movements is that they tend to reassert a position of strength in *opposition* to women, instead of *alongside* women, mistaking women for the enemy and the cause of the problem, usurping the throne by force, occupying the ear by force, occupying the land of women by force.

The best we have managed to do is invent the concept of the "teenager," a dubious distinction, a demographic that simply didn't exist in our consciousness or our vocabulary until about fifty years ago. The lengthening of childhood. There were no teenagers in all of history. There were boys and there were men.

Teenagers don't aspire to be men. They aspire to be perpetual *teenagers*. Their role models, their heroes, are not parents, teachers, inventors, explorers, writers, warriors; their heroes are other teenagers. They look to the stars of film and music—teenagers themselves—swaddled in consumerism and addicted to senseless accumulation, and they point and say "Him! I want to be like him!"

This is who you are meeting, dating, and marrying today, my love. He is a boy. A boy who equates masculine identity with lifting weights and buying fast cars. A boy trying to figure out the right clothes, the right job, the right apartment—all in an attempt to distract you from seeing how small he really feels. He hopes that maybe you won't notice—and ultimately reject—the real him.

෪ඔ

I am up early this morning—to think, to write. An hour later, here she is. She walks out of the bedroom and frumps down hard on the chair across from me, a frustrated energy, looking down at—then tossing aside—her phone.

"Good morning, lovely."

"Morning," she says without looking up.

"Hey, my girl... hello... I am over here."

She looks up, slumping, frowning.

"What's the matter?" I say.

"Nothing. I don't know... nothing..."

She picks up her phone again, concentrates.

"Look over here, baby, look... I have a little present for you..."

"No."

"Look, look, look..." I say, laughing.

She looks at me and I blow her a sweet little kiss.

A half-smile breaks but she looks down at her phone again, and the furrowed frown returns.

My voice changes now. I am in a nice mood this morning and I will not abide her bringing my energy down. "Sandy..." I say, soft and low and firm, like a father addressing a petulant child. "Look at me."

She looks.

I raise a reprimanding eyebrow and gaze at her steadily for a few seconds. "Listen to me," I say, a caressing command, "Don't be cranky around me, lovely girl. If something is bothering you, then tell me. I am here for you. But if you just woke up in a bad mood for no reason, I won't allow it. Change it." And then, the instruction complete, I smile bright and wink at her.

She continues to pout but secretly smiles.

I laugh and point to my cheek, "Come here, my sweet, and give me my sugar."

"No." But she gets up and comes toward me.

"Come say good morning to me, my crazy girl." I point again to my cheek. "Where's my sugar?"

And she sits down beside me and kisses my cheek and the beautiful day properly begins.

— The Alabaster Girl, *page 123*

ഇരൻ

We are the children of men. Every man alive on earth today had a father. Who had a father. Who had a father. Who had a father. And so on. A direct lineage, an unbroken chain of fathers and sons, stretching back as far as we care to imagine. We can go back a thousand years and sure enough, every man alive today had a father standing somewhere on this earth all those many years ago, a distant ancestor on a distant shore. Sure our ancestry overlaps the further back you go, but that doesn't diminish my little illustration.

Now consider this: It is almost a certainty that at least one of those forefathers in the last thousand years stood upon a battlefield. With both feet planted on the ground. With a sword in his hand.

Maybe he killed someone that day. Or maybe he was killed. But before he died, he created a son, who went on to create a son, who also created a son, who created a son, and so on, all the way down through the centuries, all the way down to us who are standing on the earth today. A thousand-year legacy, unbroken, unassailable, stretching throughout these many generations.

Now then, how many men who stood on a battlefield alongside our fathers one thousand years ago have no living sons today? In other words, their line died out. But not *our* fathers! Nothing could stop them. Against all the odds, against the weight of all those centuries—the upheavals of the Dark Ages, the Renaissance, the Reformation, the Enlightenment, the eras of Exploration and Colonization, the Victorian Age, the Industrial Age, the Nuclear Age, the Information Age—they persevered.

This, to me, is a truly profound thought! In spite of all the wars and crusades and diseases and famines and persecutions and plagues and migrations—our fathers created us. The implication, of course, is this: every man alive today has the *blood of champions* coursing through his veins.

We are the children of men. We had a father who stood upon this earth… on a battlefield… with a sword in his hands… with the same champion blood coursing through our veins as his… *and we're afraid to talk to that girl over there?*

How on earth is this possible? How did we lose what we once had? Whatever happened to the strength and conviction of men? What would our fathers do? *What would our fathers do?* Would they be afraid to approach her? That simple girl over there? Exactly.

What draws the heart of a man? A pretty girl? How ridiculously inconsequential! And yet we hesitate, we doubt, we sit in the corner. Is this not tantamount to letting our fathers down? Are we not betraying our entire legacy? Our fathers who lived and died and gave us a name, who stood on this earth, who had the courage to create, who created a legacy, who created us? And we're sitting over here in the corner, heads bowed, wishing and waiting, saying, "Well… I'm not sure…"

When a man is attracted to a woman and he allows the moment to dissipate because of a faltering hesitation, he is letting his fathers down. Not only that, he is also letting women down, all the women in all the world. Because… where is he? Women deserve his authentic self, his whole strength, his masculine glory, his messiness, his nervousness, his ridiculousness, his everything. Women deserve him fully present, fully showing up.

When a man approaches a woman who draws his heart, well then, no matter how nervous he is and no matter what he says to her, at least he is doing his part. He is doing his job as a man. To be aware that he is nervous and then to step forward anyway is just as much an act of masculinity as his father from the distant past standing on the earth with a sword in his hand. He has discharged his duty as a man. He has earned his right to stand upon this earth.

There is a strength that men must reclaim. We have the blood of champions. We have the whole weight of the earth beneath our feet, grounding us, giving us all necessary strength, all needed courage. We have been given a name, a name as valid, as pure, as glorious, as any there has ever been on this earth. Our fathers, those mystics, those adventurers, those holy men, those pioneers, those poets, those warriors who went before us, they paved the way… they won! Our fathers won! We are standing on holy ground. We have the right to speak our name. We have the right to occupy our space on earth, to live spacious lives, to live large, to truly embrace the gifts we've been given, to be unapologetically masculine and purposeful and mindful in everything we do. And we certainly have the right to talk to that girl over there. How can we possibly fail?

୨୦୧

Men have this idea that if they can just logic it out some more, if they can gather just a little more information, read a few more books, memorize a few more things, then they will get the results they want with women. They are searching for a magic pill, something that will allow them to get this part of their lives handled once and for all.

Woody Allen said that eighty percent of success is just showing up. The problem with modern men is that *we don't show up at all*. We are invisible on purpose.

The difference between failure and success is not the absence of fear, and the difference between a mediocre life and a grand life is not confidence. The difference is the courage, the willpower, and the discipline to simply show up. Show up. That is all a man can do. That is all a man needs to do. Never underestimate the power of just showing up.

Even successful, confident performers get butterflies just before they go on stage. It's natural. The difference is that they do it anyway. They don't necessarily have any less fear than the rest of us. They just acknowledge their fear, shake hands with it, take a deep breath, steel themselves, and do it anyway.

Sure, we make mistakes. We will *always* make mistakes. And that's okay. It is time we made friends with ourselves and then respond to ourselves with the same requisite warmth, forgiveness, and loving-kindness that we might show to others. Confidence does not stem from our belief that we know how to do and say the right things. It stems from our belief that we are *learning* how to do and say the right things.

Doubt creeps in for all of us and we must recover. Constant recovery. Recovery every moment of every day. To stand back and say to ourselves, "No, that sliver of doubt does not serve me in any way whatsoever." And phew! now we relax, for we have recovered. Three seconds later, doubt creeps right back in. The solution? Recover again. That's just the way it goes. It never ends. We will never be rid of our reining-in, play-it-safe, you-don't-want-to-get-hurt self-talk. All we can do is shake hands with that cautioning voice, acknowledge it, and recover, recover, recover.

ഇരു

Most men measure their success with women by the results they get. If a woman smiles or gives him her phone number, he calls that a successful interaction. Conversely, if he doesn't get what he wants, his desired result, he turns away dejected. He feels that he has failed. In other words, he measures his success entirely by her response.

Imagine if we pulled back our measurement of success a little closer to here, a little closer to our hearts. Imagine if we measured our success by how well we showed up as men in this world. And nothing more. If we did that, then our sense of success would have nothing to do with a woman's response at all.

Her response is irrelevant. She might tell us to get lost, she might ignore us, she might smile at us, she might give us her phone number, she might sleep with us, she might even fall in love with us. But none of those outcomes have any bearing upon our success as a man. We did our job. We showed up. We are as masculine, as powerful, as successful as any man who has ever walked this earth.

From this perspective, our future happiness, for this day, for our lives, is no longer predicated upon the favorable response of women. In the myriad of outcomes, a girl not responding to us is only one. All outcomes are possible, with her or any other girl. We can never be rejected. It is no longer possible.

ഏറെ

Here is an ancient and much-beloved parable (that I just made up):

Once upon a time in a land far, far away, there lived a young man who was in love with a beautiful girl, and he was kind to her. His kindness was genuine; he really did care about her and he really did love her. He was good to her: he held doors for her, he complimented her wardrobe, and he noticed and commented on little things, like whenever she changed the style or color of her hair. He offered her rides when she needed them. And of course, he was the one who always paid for things, because he was the guy, after all, and she was the girl, so that just seemed right. And besides, he was nice like that.

He discovered early on that she needed a lot of emotional support, that sometimes she just needed to hear that yes, she was pretty and yes, she was smart and yes, she was funny, and he was always there to reassure her that yes, she was all of those things.

His reward for his attention and kindness was a great deal of flirting from her, lots of hugs, sometimes a kiss, sometimes even on the lips! Not too much, though, you understand, because we don't want to ruin the friendship, right? Yes, of course I understand, he would say, even though he didn't, but he was willing to be patient.

She would invite him to parties and he would rejoice, even though in his heart he suspected that she just needed a ride and had no one else to ask. He would immediately dismiss this terrible thought, however, for she was always eternally grateful when he would say yes. I knew I could count on you, she would say.

Later, when the night was over and she was inebriated and bewildered, staying out far past any reasonable hour, he was always there to drive her home, to get her safely into her house and into her bed. He would tuck her in and stroke her hair and sit beside her for a while, waiting around... for what? An invitation? A thank-you? No... just in case... because, you know, he was nice like that.

And when he realized that she was passed out and the moment, too, had passed out and nothing else was going to happen, he would retire to her couch, making do with a too-small blanket, lying awake and wondering what he could have done differently, thoroughly frustrated. But he was the one—surely tomorrow she would realize?—who cared enough to take care of her. Yes, he was nice like that.

At other times, he would listen to her for hours as she complained to him about other men, how there were so few good guys like him, and how he was the only one she could trust, the only one who really understood her. She was always upset at some guy, sometimes to the point of feeling physically ill about it, and he would rub her shoulders or buy her dinner, and even though that's all she talked about and even though it was costing him dinner again, he loved to hear her voice anyway.

He secretly couldn't stand the thought that she had other guys in her life, guys that she slept with, but he tolerated it because he knew she spent far more quality time with him than with them. After all, who did she call to go to movies with her when she was bored? Who did she call to take her shopping? Who was the one who waited patiently holding her shopping bags outside countless changing rooms for her? And who did she allow to steal secret glimpses of her body by purposely leaving the changing room curtain slightly open as she changed? That's right—him, not them!

Yes, it was only a matter of time, only a matter of time. He had seen her at her worst, he had dabbed her tears, he had been there when the world was crushing in on her, when she was depressed or sad or angry, and he had watched her go home with guys who he was sure didn't care about her at all. And in spite of everything, he still loved and cared for her. For he was nice like that.

And years went by...

One day, as he reflected upon his long, lonely, and unfruitful relationship with her, he had a sudden idea. He decided he would do something completely different, something so outlandish and adventurous that it would prove to her, once and for all, his undying love for her, and surely launch their magical future together.

He had heard about the sea, a long, long distance away, and he decided he would travel to the end of the earth, find the fabled sea, and seek out for her a treasure. He would bring it back home and present it to her as the symbol of his undying devotion. Of course, he realized he could just buy her something online and have it delivered, but part of what he wanted her to notice was his willingness to endure the long and dangerous journey, just for her. Besides, he wanted the treasure to be special.

He thought about it for a long time until, suddenly, he

knew! He would seek out and obtain for her an... Exquisite Pearl! Not just any old pearl, you see, but a grand one, one that merited emphasis, capitalization, and italics.

Yes! Surely this would impress her so much she would forget all the other men and only want to be with him. After all, who would ever do such a noble thing? Ah, the more he thought about it, the more he knew he had to go!

So one day, without telling anyone, he took up a small bundle of provisions and left in the middle of the night on a journey across the land to the far and distant sea.

The journey was incredibly difficult, far more difficult than he ever could have imagined. There is no way he would have attempted it if he had known how extremely difficult it was going to be. He persisted, however, because of his great love for the beautiful girl back home and how much he wanted to impress her.

After many weeks he came upon a treacherous mountain, and he climbed that mountain, clinging perilously to the high rocks for many days, and oh how he missed her. After more weeks he came upon a scorching desert, and he traversed that desert, nearly dying of thirst for many days, and oh how he desired her. After even more weeks he came upon a deep, dangerous, and brooding forest, and he entered that forest, becoming hopelessly lost for many days, and oh how he loved her.

Finally, finally, after all these long days, after all these arduous tribulations, he found himself to be... at the sea! Oh, how immense and expansive, how shimmering and shining, how beautiful and blue! He was broken and battered but somehow the sea restored him, filling him with great energy and great strength.

He wasted no time seeking out the treasure he had come to find. "I have come from far, far away," he said to some local fishermen, "and I am here now at the sea to seek out a treasure, an... Exquisite Pearl! For the woman I love, you see." The fishermen looked at him funny, then suggested a

few local souvenir shops nearby, which wasn't exactly what
he had in mind, but the fishermen assured him there were
no real pearls anywhere around here and hadn't been for
years. So he tried all the shops and after a measure of time,
he found a large, porcelain, souvenir pearl.

It wasn't that great, actually, but it was the best he could
find, so declaring it to be the symbol of his undying affection, he bought it and added it to his little bundle. He turned
around immediately to leave the sea, to return home to the
girl he dearly loved.

But something made him pause... to look over his shoulder... to turn around... for some reason, he could not take
his eyes off the sea and all its blue immenseness.

He lingered there for many days, contemplating the sea.
Finally, after lingering and contemplating much longer than
he felt he should, with a curious admixture of sadness and
excitement, he turned around and set back out across the
land, retracing his path.

He battled again through the dark and brooding forest,
through the scorching desert, and over the unforgiving mountain, fighting the elements every torturous step of the way.
And always he thought of his dear, beautiful girl, the love
of his life, and how surprised she would be at his sacrifice
and his amazing gift.

Finally, interminably, he arrived back at his village, battered and bruised. He combed his hair, dusted off his clothes,
straightened his tie, and after a deep breath, rushed to
her home.

She was, of course, thoroughly surprised to see him, for
he had been gone for such a very long time, and even more
thoroughly surprised when, sitting at her feet, he recounted
all the details of his remarkable adventure. He told her of
all the hardships he had endured just for her. He told her
about the mountain and he told her about the desert and
he told her about the forest and he told her about the sea.
Mostly, he told her about the sea.

Then he stood up tall before her, opened his little bundle and, with the greatest flourish he could muster, presented to her with both hands the... Exquisite Pearl!

The beautiful girl was astonished and she began to weep and fell into his arms. She proclaimed right then and there that from now on, she would love no other man but him. No one has ever sacrificed so much for me! she cried. Besides, the other men are just a bunch of jerks anyway, especially the guy she met a few weeks ago. Oh and by the way, I have to go see him again tonight. I think he is just using me for sex, you see, and I want to go clear that up, to tell him that he can't just use me like that. You understand, right? But not to worry because I finally know what I want and I will call you tomorrow for sure. Or maybe the next day. But sometime this week for sure, and thank you so much for the gift, it's the thought that counts, right? You're so cute. And she showered him again with kisses and hugs and fondness.

But something was different... something he couldn't quite put his finger on. For as she was showering him with all those kisses and all those hugs and all those promises and proclamations, he found himself looking over her shoulder and out the window toward the distant horizon.

She smiled at him and he thought of the mountain. She held his hand and he thought of the desert. She hugged him close and he thought of the forest. She kissed his cheek and he thought of the sea.

Most of all... he thought of the sea... he thought of the sea. And he placed the "pearl" in her hand and walked away.
    — The Alabaster Girl, *page 128*

৪৩৪৩

Why is nice guy behavior so prevalent? Why is it so common? Why does it perpetuate? Someone in the front of the class will raise their hand and say, "I know. I know. It's because romantic comedies and movies ingrain in us the notion that the nice guy will eventually get the girl, that eventually she will notice him and realize it was really *him* she wanted all along. The whole *When Harry Met Sally* scenario." This might be true, but here's another reason… and I've never heard anyone say it before. Why is nice guy behavior so prevalent? Because it works! Ah, so insidious, but so true.

Women always respond wonderfully to little attentions: flowers, small hand-written notes, chivalry, considerate behavior—*at first*. A woman enjoys the first date with a nice guy. He is fun and funny and charming. He is cute. Finally, someone who is nice and not a jerk. She looks around and realizes that, wow, she just had a beautiful date.

He feels this, too. It was an enjoyable experience for both of them. Her laughter seemed genuine, her smiles were real. And so, of course, he asks her out again, and so, of course, she accepts. "Yes. Call me." And she is sincere.

They make plans and a second date ensues. And perhaps, a third. And because she responded so favorably to his little attentions on the first date, he turns it on even more. Look how considerate he is *now*! Look how attentive to the little details! Look how chivalrous!

Ah, but somewhere between the second and third date, he feels a drifting sensation in the air, a waning of her excitement to see him, a delay in her responses to his frequent, funny-romantic messages. She seems to be always busy these days. "I'm sorry I didn't call you back yesterday. My aunt is in town and I had so many things to do. Call me tomorrow and we will make plans, okay?"

It must be him, he thinks. After all, look how excited and enthusiastic she was on the first date. Let's see… what did he do right that first night? Whatever it was he'd better do *more* of it or he will lose her. Maybe she feels he is not attentive enough now? Maybe he needs to give her even more attention? Maybe he wasn't as fun or funny as he was on the first date? Maybe he just needs to do a little more, to really show her how much he likes her, how much he enjoys being with her, how much she means to him? In fact, maybe she has the misconception that he is interested in other girls? Oh no, that will never do!

And so he turns up the volume of his words and actions because, well… because it worked before, because she genuinely responded to it before, because she had a great time with him before. He sends her little poems, flowers, notes on her car. "Just thinking of you… have a great day!" Smiley face. This is why nice guy behavior is so prevalent, so repeated over and over: Because initially, it works. It works beautifully.

Being nice to women is not enough. If that's the only quality a man has to offer, then there is nothing in his spirit, nothing strong, nothing secure, that a woman can grab onto. Being nice, by itself, will never spark passion or create attraction. "Says here on your resumé that you're a 'good team player.' That's great, but we're hiring people with leadership skills…"

How does one wash off the sour, lingering odor of "nice guy?" Lower your center of gravity. Get in your hips. Get in shape. Get some nice shoes. Get out and meet new people. Get an edge. Loosen your tie. Un-tuck your shirt. Learn a language. Learn an instrument. Travel far and wide. Hang around your heroes. Climb a mountain and *never tell a soul.*

෧൝

Men blame women for always putting them in the so-called "friend zone." Well, think about it… what kind of women put men in the friend zone? "Flaky ones!" men shout. "Women who are not honest about what they want!" Ah, but it is a trick question. Let me ask it again: What kind of women put men in the friend zone? *None!* No woman ever puts a man in the friend zone. No woman ever has. Men do it entirely to themselves.

It went so well at the beginning with her that a man is thoroughly confused when it wanes. Straight into the friend zone. "Well, there you go," he thinks, "just like I thought—women are flaky. They don't know what they want. They just use men for free dinners and movies." But she is just following her heart, her natural impulse. Her interest in him fades because there is *nothing in him that speaks directly to the woman in her.* She has already experienced an abundance of his charm, his stories, his pleasantries. Now she needs to feel his masculine edge—his vitality, his fierce love of life, his passion, his desire. And she feels none of these things at all.

He is lacking that edge, that core of masculinity that a father would have given him. He lives in tepid apology, abandoning his damn-fool spirit, with a primary goal in life that is mostly about conquering a vagina and not at all about conquering the world.

A woman has to feel a man's thrust, his drive, his push, him living at his edge, living from his core. Ah, but today's man is not thrusting in any way at all, my love. He is sensitive and modern. He is pleasant to be around. He is a great "dater." He is attentive, accommodating, and available. Even in bed, he does everything he can to please you, please you, please you, massaging you for hours, going down on you for hours, shunting aside his own desires, his own impulses, his own primal thrust, and all the while imagining himself to be a great lover.

In other words, he is a wonderful *friend.* In other words, he measures out—then steps into—the friend zone entirely by himself. And when she tires of waiting for him to be a man, he blames *her.*

Thus is planted the seeds of vendetta in the heart of man. "Slut" is a nasty term we use for a woman who exercises her right to say yes. And "friend zone" is a nasty term we use for a woman who exercises her right to say no. In other words, women are damned if they do and damned if they don't.

ଚୈଙ୍

Let me make a distinction between a nice guy and a Nice Guy. You are already aware of the difference, I am certain. Genuinely nice guys have good intentions. They are honest and sincerely want to have good experiences with women. They do not know and they really *do* want to know. They treat people the way they would want to be treated themselves. They like people and want to do good things and be a positive influence. They want others to like them, yes, but they have no sense of entitlement, or feel that the world owes them something. They are inherently nice, no matter what others may say or do. They are nice because, well, because they are nice. They would love to share a great relationship with a great girl. Sure, they are confused about how to *attract* a great girl, and yes, they feel they are perpetually in the "friend zone," in spite of their best efforts, but they have no hidden anger toward women, harbor no ill will toward women, and do not complain about women or blame them for all their woes. They blame *themselves* for their loneliness, not women.

Nice Guys, on the other hand, are a scourge, a plague of locusts that blocks out any vestige of sunlight. A Nice Guy is too "nice" to simply ask for what he wants. He hangs around a woman for days, months, years, like a beaten and angry little puppy, hoping for a blessing from above. He is there to help her move, to carry her shopping bags, to pick her up at the airport. But he never speaks one word to her about his true desires. Instead, he shifts his feet and smiles his weak, obsequious smiles, repeating the same lies over and over, "No, no, it's okay… I don't mind… I'm fine."

The Nice Guy puts a woman on a pedestal and then blames *her* when she falls. He hovers around her for weeks, months, years, then gets angry at her when his pretending to not be romantically interested in her fails to get her into bed. He fumes and spits vitriol about her to others when he realizes she is not going to reward his sycophantic and treacly kindness by spreading her legs reverently for him. He confronts her and demands to know why she is not dating him. He is angry and offended that she could be so shallow as to be interested in other useless men. How can she not see what's really going on?

Nice Guys are surrogate boyfriends, volunteering to be stand-ins for the real actors in a woman's life, then furious when they don't get a speaking part in the movie.

Nice Guys sidestep all personal responsibility by blaming women. In fact, it is convenient for them when a woman fails to respond to their excessive niceness because it allows them to justify their innate belief that all women are shallow, flaky bitches with issues.

Nice Guys have a sense of entitlement. These are the same guys who complain about *women* having a sense of entitlement, that women are fundamentally selfish, that they only consider what they can take-take-take from men, a what-can-you-do-for-me attitude. These men think that not being a jerk entitles them to receive favors from whatever woman they happen to latch onto. They feel that because they are so nice and accommodating, women are *obligated* to like them. They really do believe that women owe them something for being so attentive and nice.

The Nice Guy isn't really nice at all. His only agenda is to gratify himself. Even though he is hung up on her and obsessing about her, in reality, she is interchangeable. If it doesn't work out, well, he will feel sorry for himself for a while, then just go out and hump someone else's leg. A Nice Guy hides behind a veneer of "sensitivity" and "respect" but his watery behavior is just an unctuous attempt to manipulate her into doing what he wants. It is the ultimate form of manipulation. It is weak. It is vindictive. It is wrong. Nice Guys are the real assholes.

Some women, with apathetic hearts and ulterior motives of their own, will feed off a Nice Guy, giving him just enough hope and attention to keep him going. Hey, if he wants to buy me things and drive me around all the time, it's not my fault! Other women choose to ignore it because it is too awkward to address it, hoping that he will eventually get the hint. And other women, of course, have no idea what is actually going on, never once considering that he wants to be more than friends.

Yes, there are shallow women in the world, taking advantage of Nice Guy behavior. But there are also volumes of honest, lovely women who are trying their best to be real. The problem is that the intentions of women are often misinterpreted by Nice Guys. If she displays her feminine side in any way in a social, or even a professional, environment, if she is nice and courteous, smiling and kind, the Nice Guy often interprets it as signals of romantic interest. She is coming on to him, she totally wants him, or at the very least, she is inviting him to proceed. Just because a woman is engaging and sweet, doesn't mean she is constantly flirting.

Let's simplify and generalize, because we can. Men want sex. And a girl who is too quick to give that up to every man nearby is said to be too easy, too available—in short, what society labels a "slut." So now let's look at it from the other side. Women want a strong emotional connection. And a man who is too quick to give that up to every woman nearby is said to be too easy, too available—in short, an emotional slut. So there you go… a Nice Guy is a slut.

Am I, perhaps, being a little too harsh on men? A tad pharasaical? So be it. I can live with that. I *am* that man. Everything I say here is what I wish someone would have told me all those years ago when I was young and cloying and apologetic and "nice."

෨෬

I like talking to her, I decide. She is pretending to be bitchy but she is not really bitchy and she is making me laugh. Blonde girl again. Why is it that, even though I am sublimely attracted to brunettes (I always say I would walk past three blondes to get to a brunette), most of my girlfriends end up being blonde? Curious. This makes me laugh and she almost laughs too, but catches herself because, of course, she is trying to be bitchy. And that makes me laugh even more.

The bar is full of people, the music is good, and she is standing before me with a drink in her hand and a sniffy, faux bitchiness in her attitude. She smells nice and she is fun.

"I like you," I say. "What's your name again?"

"Not interested."

"No... but you're still here talking to me when there are all kinds of other areas where you could be. You could easily walk away if you wanted to, but nope, you are standing right here beside me and you know exactly why. And so do I. Not my first rodeo, as they say."

She starts to say something, but out of the corner of my eye... something else, something across the way: a girl (brunette) has just arrived. She is milling about near the entrance, like she is not sure if she should stay here or go.

There is something about her, this brunette arriviste... in a bar full of pristine women, there is something magical about her.

What draws our hearts? Ah, who knows? Mystery draws our hearts, or incantations, or stars, or destiny.

Without hesitation, I interrupt my pretty blonde accomplice in mid-sentence. Hold that thought, I say, and I turn and walk away, straight to the other woman, who is beautiful, who has dark hair, and who... something, something about her... takes my breath away.

I don't live here in Vancouver, she says. I am from Bucharest, she says. (Of course! The prettiest girls in all the world are Romanian.) I am just looking for my sister, she says. I would love to stay but I cannot, for we have to catch a plane early in the morning, she says. Yes, contact me when you come back to Bucharest, she says. Here's my card, she says.

And just like that, she is gone. I pocket her card, turn around, and walk straight back to my pretty blonde girl who is still standing in the corner, with her drink still in her hand, watching the whole encounter in wide-eyed bemusement.

I smile sweetly to her because I like her. "Hello, my dear. I'm back. You were saying…"

"Did you know that girl?" she says, indignant.

"Which girl?"

"The girl you were just talking to."

"Did I know her?"

"Yes."

"No."

"You didn't know her?"

"Nope."

She shifts her drink from her right hand to her left hand. Then she shifts it to her right hand again. Then she sets it on the counter beside her. Then she raises both hands before her, toward me, palms up, as if showing me a toy boat she had made, and in a measured schoolteacher voice, a reprimanding disbelief, she says, "Okay, let me get this straight. You were just over here talking with me, right?"

"Yes."

"Then another random woman happens to walk in, a woman you don't even know, and you just… leave? You just walk away from me? To go talk to her?"

I laugh, "Yes, of course I did! Did you not get a look at her? Did you not see the way she was dressed? She was gorgeous! Of course I went and talked to her. Plus, she was wearing red lipstick. How could I not?"

She looks at me, mouth and eyes hanging open.

"But not to worry… here I am back again talking to you," I add with a smile.

"You've gotta be kidding me!"

I laugh again. "Yeah, well… what am I supposed to do, girl? You already let me know how fundamentally disinterested you are in me. Remember? 'How do I abhor thee? Let me count the ways!'"

"Well, you could have the common courtesy to not just leave

in the middle of—you know—our conversation."

*"Yes, it's terrible, isn't it? Run away, little girl. I'm nothing
but trouble. I don't even know why you're still here talking
to me."*

"I'm not," she says quietly, looking at the floor.

I lean in close to her, my voice low, "Oh, but you are."

She looks at me. I look at her. She almost smiles.

"You're still here—" I say.

"No, I'm not."

"—right here with me. Yes, you are."

"I don't even like you."

"Yes, you do."

— The Alabaster Girl, *page 133*

ഇരു

A common lament is that women are only attracted to jerks. Bad boys,
yes. Jerks, not so much. Oh sure, there are lots of women who return
again and again to abusive situations no matter how much help they
are offered. Why? Who knows? To quote Lucy Maud Montgomery:
"A body can get used to anything, even to being hanged." I will let
others with a more psychological predilection construct their charts,
conduct their interviews, and posit their explanations.

But putting these extreme cases aside, I think we can all agree that
a lot of women are excited by bad boys. In fact, even though they
might eventually marry a nice guy, a lot of women will always feel
that rushing twinge of attraction to bad boys.

So why is this? Why are women attracted to bad boys? Someone
might thoughtfully stroke their chin and say, "Well, it is obvious
why… they are a challenge." And that's as good an answer as any.

The challenge is that he has drama in his life *that isn't her*. He is too
wrapped up in himself to pay much attention to her. She wants what
she can't have and she can never really have him. She can't get over

the fact that he is not focused exclusively on her, and it becomes her subconscious mission to change all that. If she can fix his character flaws, perhaps he will be so grateful to her for making him a better man that he will never leave her. She wants her friends and family to see what she sees in him, the good guy that he really is. He just needs a few adjustments, nothing much really, and they will see. Yes, this is an excellent project for her.

Few men have the courage and authenticity to speak their truth to women. This is one thing that bad boys have going for them. They say it like it is. I once heard a man ask a group of women why they always seem to get together with bad boys and one of them thought for a moment, then answered, "Because they ask." There you go.

Women *say* they are tired of all the jerks. For once, they would love to meet a normal guy with a normal sense of humor who is nice to them. Ah, I say to them, are you sure? Within a five-mile radius of where you are right now, there are *volumes* of nice and normal guys who would be extremely happy to be that man for you. They will shower you with flowers, gifts, and sweet nothings. They will pay attention to your every whim and desire. They will be so nice to you, your head will spin. But you don't really want that, do you, my love? See? You laugh because you know it's true.

The problem with those volumes of nice guys within a five-mile radius of you, those wonderful men who would do anything for you, who would be so sweet and nice to you, is that they would make you their whole reason for existence. They would place all their hopes and dreams in your hands. They would make you responsible for their self-worth. They would make you responsible for their future happiness. And you know that. And you don't want that. That is too much of a burden for anyone to carry.

How's this for an idea, my love? Imagine a man who is all the things a woman says she wants. He is funny and charming and attentive. He loves her mind. He loves her body. He wants her in his life forever.

Yet he still has the *untamable spirit of adventure in his heart*. He speaks his truth. He compromises *never*. There is no discrepancy between his immense passion for her and his immense passion for life.

This is the "real man" that women seek, a combination of all the desirable qualities of the nice guy and all the desirable qualities of the bad boy. The nice guy is attentive but boring. He is focused only on her. He gives and gives. The bad boy is inattentive but exciting. He is focused only on himself. He takes and takes. The real man is attentive *and* exciting. He is focused on the great adventure that is his life and can't wait to include her. He shares and shares.

A woman doesn't want to *be* the adventure, she wants to be taken *on* an adventure. She wants to be caught up in something greater than herself. She wants a man who has a purpose in his life, a purpose that isn't her.

❧

As in everything, the answer for a man is to ask, "What do I want?" This is the greatest thing he can do, in every situation, in every inter-action, in every aspect of his life. To ask that question, to examine his heart for the answer, and then to express it to all. It means to engage with yourself first, entertain yourself first, please yourself first.

We think this is selfishness, but this is not selfishness. It is the *opposite* of selfishness. It is a gift. To stay connected to who we are and to celebrate what we want for ourselves is the highest good, the greatest gift we can give to others and to the world. It is the greatest expres-sion of our true selves and the only true commitment of our lives. Our authentic desire is glorious beyond words.

A woman will naturally punish a man who is weak and doesn't speak up about what he wants. It's automatic—she won't even realize she is doing it. She just follows his cue. She will tend to please whomever he tends to please. If he pleases himself, she will please him, too.

However, *if he only pleases her*, as so many men do, she will oblige by also pleasing herself—and *only* herself.

Here's something I've never heard anyone say before: The greatest lovers please only themselves in bed. What? Yes, you heard me right, my love. I will say it again: *The greatest lovers please only themselves in bed*. No, no, no, you are almost certainly thinking. That isn't right at all. Oh, scandal! Why do I insist on saying such controversial things? Yes well, let me *attempt* to explain…

There are three stages in the sexual experience of a man. In *stage one*, he is a little lost in bed. He's not sure what to do, where to touch, where *not* to touch, or just exactly what works. He tries various things, fiddles with a knob or two, speeds up when she breathes deeply, slows down when she doesn't, trying all the while to get a sense of whether or not she is enjoying it, but never sure at all if she is. Smart women will pretend to enjoy it, giving him little taps of guidance and sounds of encouragement. Smarter ones will talk him gently through it, leaving nothing to chance, telling him exactly what they like best.

Later in life, if he has paid attention and has a desire to learn, he eventually moves on to *stage two*. He is now considered to be "good in bed." He has more experience now. Perhaps he has even read a book or two: on the basics of female anatomy, on how to touch a woman, on how to go down on a woman, on the notion that "she comes first," and all that. Women enjoy the experience with him now, for he knows what he's doing, he knows where to touch her, he knows what feels good for her, his foreplay is extensive, his rhythm is sound. If you ask women, they will say that, yes, this is exactly the kind of man they want in bed. All books and programs on sex seem to agree, and are brimming with various positions and techniques—textbook examples on how a man can achieve this pinnacle of proficiency in bed.

But if we measure a man's sexual prowess by his ability to run through an orgasm-inducing checklist, well… women can give themselves an orgasm far faster and more efficiently than any man. She can please herself, expertly and at will, if that's the ultimate goal.

So here's my novel notion: The best lovers are the ones who did their time in *stage one*, then moved on to *stage two*, spending years punching that particular time-clock, and now have moved on to *stage three*. This is a stage very few men will ever attain, but when one does, it is remarkable indeed!

A man in stage three pleases *himself*, not her. For he has come to the profound realization that by pleasing himself, he is ultimately pleasing her. He does exactly what he wants to do to her and when he wants to do it. He goes down on her because that's what pleases *him*. He turns her over into a new position, then changes his mind and turns her over again, because that's what pleases *him*. And he is constantly describing to her, in glorious detail and in a low and vibrating voice, exactly what he is doing to her in that moment and exactly what he is about to do to her in the next.

In other words, he has his way with her. He uses her. He bends her over. He pleases himself... *through her body*! And in doing so, he takes a woman to places in her *mind* where she has never been—soaring anthems of emotion, waves of pleasure, an entire opus of imagination.

A man in stage one pleases himself and occasionally her. She is kind and understanding. A man in stage two pleases her and occasionally himself. She has nice and consistent orgasms with him. A man in stage three pleases himself through her body. She loses her mind, starts speaking in tongues.

Now then, I must tread softly here, for this is a phenomenally incendiary concept. There is a very real and present danger that men will think that I am suggesting they can dispense with any foreplay or attentiveness. I am not suggesting that at all. In fact, a man in stage three might attend to his woman for hours. But it isn't because he is trying to please her. It is because it pleases him.

Here is an extremely important point: A man can *never* successfully move to stage three without a thorough understanding and volumes of experience in stages one and two. And he certainly cannot move *directly* from stage one to stage three. There are absolutely no short-cuts. You can't have one without the other.

A man in stage three is the quintessential lover, he has pleasure embedded in his fingertips. The essence of the lover shines through everything he says and everything he does. He knows how to touch a woman, and he uses that knowledge to enhance *his* pleasure, thereby enhancing *hers*.

ഓരു

Men today are tanned and sculpted and groomed, but it's all shiny, polished surfaces. There is no ragged edge in men, nothing in them for women to grab onto, nothing strong at all, so women are forced to settle for men who are soft, accommodating, dispassionate, and for the most part, asexual. Either that or try their luck with jerks. Why is there nothing in between?

Most men live their lives in sexual shame. We are taught to hide our sexual nature, to hide our light under a bushel. Followers of Attis, castrating themselves in frustration, lest mother be offended. In our Western society, sex is reduced to a "piece of ass," wrapped in guilt and regret, and devoid of the exultation of the soul in contact with beauty.

Our shame about being men is by far the biggest reason we have dysfunction in our relationships with women. It is why we can't get a date, it is why a woman will not trust us with her body, it is why we can't keep her, it is why we put her on a pedestal, it is why she doesn't respect us, it is why we mistreat and abuse her, it is why we are manipulative, jealous, controlling, picking at her and knocking her down in all kinds of subversive ways. It is why we are so unful-filled and so lost today.

Oh, what a loss! For men. For women. Our sexual nature is God's gift to us. It is divine. It is our birthright. We have every right to reclaim it. In fact we have an *obligation* to reclaim it, an obligation to all the women of the world. Women are waiting to feel the thrust of men, and men are not thrusting in any way at all.

There is a masculine joy men need to reclaim, a return to the spirit of men. Men don't need more therapy, more enlightenment, more finding themselves. Men need a return to courage. The courage to choose. The courage to create. The courage to lead the dance. The courage to say to a woman, "You are beautiful to me and I like that." Men deserve it, it is theirs for the taking, and once they reach out to take it, the whole world will respond.

There is a sublime grace in a man who embraces his masculine edge. Our masculine edge, our sexual energy, should be the first thing that enters a room when we arrive. It should never be suppressed. Ever. We have dialed it down all our lives. No more. This has to stop. The world needs men who are fully presenting their sexual energy to the world. Who are proud again to be men.

Ⅎண

I need to get to know someone first.
To feel comfortable.
You know and I know that we have been connected forever.
I am different from other men and you know it.
We have been comfortable with each other from the moment our eyes first met.
We are lovers.
Lovers?
We are not lovers.
Lovers make love to each other.
We've never made love to each other.
Ah, that is where you are wrong.
We are lovers.

In the truest sense of the word.
We haven't made love to each other yet?
What do you think we have been doing this whole time?
— The Alabaster Girl, *page 135*

଼ଠଔ

All men have a center of gravity, an equilibrium, centered around their heart. Now consider this: If we can accept that a man has a center of gravity, then it can be said that he has an *outward-flowing* energy—from his heart and into the world before him. All the expression of a man moves outward from this center of gravity. This is how the world experiences him.

Picture a flow of energy from a man's center of gravity that moves *upward* and outward. It starts from his heart, his center, his core, and moves up through his chest, his arms, the tips of his fingers, his face, his smile, his eyes. A welcoming radiance. This is the essence of man in his charm. This is man fully charismatic and alive. This is man full of curiosity, invitations, aliveness.

Through this upward energy, he is connected to the sky above him and the horizons stretched out before him. This upward-flowing energy is how the world perceives his beauty, his empathy, his curiosity, his honesty, his aliveness, his humor, his clarity, his grace. Everything good about this man is present in this energy flow and fully presented to the world.

For instance, imagine a man on a job interview. Everything about him could be said to be *high*—his smile, his posture, his energy—all flowing from his heart, upward and outward. He sits up straight in the chair, he focuses, he is attentive, he summons the requisite lyric bravura of charisma and charm. Even his eye contact with the interviewer is high and bright. A perfect example of a man's upward radiance.

Now imagine the same man with another, equally powerful form of energy that moves *downward* and outward. Also originating from his heart, his center of gravity, this energy moves down through his stomach, through his loins, his legs, through his feet, into the ground, and outward into the world. This energy force his stability, his connection to the earth. It is low and floats before him on the floor, like a heavy-bass hum.

This downward-moving energy is his sexual energy. It is his darkness. It is all the things that make him strong and mystical and dangerous and sensual and scandalous and mysterious. This is the knowledge in his heart that he has what it takes. This is his power to destroy. This is his conquering self. This is the part of him that will ravish the world.

These are the two halves of true masculine energy. Upper and lower. Like a tree, a man has foliage that reaches up to the sun, with fragrant, colorful leaves for all to see, full of birds and light and grace. But he also needs roots that go deep, that keep him grounded, confident, unmoved.

If a man is only projecting one kind of energy, he is out of balance. If he is all upper energy, he is agreeable and engaging and charming, the life of the party, and fun to be around. But he has no excitement, no ragged knife-edge to his personality. He has no mystique. No one looks at him and sees a man of strength. Women all *like* him, to be sure, and want him around, for he is entertaining and fun. But they will never truly *desire* him. They will never be sexually attracted to him. He will never be their fantasy. He will forever be "just a friend."

A typical man today is too top-heavy. He has forever suppressed his lower energy. But it's not his fault; there is little in his instruction today that teaches him how to embrace the quiet strength of his sexual nature. In fact, he is taught to *apologize* for it. He is so afraid to offend that he does nothing. Nothing at all.

Most of the dating and relationship advice out there is focused on improving a man's upper energy. He learns social skills. He takes classes on how to be a better conversationalist. He learns ways to be more charming, charismatic, and chivalrous. He learns to be funny. And this is good, the essence of charisma. These things will certainly make him a *nice* man. But they will not make him a *magnetic* man.

On the other hand, a man who has only lower energy is too aggressive, too sexual, too controlling. This is the jerk, the asshole, the chauvinist. This is also the leering, lurching, creepy guy. Because his lower energy is not balanced and refined by the charm and the respect and the empathy of the upper energy, this man can be scary and dangerous to women. He suppresses his upper energy because he has confused romance with supplication, sensitivity with passivity, empathy with softness, authentic desire with selfishness, grace with weakness. His sexual energy is untempered, rapacious, simmering, out of control, usurping all rational thought—the unfiltered, primal, sexual urges that Kingsley Amis likened to being "chained to a maniac."

Upper and lower. North and south. Light and dark. When a man is in true balance, both forces are of equal measure, both are necessary, and both are full-flowing for all things and for all people.

Why do women never get the sense from men that they would, without hesitation and with full respect and delight, bend them over and ravish them? This is what women are *desperate* for. The magnetic pull of truly balanced masculine energy. Instead, they are stuck with an entire generation of nice guys. Or aggressive, tone-deaf assholes.

An integrated man has both energies, and the balance of both has an incredible impact. He is always shifting, as necessary and without effort, between upper and lower energy. This is a real man. A man who projects both of these energy fields into a room is never forgotten. His upper energy invites others into his realm and his lower energy lets them know why they are invited. Women all want him and men all want to be him.

Both energies are needed in this world. This restores a masculine beauty to the earth. To be unapologetic for our sexual nature, to let women know that we are on their side, that we are delighted to be men, that we are delighted that they are women, and that yes, we are delighted to desire them. This is the essence of the real man, the one that women have almost lost hope in finding. A return to the glories of masculine edge—empathy, respect, desire, sexuality—is what is needed to go from a nice man to a magnetic man, from a good "dater" to an irrepressible lover.

ॐ

A typical man today is too afraid of his dark side, yet this is the part of him that is so desperately needed, so desired in the world. This is the side of him that represents mystery and danger. It is his mystique, his dark forest, an essential part of his glorious masculine edge.

A man's mystique is a profound and rich concept, difficult to describe in words without being massively misunderstood. It is hard for a man to understand his darkness. It is even harder to teach or acquire.

An exploration of his mystique, his myth, is a lifelong quest at the edge of all understanding, but it is crucial for a man to ceaselessly explore it. It is impossible to experience it without simply experiencing it. It can only come from testing the edges of everything. Travel, adventure, taking risks. And wow, when a man first glimpses the essence of his mystique, and ventures into his dark forest, he is forever changed.

All great men have the power to destroy. There is a reason that angels are depicted in paintings with swords in their hands. These are swords of justice and honor and truth. These are not swords of indiscriminate destruction, of malicious attacks, of wanton aggression; but make no mistake, these are swords unsheathed, ready to cut and wound and slay.

True masculinity includes both the power to destroy and the grace and refinement to restrain it. We are riding a great and magnificent stallion, snorting and bucking and pawing at the earth, and we need the courage to let it run free and at the same time, the strength and restraint to rein it in.

This is what is missing in the spirit of men today. We are *Laodiceans* and God has this to say: "So then because thou art lukewarm, and neither cold nor hot, I will spew thee out of my mouth." And rightly so. There is no sense in us that we have what it takes. There is no sense in our women that we would stand up for them. We are watered down, tepid, somnolent. In the history of hunters and gatherers, we are a generation of gatherers.

We are taught that it is noble and honorable to dedicate our life to a cause, to sacrifice mightily for a cause, to even die for a cause. *But would we die for our own cause?* For the cause of us? If not, why not?

Where is the sense of justice, truth, and strength in men? Where is the flame in men that scorches the earth, bringing forth new life? What is our own myth? What is the relevance of our lives? We are carrying fire, and others depend on us for its life-giving powers. *We dare not drop it.*

How many men truly rage against the elements? How many ever bind themselves to the mast, with the surge and roll of the majestic sea all about, and the boat and the sailors all coming apart at the seams? And shouting, like Dumas, against the storm: "Do your worst, for I shall do mine!"

It is time for men to gird their loins and join the fight! Not a fight against women. A fight against mediocrity. This is a call to leadership, not a call to false strength, to braggadocio, to machismo or aggression. This is a return to power, not force. Force breaks things. Power contains things. Force lashes out. Power remains unmoved.

six

The Way of Women

A poem, a prayer, the flicker of time
in sepia tones, a tinge of blue

From our heart's first cry to our dying light… all of life is a journey… from the faith-brimmed optimism of our youth to a measured hesitation, from wide-eyed wonder to wistful mystery. Time, why do you not do as you are bid? Do you not hear our pleas?

Have you ever fallen in love? she said.

All the time.

But you never stayed.

No.

Is that fair?

No.

Then why go?

Ah, something there is that calls my name. Something… beyond the horizon, I suppose.

And what is that something?

I don't know… The sea. Or sin. Or treasure. Who knows? It's not easy. It's not like I just walk out the door and skip away down the road with my hands in my pockets, whistling a bright little tune. It's very hard to go, to leave a beautiful heart behind.

Then why don't you stay?

Well now, that would be an entirely different type of sadness, would it not? There is a greatness in remaining true to one's spirit, no matter what the cost. Does anything last? Beauty is evanescent and beauty is impermanent. All is impermanent. Willa Cather said it this way, "This is the joy of the rose, that it blows, and then it goes." It is one thing to live with a hint of sadness. It is another thing to live with regret.

We get on trains to escape, to get away. From what? Our past? Entire lives spent reviewing in hand-wringing detail the film-reels of the past—what sagging failures! what towering disappointments!—then projecting these same dismal shadows onto the film-screens of the future. But isn't the past irrelevant? Mere kitsch, a trinket, a baubly souvenir laden with dust? Yet the past somehow continues to masquerade as the single most defining symbol of our lives. Only dreamers and lovers travel toward something, not away.

So... there is a part of you that does want to stay? she said.

Absolutely. I wish I could be that guy for her. Casanova was always reluctant to leave behind a woman he loved. This I understand completely. He found it difficult to leave, because he couldn't bear the thought that this dear, sweet girl who loved him so much might be sad because of him. There was always a part of him that wanted to stay. He almost did a few times. But then the wind would call his name again—it always did—and his desire to go was far more powerful than his desire to stay. But he couldn't just, you know... *leave.* So he would try his best to find her a suitable replacement, introducing her around to dashing young men, seeking for her a potential paramour. Or he would arrange a highly coveted theater engagement for her—she was almost always an actress—that sort of thing. Only then, when he knew she was going to be okay, did he feel free to leave.

To assuage his guilt, perhaps?

Perhaps... but I like to think that he just cared about her heart and didn't want her to be sad, no? A simple explanation is usually best—Occam's Razor and all that. Not all men who go are bad. And not all men who stay are good.

ഔൽ

"*Was will das Weib?*" lamented poor Doctor Freud, then tried to find the answer by observing a few cases of frothy, hysterical, and bored Viennese women. *What do women want?* An age-old question, pondered by men throughout all of recorded history, and presumably before that. Even King Arthur bet his life that he could find the answer to "what womyn desiren most" (he was saved only by the courageous marriage of Sir Gawain to the "loathly lady," Dame Ragnelle). Is it possible that the cave paintings of Lascaux were nothing more than attempts by cavemen to describe to other confused cavemen what those crazy cavewomen want?

What do women want? For men today this question has taken on considerable gravitas. It has shifted away from a light-hearted chuckling about the frivolity of women, a good-old-boy wink and nod and a subsequent carrying on of the status quo—*Ah, dear boy, women are silly and fickle and fancy, but we love them anyway!*—and into a very real existential crisis for men. What do women want? A life-and-death question. What, oh what, do women want?

Throughout the centuries, men have always known their role. They have always been the providers, the protectors, and the procreators. *We will build and battle, we will sail and sing, and all for you, our darling girls.* But not any more. Those traditional roles of men are gone, long gone.

Today's woman is hardly the "weaker sex." She has girded her loins in battle dress. Today's woman *protects* herself. And today's woman is perfectly capable of *providing* for herself, thank you very much. And *procreation*? Science is only a few beakers and pipettes away from eliminating that need for men, too. No wonder men feel lost.

What do women want? Let me attempt to answer the question, my love. Because, why not? If I am prone to absolutes, let me over-step my bounds once again and do it large. My answer is this: *Every woman wants to be in a love story.*

Women want the same thing they have always wanted since they were little girls. To be noticed. To be adored. To be seen as lovely. To be celebrated. To be in a love story.

Amid all the confusion, despite the fact that today's woman has been raised on books and magazine articles dedicated to putting men and their motives under a microscope, and despite all the considerable warnings from their squinty-eyed, self-appointed spiritual guardians, women will always need men to *celebrate* them. Every woman remains, at heart, a female. This is a beautiful thing, for it means this is a role that can never be taken away from men.

Women will always need men just as surely as men will always need women, my love. No matter how independent women become, no matter what their role in society, no matter how they were raised, no matter what their friends or family think, women will always need men to celebrate them. And men, in return, will always need women to inspire and contain them.

I have known powerful, influential women in cities around the world—investment bankers, real-estate moguls, company presidents, visionaries, women of success, women of authority, women who command respect, women who are efficient, knowledgeable, and independent. And yet, in quiet times, they cry. Why? Because they are sad and because they are lonely and because they are in love with love, that's why. And in those quiet, crying times, do you know what those sophisticated, worldly women say to me? That they would give it all up for romance.

Men are intimidated by women of power and influence. This is why the relationships of these women always turn to dust. This is why women across the spectrum are starved for men who are skilled in the art of love, men of grace who can delight in them, who are strong enough to put them in their place when they deserve it, who can artfully sweep them off their feet just because, who can awaken again even the tiniest spark of the innocence and passion and wonder they had as girls.

Every woman wants to be in a love story. To be noticed, adored, desired… this is a vital element to the heart of a woman, as necessary as air and water. She can't live without it. Nothing will ever supplant or replace that. The man who understands this understands everything. The man who understands this is forever surrounded by beauty.

ഇറ

There was a time, not so long ago, when she was a girl, skipping happily through the fields of her childhood. She danced and sang on those lazy, forever days, through perfumed meadows, beside sun-stippled brooks, her dreams floating all about her on little dandelion puffs. And oh what dreams they were! She was going to be the heroine of her future story, desired and romanced by a dashing hero. She would be sought after, fought for, and ultimately won. She would be seen. She would be exalted. She would be lovely. Her life would be an exhilaration, an adventure, ascending higher and higher every day, happily ever after. Amen.

What happened? When did those dreams die? When did doubt set in? When did the hesitation and accusations and shame begin? When did life start to close in on her? She wanted to be seen as lovely, to be noticed, to feel worthy, and instead she found herself buried under an enervating, tangled morass of classrooms, career choices, responsibilities, and obligations. Society and the media set unattainable standards of beauty and accomplishment. She was expected to be everything to everyone, and all at once. The men she encountered were *not* heroes. They hurt her sometimes. They betrayed her sometimes. They abandoned her sometimes.

Her relationships, castles of sand, so carefully constructed and measured, that once seemed so promising and perfect, always seem to wash away at the slightest wave. Eventually, the original wonder of that wonder-filled girl, assailed on all sides for years, gives way to hesitation and doubt, a dampening down, a giving up, until that sense of wonder is ultimately suppressed so deeply inside of her that she no longer really believes.

We have lost the eternal youthfulness of summer and have aged into calculating adulthood. Year after year, our rapturous dreams fall away one by one, like feathers dropped from flying wings.

When a man comes along who can show her those dreams again from her childhood forever days, *she will follow him to the ends of the earth*. When a man touches a woman on that level, where she can feel free again, feel young again, feel beautiful again, then no matter how many husbands or boyfriends or partners she will have throughout the rest of her days, she will always, *always* think of him. This is a gift… a gift he gives to her, and a gift she gives to him.

₧₧

You and I are meant for hotel rooms. The half-pulled curtains, the blankets all around, the singular taste of intrigue and sex in the air. It is our secret place; no one knows, no one will ever know…

Here's a fantasy I have of you: You lie back on the bed, your golden skin dark against the white sheets, your legs spread wide, and the heels of your shoes digging in deep. I kneel down and kiss your entire body, unfolded before me, natural and sublime. Your body and I are lovers, ancient lovers with ancient songs.

This fantasy is one of many… oh yes, I have many ways to dream about our secret trysting tree, with my voice a vibration on your neck and in your mind, my hair brushing upon your belly, my lips on the soft and secret insides of your knees, my breath like a feather upon every surface of you. You ask for nothing, but you take everything. My silent offering. You relax into trust, opening, opening some more. Yes, you take all I can give, a selfish ingathering, a perfumed, rushing devouring.

I adore the way your body looks to me; I tend to it like an unhurried gardener. I love your scent, your taste, the lilt of your voice, the softness of your skin against my lips… Oh boundless love! I can't resist. To aspire to celestial visions, though mortal and earth-bound and blind.

You run your fingers through my hair, without intent, until an ancient, original, and primal urge overwhelms you, causing you to push my face down hard. I cannot breathe and yet I breathe. I follow the impulses: your unspoken directions, your implicit requests, your infinite signals of voice and rhythm. I stay right there, right there with you, never hurried but never slow, until your breath wells up within you and escapes in ragged sounds, and I kiss you hard, and you want it even harder, and you wrap your legs tightly around me, with your fingers in my hair, and you embrace me strongly, holding me there upon the wave, and with my eyes softly closed, an indescribable emotion releases from within... and a single tear flows from me and mixes with you...

I take your body now, in all of the ways you give it to me. I melt into you, my delectable lover, and in the final triumphant throes of this black velvet night, you draw me down upon you, down, down, dreamy soft, and sink we two into the earth, for we have seen the light, seen the light.

The opus crescendos, completes. We have climbed the bountiful slopes of Olympus; we have received blessings at the feet of Cytherea. And now to rest, my angel, to sleep in each other's arms, until the dawn-chorus of meadowlarks stirs our daydreams once again.

— The Alabaster Girl, *page 137*

ೞೞ

Every woman wants to be in a love story. And yet... few ever find one. And why is this, my love? Well, let us suppose and imagine some more, shall we? Imagine two ribbons in a woman's life, guiding ribbons, parallel ribbons that are always, ever stretched out before her, diverging and converging at times, and she seeks them out and holds onto them both with all of her strength as best she can.

Let us call the first ribbon *Security*. It is an ancient ribbon, soft and wide and easy to hold onto, and she loves this ribbon for it is the promise of home, comfort, abundance, knowing, companionship, stability, children, career, and responsibility. This is the ribbon of warmth, of sitting close together and of popcorn-movies at home, of working in the garden, of yoga, of education, of business acumen, of motherhood. This is the ribbon of strength, and she holds this ribbon tight and close and she follows it forever in her sensible shoes, with her hair up and her gaze steady. She is Woman here... capable, responsible, creative, for she holds in her hand the *Ribbon of Security*.

The second ribbon in a woman's life, on the other side of her, is equally delightful and compelling. This ribbon we shall call *Romance*. This ribbon is sensuous and sinuous, undulating, floating about her as light as air, often tangled and a mess, but oh so velvety and rich to the touch. It, too, is an ancient ribbon, an ancient need, like the waistband described long ago in the *Kama Sutra* of Vatsyayana: "Soon she won't object to fingers that stray under her skirt-hem and linger at her lightly knotted waistband; when her eyes are dreamy and her breathing's harsh, send the servants away." She loves this ribbon for it is the promise of the kiss, of romance, of being swept off her feet, of letting her hair down, of losing control sometimes, of being caught up in the dizzying, irresistible embrace of love. This is her ribbon of delight and enchantment, of seduction and mystery, of secret trysts and intrigue, of longing and desire, and she holds onto this ribbon tight and close, in her red heels and her red lipstick and her red desire. She is Woman here... ravishing, sensual, lovely, for she holds in her hand the *Ribbon of Romance*.

Two ribbons in a woman's life, essential, like air and water. She needs them both and can't live for long without either one, so all her life is a relentless search for both of these ribbons to hold onto, and all the fulfillment they represent. And ultimately, her greatest desire and her greatest joy would be the convergence of these two ribbons into one, joining together to become a single constant thread in her life... Security and Romance intertwined forever.

Every woman wants to be in a love story, and this is that love story. But what usually happens is this: at any given time in a woman's life, she has a tenuous grasp on only *one* of these ribbons. Or neither.

Consider the two kinds of men she meets, my love. If we want to continue to simplify some complex realities (and we do), then men can generally be divided into Companions and Lovers. This is no secret. We are borrowing these terms. They have been widely used, both academically and intuitively, for a very long time.

Imagine a woman who has a Companion in her life. This makes her secretly smile. She loves him because he is a good man, considerate, attentive, a kind soul, her best friend, her support, and a wonderful father to her children. Yes, he is all those wonderful things and now, happily, she can relax, for she holds in her hand the Ribbon of Security. And this is very good.

Imagine a woman who has a Lover in her life. This makes her secretly smile. She loves him because he is a good man, passionate, spontaneous, romantic, seductive, with just a hint of danger and adventure. Yes, he is all those wonderful things and now, happily, she can relax, for she holds in her hand the Ribbon of Romance. And this is very good.

And yet… something is missing in the hearts of both of these women. Having only one of these ribbons is not enough. A woman who finds she only has one of these ribbons will *always* reach out for the other ribbon with her other hand. Oh sure, she will be content for a while with only one ribbon in her grasp, perhaps for many years. But inevitably, unless she steels herself and wraps herself in resolutions, or she has no imagination at all, or she just decides to buy a rocking chair and get old, she *will* reach out for the other ribbon. She has no choice.

A woman who has a found a Lover has found something extraordinary. She loves it, and why wouldn't she? The time spent with him is thrilling and electric; the sex is breath-taking, transcendent. This is perfect for her… for a time. Eventually, it is no longer enough.

There will come a time when she finds herself looking for the security and commitment that is missing from this relationship, a shared vision of the future, a sense of belonging, of knowing that she is partnered with someone who is looking in the same direction as her, that they will be strong together through good times and bad, and that he is ready to go the distance with her forever.

A woman in a relationship with a Lover spends her entire time trying to get him to stay, to commit, to make promises to her. And when she realizes he is not going to change, he is not going to settle down, he has no promises to make, she loses heart. Even though she loves him with all her being, she knows that this must end. The need for focus and stability is so strong in her that she must eventually seek out the Ribbon of Security.

A woman who has a found a Companion, on the other hand, has found something extraordinary. She loves it, and why wouldn't she? She can relax now, all pressure is gone. The time spent with him is calming, assuring, and serene. This is perfect for her… for a time. Eventually, it is no longer enough.

There will come a time when she will examine her life of stability and comfort, a measured and predictable path stretching out before her like a long fine boulevard. And a sadness will descend upon her, a longing for passion and romance, for the colors to mix together on the paper and run free. As the dancer Isadora Duncan once admonished, "You were once wild here. Don't let them tame you."

A woman in a relationship with a Companion spends her time trying to get him to notice her, to desire her. And when she realizes he is not going to change, he is never going to ravish her, he is never going to lust after her, she loses heart. The need for passion and romance in her is so strong that she must eventually seek out the Ribbon of Romance.

In our simple analogy, a woman who only has passion in her relationship will eventually reach out for security, and a woman who only has security in her relationship will eventually reach out for passion.

But wait! we protest. Why must it be this way? Surely it's simply a matter of waiting for the right man to come along? An excellent man who embodies all of the qualities of both of these ribbons? Security and Romance bound up forever in the spirit of one man? Surely he's out there somewhere? Yes, well…

Am I generalizing? Of course. Are all women like this? No. Are all men like this? No. And isn't it true that we can never find happiness in others, that no man or woman can ever make us happy, that we have to learn to stand on our own two feet, and that happiness comes only from within? Sure. Why not? Sounds good.

                                        ഇരു

There are few things more interesting to my mind these days than the way you and I wake up together. It feels forbidden and hot, like a secret affair on a sticky Louisiana morning, with a slow fan looping silently in the background. We wake up drenched in sweat and a strange and surprising sense of confusion. The sheets are off to the side, our clothes are scattered all over the floor, we are consumed and dishevelled and messy. Everywhere in the air is the smell and feel of sex.

And yet not one significant thing has happened at all.

And I think, how can this be? I wake up shocked. How can I lie beside you all night long with your breast in my hand and your nightgown pulled up around your waist and your panties brushed up against my leg? How can I breathe in the aroma of your body, the aroma of a goddess of the sky, and just lie here doing nothing, listless, like some kind of apathetic opium poet? How can I listen to the ragged little whisper-breath you make, the hum-vibrations on my skin, and not want to run with you into every dark alley and plush bedroom we discover, forever? Am I losing my mind? Am I going insane?

This is the way you and I wake up together... like we have lost all sense of sanity. We made a pact a week ago that we would abstain, to try to understand and explore the concept of intimacy without sex. A tantric experiment.

We tell each other all kinds of stories about why it is so important to not go beyond our secret kisses. We are artists, we say. We need to try to understand abstinence, physical distance, we say. The sexual tension is necessary for our understanding and for our art, we say. We will diminish our mutual experience if sacred love devolves into the profane, we say. Let's replace sexuality with rituals, we say. Our dedication to the experiment, to exploring the furthest and purest forms of intimacy, is so palpable, so soaring, so lofty, that we must do everything to stay in the very center of this ferocious river, hanging on for dear life and never letting ourselves drift off to the side, into the backwaters of pedestrian, ordinary, and unremarkable sex.

These are the stories we tell each other, and I wake up weary because I have no idea anymore. Are we really exploring the deepest and most profound levels of intimacy, you and I together, so close with no sex? Or are we just being sentimental and stupid? What the hell? Who invented this torture? I need to get out of here. I need to find a beautiful new lover and fast.

It's only a matter of time. The moment I touch a certain part of you, it will all be over, and we both know it. My fingers have an instinct, a knowledge, an intuition. The moment my fingers touch that certain part of you, beckoning to you, summoning you forth... in that moment, I will discover the universe of you and all of your eternities... in that moment, your back will arch, your breath will quicken, and you will be mine. I will be the expert of your body like no other. I will take you then, hard, and push you across the bed, in

three positions, maybe four, and I will fill you so full that
your heart will ache and your eyes will cry.
— The Alabaster Girl, *page 140*

ଚଚ୍ଚ

There comes a time in every man's life when a woman arrives who loves him for him, who becomes his ardent muse and source of inspiration. Her presence in his life is like a thread of spun gold; the fabric of his future is forever embroidered with its color. He loves his girl and she loves him. She brings him far more than companionship and intimacy; she brings him inspiration and magic.

And here is the tragedy. Most men rarely understand the magnitude of this gift, this elevation of their lives and souls. And because most men do not understand the magnitude of this gift, someday that same woman will almost surely slip away.

A man forgets because, well, because he is a man, and it is the way of all men. He forgets to notice her, his woman, his wife, his beauty. He who was once so giving, so attentive and aware, so alive, has become nothing more than a shell, a mere caricature of what she first fell in love with; he has become one of Thoreau's men of quiet desperation.

And now here she is in a relationship with him, listless and bored. He takes her for granted now, tending to her occasionally, like a watered plant. She feels so unappreciated. Their relationship, propped up and patched, has devolved into a series of slow-motion days. What was once vibrant and spontaneous is now pedestrian and tired, each day saturated and heavy, a listless somnambulism.

Oh men, I have given you everything you need to guard against men like me. I have given you everything you need to keep her attention focused on you and not looking out the window, hoping and wishing and awash in distant dreams. And yet… you won't listen, or can't hear, and I will be in the end-zone, in your stead, ready for her. I will be ready for her, because she is certainly ready for me.

Women are a gift from men to me. With their clumsy and faltering hands, men wrap women up in their paper hopes and fading dreams, in a little box with a little bow, and hand them to me.

෴

He knows. He knows he needs to spend more time with her. He knows he needs to sit and hold her hand, to listen to her for awhile. He knows that flowers are meaningless if only bought on Valentine's Day. He knows she wants to go out and do something new and exciting. He knows she wants him to trail his fingers in the water when she is taking a bath. To like her dress. To read to her in bed. To touch her hair. To throw her on the bed and ravish her, *yes please god!*

He knows all these things. But he is so busy these days, and surely she understands, and surely she knows he loves her even when he has no time to show it, and surely… well, he really does mean to do all those things. After all, he is doing all this for her. For both of them. That is why he is so busy all the time. She sees that, right?

Ah, the folly of good men who think the greatest manifestation of love they can give to their families is to work hard in order to present them with a better car, a better house, a better neighborhood. Oh, but his family doesn't want all those things, my love… they want *him*.

A man knows in his heart the exact moment when it is too late, when she has been neglected just a little too long. He hears but ignores all the rumblings and signs for months, for years (nothing makes a woman prettier than an unhappy relationship that is about to end) until suddenly he feels something rushing toward him, like an avalanche pushing the air before it, creating a vacuum where it is impossible to breathe, and in that moment, inescapably, achingly, he knows he has lost her. And everything stops.

The saddest a man will ever be is the moment he discovers his woman is slipping away. The night descends heavily upon him, the colors wash away, his world transforms into a cemetery with only one grave. All the things that were once so important—his work, his friends, his hobbies—are swept unceremoniously into the distant corners of his consciousness.

Now there is nothing else *but* her. Now he does all those things he knew she wanted him to do all along. Now he rushes out to buy her flowers. Now he compliments her. Now he writes her that long, labyrinthine love letter. Now he promises her everything, swears that he will change. But it is no use; she becomes more and more distant and disconnected in spite of, or perhaps because of, all his considerable efforts. It is too late, the door has closed, and she is slipping away into the fog.

ಸಿಂಚ

A woman is a butterfly that lands on your hand. Hold still... *hush*... look closely, savor this moment, this slice of life. Delight in this butterfly, and the amazing beauty she is adding to your life, the blessing of her grace. She is your gift, your muse, your inspiration. All you can do, and all she is asking you to do, is to hold her high before you and praise her pretty wings, iridescent in the light, keeping your hand steady, curling your fingers up ever so slightly to protect her from the wind and allowing her to rest there, where she knows she is safe and she knows she is warm and she knows, above all, that she is wanted. She may stay forever.

Or she may fly away. At any time and for reasons a man may never understand—or even for no reason at all. It is a gift but never a given. He will be sad. She will be sad. And he will miss her for the rest of his days. But the memory of the beauty and grace she infused into his life will never be overshadowed by the poison cloud of a deteriorating relationship, and that is a beautiful and profound and right realization.

One thing's for sure... she will fly away if she doesn't feel lovely in his presence, if she doesn't feel noticed, if she is no longer seen as a gift to his life. The moment he takes her for granted, the moment he takes his eyes away from her, the moment he is distracted by frivolities and needless things, she will feel it and if he does it long enough, she will fly away forever.

Sometimes a man, because he can't bear the thought that she might fly away, will try to contain her, to hold her fast. He closes his hand tightly around her, to keep her at all costs, to restrict her movements, until she can barely breathe anymore and her wings are crushed. As Blake wrote, "He who binds himself to a joy... doth the winged life destroy... but he who kisses the joy as it flies... lives in eternity's sunrise." A woman must be free to leave. Only then might she stay.

There is a harmony in life, an alignment, when a man heads toward his vision of the future, when he dedicates his life to a love of beauty, all the while delighting in the butterfly that lands on his hand. She can never be his purpose in life, his *raison d'etre*... but she is an irreplaceable part of his magnificent journey, adding to it in impeccable ways.

₧₧

How many times does a woman in a stilted relationship try to get her man to notice her? How many wives in this world have paraded in front of feckless husbands, dressed in the sexiest thing they could find, soft-framed in candlelight and wine, trying to get him to find her desirable? Just that... please desire me! Please see me! *Please notice me!* Here I am before you... take me now! Push everything between us aside! Flip the table over, rip my clothes from my body, destroy *everything* just to get to me! Take me! Overpower me! Bend me over! Ravish me! Ah, but there is work to catch up on... football to watch...

We moralize and hypothesize about a woman who has an affair. Scandal! The nerve! Boo! Hiss! How could she possibly do such a thing? What was she thinking? Why would she jeopardize everything she has—her home, her children, her reputation—all for a ridiculous little fling? Why would she throw it all away? How could she be so careless? How could she be so weak? It makes no sense to us at all.

But think about it… would a woman really throw it all away for the fleeting notion of a mere fling? Does she really desire that fantasy-romance-novel life more than the one she currently inhabits? Would she really trade her life with her kind, caring husband and her much-loved children for some alternate life of wild abandon? No, of course not. But like a prisoner in a small cell, with everything taken care of, food and water and books and all the amenities supplied, she still dreams about that one hour of exercise a day, in the little square prison yard outside, where she might see a cloud or a bird, and feel the grass beneath her feet.

There is a zephyr that blows from the meadows of a distant land, a wind of solitude, redolent of lilac and honey and miracles. If she closes her eyes in a quiet place, she can feel it dancing softly in her hair and whispering in her ear. Her body knows these rhythms, even if her mind has forgotten. The need to be desired is so strong in her that she must risk it all—she *will* risk it all. And it's not her fault when she does.

ॐ

I taste you each time I enter the room. You don't know it because it's just a kiss, really… a small kiss on your neck in that divine part, the deep part where your neck meets the curve of your shoulder.

The men arrive exactly at their appointed times, nervous and nodding to us who wait outside, and I greet them warmly, like some kind of pimp guarding the door and marking time.

This Soho hotel is beautiful and old, baroque, with red brick and avant-garde furniture, and I see none of it. I sit here surrounded by all this quaint opulence, in style, like a king on his throne, and I can only think of the room behind me. My thoughts swirl like discolored leaves in a furious wind.

I have a ritual, unwanted, that repeats throughout the day. Before I introduce the next man to the room, I come in to check on you, and here I am now, smiling and sure and looking around, asking if you need anything—more food? more wine? more videotapes?—but the real reason I come in to check on you is to put my lips to that divine part of your neck for that kiss, for that taste of you that I crave.

And you are so sweet and so dirty and so breathless and excited. The room is a mess, your hair is a mess, and your dress is kind of sideways around your body and hanging off your shoulder, like the accidental flourish of a woman ravished mere moments ago.

And everything speeds up now, in a rush of red lipstick and fresh dress and the ceremonial placing of another cheap plastic-wrapped hotel cup, ready to receive new wine with a new man. You haven't eaten or slept all day and yet in the blur of the few moments I spend with you now, you recover to a freshness of beauty that stops my breath... in an instant... like a magic wand has been suddenly waved and, as the magic sparkle dust clears from the air, there you stand, poised and perfect and ready for the next date.

You transform before my eyes and I am amazed, and you turn to me and smile, so sweetly to me, and everything frantic in the whole wide world simply comes to a stop. You stand there before me in innocence, yet underneath that raffiné elegance is a dirty, dirty girl, a trollop, a siren, a possession, a tramp, your body not perfect but fully embraced, and there is something lyrical and serene in the madness of it all. And I wonder, what is the meaning of your film project, this performance, and my role in it.

"The last boy... he was so sweet... ah mon dieu..." you breathe, and you gasp at the thought of the experience you just shared with him. You have consumed him in a passion *he has never felt before and will never feel again. His fantasy is now complete. You have just given him the only wet dream he will ever need. Never again will he imagine random girls in random scenarios, no more darkening of the room and covering of the windows to watch grainy porn. There is no need; you have just become the only woman he will ever masturbate to, replayed over and over again in all of his dark nights.*

You come to me now, so joyously to me, and you embrace me and thank me for helping you with your little film project. And that is when I give you that little ephemeral kiss on that divine part of your neck.

This moment is mine alone. This is my date with you. My thoughts swirl like discolored leaves in a furious wind.

You don't even know that I taste you each time I kiss your neck, but I do. And there in the exalted softness of your skin and in the salt of your sweat and in the desire of your perfumed essence, I linger and I taste you... as deeply as if you were mine. I kiss and taste the wonder of you and I desire you completely in that moment; I want to take you right here, right now.

And then the moment is past and the kiss is done. I have tasted you, my love, I have drunk deeply at your well, and it is enough. I look around at the banality and profanity of the room, at the camera on the "tré-pied," at the half-empty glasses and the half-eaten food and the detritus and blankets on the bed. I look around and I am in awe of you and your art and at the same time, repulsed at the cloying scent of men in the room.

I am Henry in this moment, and you are Anaïs, lost together in some smoky back room in the Paris of the '30s. You with your bohemian, sultry moods... with your temptations ripe and irresistible to every man and every woman.

Yes, you are Anaïs and I am Henry, loving and fighting and fucking others in Paris on those gray days of no writing...

— The Alabaster Girl, *page 143*

ഐ൚

And what of jealousy, my love? What is that all about? It takes no little imagination to intuit that jealousy is fundamentally about fear—fear of the unknown and of change, fear of losing power or control in a relationship, fear of scarcity, fear of loss, fear of abandonment. It is a reflection of our own insecurities about our worthiness, anxiety about our adequacy as lovers, and doubts about our desirability.

No matter how enlightened we think we are, most of us experience a measure of discomfort if our partner strays in some way. This discomfort might range from a twinge of mild annoyance— "Where is she?"—to the terrifying reemergence of our latent fear of abandonment.

Infidelity is the big one, the deal-killer, the devastating blow to a relationship for most people. Why is this? Why does infidelity bother us so much? A quick answer is that the most sacred things a couple shares—trust and intimacy—have been irrevocably broken and our hearts don't know why. It doesn't matter why. We feel hurt and betrayed and abandoned.

Do we even know what we are jealous about? Let us imagine two scenarios. A woman is in a relationship with a man and they are both in love. Their home is wonderful, their life is wonderful, the two of them are wonderful together. All is good.

In the first scenario, the man goes away on a weekend business trip, a conference. When he returns, he says to her, "Sweetheart... love of my heart and my dreams... I, uh... I need to tell you something. I want no secrets between us. When I was at the conference, a bunch of us partied at the hotel bar, well into the night. Everyone got exceedingly drunk. Now here is the part I feel I need to share with you, to open my heart to you, because I want no secrets between us... I met a woman, not all that pretty, not as pretty as you, who was, you know, also quite drunk. I didn't really talk to her at all, but somehow she stumbled into my hotel room, and one thing led to another. And oh, my sweetheart, the next morning, as my senses returned and I realized what I had done, I was mortified! She was already gone by then, but the thought of what happened repulsed me, made me sick. All I could think about was you and how much I love you and would never want to hurt you! I didn't care about that woman at all. She was nothing to me. I don't even remember what happened exactly. All I know is, I only love you. And I only want you. And I am so sorry."

In the second scenario, the man goes away on a weekend business trip, a conference. When he returns, he says to her, "Sweetheart... love of my heart and my dreams... I, uh... I need to tell you something. I want no secrets between us. When I was at the conference, I met a woman who was quite... interesting. We had so much in common, like we had known each other for years. We talked and talked, well into the night, watching the stars and the moon. Time escaped us and before we knew it the sun was coming up on the horizon. It was so peaceful and serene. I felt so alive, so connected to the universe. But, I am proud to say, it was nothing physical. I didn't touch her at all. In fact, we even talked about you. And how was your weekend?"

You can anticipate my question, my love: which scenario would break your heart the most? Exactly. It is striking to me that relationships end far more frequently from the first scenario than the second. Why are we so quick to call the first scenario infidelity but not the second? Which was the greater betrayal of trust? Which was the greater intrusion upon the sacredness of the intimacy they both share? We might answer that both are bad, both are irresponsible, both are a betrayal of trust. Well, sure... but then why does the first scenario have a much stronger chance of killing the relationship dead than the second? The only possible answer seems rather weak: that in the second scenario he at least remained "faithful." So strange. As Alice would say, "Curiouser and curiouser!"

Some would say that jealousy is unrealistic and shouldn't exist. The physical act itself? What of it? Sex and love are two different things, are they not? Why would we destroy a home, a bond of affection, and lifelong mutual plans, all because of the simple biological urge to copulate? Oh, but the physical act is not the problem, if we are honest with ourselves. It's the deceit. Absent the deceit, it's the *turning away*. This is the crux of the problem. The face of the one we love has turned away, however briefly, from us toward another, and we have never felt that utter sense of loss in the relationship before.

Me? I am never jealous of other men. Another guy is hovering around, trying to get my girl's attention? So what? He is not me. A man gets upset at another man who attempts to "steal" his woman. Why be jealous of him? Is he not just following his heart? He's just being a normal guy, moving through life, and he happens to like a girl. How on earth has he wronged *me*? It's no intended slight to anyone.

If the beautiful, wonderful girl who is with me, who I say I respect and adore so much, ever meets another man she would rather be with, then who am I to stop her? What right do I have to impede her happiness? She is not my possession; she has the right to be happy in life, and if she would be happier with someone else, then she should be allowed that freedom. If I truly love her, how can I not give her that freedom? No one ever steals your woman. She leaves because she has to.

ഹൈരു

Counter to what we might assume, while men and women are equally capable of romantic passion, it is usually the men who fall in love the fastest and the hardest. They are the sentimental ones, the true romantics. Women, on the other hand, tend to treat their relationships with at least a modicum of pragmatism and common sense.

In spite of the sensitive, softer side of women, when it comes to relationships they are logical and efficient. And in spite of the seemingly more logical and practical side of men, when it comes to relationships they are weak, soft, a dripping bag of mush.

Women are more proficient and creative in dealing with a leaky boat. Women respond to the leak, doing their best to maintain and patch the hole, but when all else fails, they set about abandoning ship. Men sometimes accuse women of being heartless or cold when it ends, but women are simply finished and moving on. A man will pine over a woman for years, never really knowing exactly what happened.

A man tends to have a harder time getting over a break-up than a woman. This is because for her, everything has already been analyzed and scrutinized to the highest degree. It has already been discussed *ad infinitum* with all her girlfriends. What went wrong? Well, she already knows. What does she think and feel about it? She already knows. What will she do when it ends? Again, she already knows. She has come to terms with the fact that it is over, *before* it is over. He, on the other hand, has been throwing a few token flowers at her now and then, hoping the problem would just go away. And just when he thinks he has everything nicely tamped down and sat upon, the whole thing ends. It's over in her mind. Her soul-searching analysis is done. His is just about to begin. And he doesn't even know it.

When a relationship ends a man is shell-shocked, taken by surprise. In spite of all the signs, he never saw it coming. He knew she was unhappy but he thought, ah, this too shall pass. Then the break happens, jarring him into the present, and now the light comes on, a frenzied, frantic realization, a punch to the stomach. Now he has to deal with his emotions, fears, and thoughts all at once—the very things she calmly came to terms with long ago—in a jumble of confusion, in compressed time. He becomes spectacularly incapacitated. He can't work, can't eat, can't breathe. He lies on the floor, gut-shot and writhing in profound, debilitating despair.

Both men and women are desperate to revive a broken relationship, to re-create the great love affair they had at the beginning. The difference is that women try to do it while it is ongoing, and men try to do it when it is over.

✂✂

Not only can a woman get over the demise of a relationship faster than a man, but she can get over a crisis of infidelity faster than a man. This is because the self-esteem of a man who has been cheated on is utterly destroyed, whereas the self-esteem of a woman who has been cheated on is battered and bruised, but recoverable. He despairs of ever seeing the light again. He feels so lost, so helpless, so alone. She, on the other hand, reaches out and leans on her extensive emotional support network.

Men put all their intimacy apples into one basket. A man has camaraderie with his friends, to be sure, but not necessarily emotional support. His woman is his *sole* support. She is his confidante, his sounding board, his cheerleader; and when the relationship ends his entire support network disappears, with nothing but a puff of smoke lingering in the air. He has invested all his emotional capital into one stock, the market has crashed, and now he is bankrupt. A woman, on the other hand, diversifies, with a well-rounded portfolio, a mutual fund that includes her friends, her family, and him, of course—a tried and true, well-established safety net.

A woman's friends will rally around her, commiserate with her, put their arms around her. A man's friends will tell him to "hang in there… come on, let's go get you drunk and laid." He must deal with the whole emotional aspect internally. Any recovery must stem from his willpower. He is alone and must bear his burden alone.

✂✂

I am surprised at how ordinary it all seems, like I have seen it hundreds of times before. And I have, of course, but not with you. I am curious that watching you touch yourself seems so normal to me, almost bland, like you could color the whole scene beige and it wouldn't make a difference. In fact, the only thing I am curious about in this moment is my complete lack of curiosity about you.

I glance at you out of the corner of my eye and I can tell you are getting close. Your eyelids flutter, closed but not quite, a quickening of pace and intensity. Your lips part slightly, flushed and red like wine, the only brush-stroke of color in this beige-bland room.

I've seen it all before. I know exactly when you are going to come, yes I do, and how long it will take. I know you will pause to take a little break, and there you go... you just did. Every woman takes a little pause or two when she masturbates. She gets to a certain point where she knows she will not lose it now, it is good, and everything will stay poised at that heightened point, like arriving at the very last camp on the slopes of Everest. She rests there, taking a few moments to gather her fantasies and her energy for a renewal of her assault on the summit, the last heroic push through to ecstasy.

You take your little break now, there on the bed beside me, just a few seconds, just enough to relax the tension in your body and to smile a smile at me, and then you close your eyes once more, turning your face away from me slightly, and resume your rhythms.

I can see the way your mind works as you touch yourself. You realize you might get a better story out of me if you give me a better view, so you turn your body around so I can see the movement of your hand between the blanket, with your fingers reaching between your legs. You keep the blanket there, of course, because it is "best that we remain platonic" and we certainly don't want anything sexual between us. Oh, how you haunt me.

I watch you from the corner of my eye when you come. You convulse three times, your back arching just so and your voice in little serrated gasps, not loud at all, and not feminine and high-pitched, like I imagined, and like you described.

And then it is finished. It did not seem intense to me at all. It did not turn me on at all. It all seemed kind of flat and uninteresting, beige like the room, now that I think of it. You turn me on; you, masturbating, do not. I was far more excited by the innocence of your sighs as you slept beside me last night, and by the anticipatory impressions of your body pressed beneath the silk, and by your hair, like sun-colored straw, scattered gloriously across the dark pillow.

And it doesn't matter anyway. You were not masturbating for me at all. In fact, you weren't even masturbating for you. Did you even enjoy it?

I look at you and you look at me and... nothing. There is nothing here, nothing erotic, nothing exciting. There is no chemistry between us, no seduction, no scent of intrigue in the air. There is no attempt to include me in your singular tryst, even as a voyeur. This is manipulation, is it not, my dear? This is all a one-way attempt to excite me so I will write something good for you, for your art. You wanted to hear me typing at my desk as you masturbated, and I typed all right, the whole time. Even as you came, I just kept right on typing, but not about you.

Sex with you would be like the way we walked through MOMA yesterday. You were quick, and direct and fast at every display. You knew exactly what you wanted to see, and we were headed there all right, but you felt compelled to see it all, every floor, even for the briefest of seconds. No section escaped you at all. Me? I was just enjoying the wonder of the moment, content to hang out in any old room and study the art a bit and read the little cards on the wall, but you, efficient, would circle back and grab my hand and lead me somewhere else, because this room was done.

Yes, sex with you would be a rushing chore: mechanical, formulaic, distracted, and with no spontaneity and no fun. You would not be content with anything less than elaborate and shifting symphonies, with structured themes and

measured movements, and I am too weary, to be honest.
Sometimes I just want to hang around and play my guitar.
— The Alabaster Girl, *page 146*

ഇൻയ

Let us consider a universal yet remarkably little-known concept
about the mind of women, my love. Men will shake their heads in
umbrage, emphatically disagreeing because, well, because they can't
grasp it at all. Women will also shake their heads, but in wide-eyed,
hands-over-their-mouths recognition. The concept is this: *Women*
understand affairs. They understand why women cheat on men and
they understand why men cheat on women. Men, on the other
hand, *never* understand.

To most men, a woman who cheats is a vile, disgusting wretch with
no morals. Men get hurt and swear they will never trust women
again—conniving, lying bitches!—a blast-furnace, scorched-
earth reaction. This is because they do not understand the mind
of women.

A man's belief system is blanketed in a cerebral, over-riding sense
of justice, an objectivist vision of pure right and pure wrong, and
she has violated these universal principles. Women, on the other
hand, view the world a little more subjectively, with a more fluid,
pragmatic sense of relative right and wrong. You could even say,
surprisingly, that in affairs of the heart, women are more primal,
animalistic, realistic.

When a man has an affair, he feels guilty of the inherent breach of
trust. A woman who has an affair feels just as guilty, of course, but
not necessarily because she thinks it is wrong, that some kind of
universal trust code has been broken. No, instead she feels a profound
sense of guilt because she betrayed a relationship, violated a shared
vision, and caused deep hurt to him and to others. And as we have
seen, relationships are sacrosanct to women.

When a man has a partner who cheats on him and he finds out, he is stabbed with a thousand blades, cut to his very core. He feels fundamentally, heart-wrenchingly betrayed, as if all the trust in all the universe has been irrevocably sucked into the blackest of black holes. He is in a seemingly eternal pit of despair. His ego, his heart, his whole life is crushed.

Conversely, when a woman has a partner who cheats on her and she finds out, she is really, really *pissed off*. How could you do this to me? You asshole! How dare you? You don't do it to me. I was the one neglected for years; I should have done it to *you*! In a nutshell: men get hurt, women get angry.

A man who is cheated on, is in profound despair and confused. He is not sure where to turn, what to do. A woman cheated on springs into action. She fumes, rallies her phalanx of emotionally supportive allies, spreads out the map upon the war-room table, and with determined strategies and decisive maneuvers, lashes out with devastating precision.

Here is the part that men will never understand: *This does not mean in any way that women are inherently deceitful.* To a woman, there are things that make sense that will never make sense to men. To a woman, there are certain things that simply *do not count*. Men wring their hands and say, "Well, if this is true, then women need to change. They shouldn't be like that… it's wrong!" Oh, but women *are* like that. Men need to get over themselves. Women are simply wired in a different way. The minds of women work in far different ways than the minds of men. Theirs is an analog system, while the minds of men are binary. And yet, far and wide, we vilify women.

Some will denounce me as an apologist for women. I can live with that. Let me just say this: I have been there. I know what it's like to be hunkered face-down in a mud-drenched trench, as the foul and acrid mustard gas of betrayal drifts over everything I know and love. I have experienced the guttering, gasping loss of vitality and the inability to see anything before me, for I, too, have been spectacularly cheated on in my past and I, too, was broken, broken, broken, couldn't think, couldn't work, couldn't breathe.

ଞେ୦ଓ

Let's continue our sweeping generalizations and extend this concept even further into the corners of philosophical abstraction, shall we? Here you go: There are other things that, in the mind of a woman, simply do not count.

An example? Many of us tend to lie about the number of sexual partners we have had. When a guy says how many women he has slept with, a good rule of thumb is to divide by three. And the number a woman will offer? Well, sure, why not? Multiply by three. Okay, no surprise there. But here is where it gets interesting. The difference is that men *know* they are telling a lie; they know the actual number, but tend to inflate it. Women, on the other hand, actually *believe* what they are saying. They aren't really lying at all, because they have convinced themselves that some sexual experiences simply do not count. Let me say that again: for women, there are some sexual experiences that *do not count*.

Moments of regrettable vulnerability or drunkenness or fleeting indiscretions are often edited from a woman's mind. They really do *believe* that the number of men they have slept with is "eight," even though the actual number is likely quite different. Am I generalizing again? Why, of course.

In addition to this, there are certain men in this world who get a free pass from women. None of the normal rules about dating or intimacy or whatever applies to them. Women allow them things they would *never* allow to other men. This includes their time, their attention, their bodies, everything. She can go to bed with him and yet it doesn't count in her mind. "Him? No, that doesn't count. It's just, well… *him*."

This is a secret of the world, my love, a secret known only to women and only to these lovers of women who have experienced it. And yet it is widespread and *common*. Other men are oblivious to it. You can tell them about it, but they will never believe it. Like trying to imagine infinity or divide by zero. They nod their heads as if they understand, but they do not understand.

How many times have I been in bed with a woman who is telling me about the guy she really likes? "What should I do?" she asks me. "Should I call him? Look at this message he sent me. How should I respond?" And there I am, relaxing in her bed and giving her advice about how to land the guy she wants. The irony is not lost on me. It makes me smile, makes me realize that all is right with the world, for I am completely in my element here. I am not "the one." I am not her boyfriend. I know my role in her life and so does she. I am her lover, her secret lover. I am the man who doesn't count.

ℰᏰᏉ

On this slow, blossom-drunk day in May, she holds my hand and asks me a question that breaks my heart, the hardest question I have ever been asked by a woman. Oh... her eyes today. I can see the loss-tears starting to form in those blue, eternal eyes. I love her so much.

She asks, "Is your freedom more important to you than me?"

And my answer, simple and true, "Yes."

There is a space around moments like these, a kind of chasm in time, a slow motion that descends all around, like the air is gone, but you don't care, for there is no longer need for air. I will never forget this moment, as she bows her head low and begins to cry, her hair lifeless and long and hanging down over her face. I watch as a single tear falls, slow like a dream, onto my hand holding hers.

I look down at her knees in silence, and we sit together close on this long, lazy bench in the park. How many times did I rest my hand on those knees, in the calm, casual way of all lovers? How many times did I kiss the backs of those knees in that soft, sacred way that she adored?

I have an overwhelming urge to temper my answer, to give her some measure of comfort, to soften the blow in some way, by adding some inane phrase like, "...but you never know what might happen in the future" or "...let's just see how it goes." But those are lies lies lies. Instead, I just hold her hand and contemplate her knees that I love, and we are both silent.

I cry too. I cry because I love her heart. I cry because I am losing her here. I cry because there is something in me that cannot compromise, cannot settle down, and sometimes I think it would be easier if I could. I cry because I cannot give her the domestic promise she desires, and because she wants so much to be happy, and she is not happy.

She is beautiful and interesting and intelligent and will certainly find another, but in this moment, she doesn't care about any of that. She just wants to be sad. So she is sad, and I am sad too, in this time and space with her, with a single tear falling on my hand holding hers.

There is nothing to say. Nothing will alleviate her feeling of loss in this moment, her feeling of abandonment, like she is clinging to a branch on the side of a cliff, looking up to me with eyes of distant hope, and I... I simply turn and walk away. I have nothing for you, as if to say.

Be brilliant, I tell others. Be magnificent, be aware of your impact, don't be afraid to take a stand, then change it later, I say. Ah, but there is no room for brilliance here, no room for being magnificent. I am alone with my thoughts, and what are they? I have layers I move through, pulled from the poetic longing of my heart... the air is gone... and all I see is dust.

Why do I care so much? Why does it break my heart to say no to a woman? You wanted security and a promise from me. I am not security or a promise of anything. I am the man who goes. Why can't I just go?

*In this world of so little caring, it is an unbelievably pro-
found thing to tell someone who loves you, who cares about
you, who would be sad if you were hurt or hungry or lost, to
stop caring for you, stop longing for you, and to look away,
look away.*

*I look at her knees and I cry... because of all these things,
because I can't bear the thought of her unhappy or alone,
because I love her heart, and because she deserves a clear
happiness.*

— The Alabaster Girl, *page 148*

ഓരു

Now then, let me answer your unasked question, my love: Yes, I have
jumped out of a few bedroom windows in my time. I've had all kinds
of affairs with all kinds of attached or semi-attached women. There
was a time in my feckless, voracious, and self-serving youth when
I paid little heed to the destruction I might be causing. Shake your
head at me if you must. I understand completely and I accept your
reprobation. You asked for the truth. It is not something I advocate
nor am I proud of it, but it *is* the truth.

Not anymore. Not for a long, long time. But don't rejoice and kill
the fatted calf for the prodigal son just yet. It's not because I have
magically transformed into some kind of altruistic, wonderful guy. I
am always aware of my own shadow. I am still a scoundrel, after all.
And I thoroughly believe that *every* woman deserves to be seduced,
deserves to experience passion, deserves to be desired.

No, nowadays I stay away from women with less-than-significant
others because it is far too damaging. There is too much hurt and
destruction, too much aftermath. And I am not talking about *her*.
She will be fine. Her eyes are wide open. Instead, it is the potential
sadness of the others in her life that gives me pause. After all, even
though her man might be oblivious to her and her physical needs,
he might be a good man, with the best of intentions, and treat her

well. They have created a life together, a hidden collection box of little things: mutual friends and family, the home they share, years of photographs and memories. That belongs to them and them alone and I want no part of it. And (for me, the most important thing) they might have children, innocent, innocent, whose little hearts will surely be broken. Oh the promises we make, the promises we break.

A woman in an affair has a hidden desire to get caught. If nothing else, she will *always* eventually confess. In my experience, every single time I was foolish enough to cavort with an attached woman, she would always (with one notable, long-lasting exception years ago… thank you, dear) confront her man with the evidence. Why is this? I don't know. It always baffled me. I never said a word to anyone ever. I suppose it's because, for her, the affair represented much more than a primal need for passion; it represented a revolt against the soul-killing mediocrity she felt in her relationship. She needed him to finally get it, to understand what she had been trying to tell him for years. As in a screaming and tearful tirade: "You don't notice me any more? You don't find me sexy? Oh yeah, well guess what? *Someone* still finds me desirable! So there!"

The result? Oh, I've had a few scrapes and jumps and close calls. He who dares wield a sword shall surely know the sounds of battle! Men banging on my door in the middle of the night demanding to "speak" to me. Men accosting me in clubs and bars and driveways and parking lots. Fortunately, I am an excellent talker and brilliant negotiator (under pressure!) and, failing all that, I can take care of myself. Wow, how thoroughly asinine I was, sitting for all those years beneath the Sword of Damocles!

So there you go, my love. A relationship post-affair might recover, might survive, might even thrive. But the damage is severe and never worth it. It will always, always hurt, and no amount of time will make it completely go away. So no, no, no, there is a lot of sadness in this world and it increases immeasurably when a relationship comes crashing down for whatever reason. And I am not going to be that reason. I am, of course, not the reason at all. A moribund relationship is heading straight for a wall anyway. Almost everyone in a dreary relationship will eventually reach out to someone else. In other words, if not me, *it will be someone.*

Every woman needs a lover. A woman with a lover is more beautiful than she has ever been or ever will be. And if it isn't her husband or boyfriend, it will be someone. But not me is much better. I have seen enough; I no longer have the dexterity to dodge all the falling, flaming debris of a sad and broken relationship.

seven

The Way of Love

You're there on the surface of the wine
You impinge; I allow

Out there, a lifetime of lessons learned, reflected against the ascendant, pale blue of a bountiful sky. In here, questions and curiosity and timeless wonder. Where is the real mystery? Out there in the abundance? Or here in this passenger car with this increasingly intriguing and intricate girl?

Do you ever feel lonely? she said.

No.

Never?

Well, am I ever alone? Oh sure... plenty of times. But lonely? Never.

Okay, but don't you feel you are somehow... missing something?

I miss some things, yes. There was a time when I would fall madly in love with a girl and there was an innocence about it, a *naiveté*. I was love-struck—struck with love!—felled like a tree, and I didn't know what was happening or what was about to happen. I was just excited and in love. That is the only thing I knew. So yes... yes... those were the days... sublime joy and crushing heartbreak, one right after the other... and not knowing why or how.

And now you know...

Now I know. Now I choose my battles. Now I hold my hand out to her or I don't hold my hand out to her. Now I take her to my bed or I don't take her to my bed. I already know how it is going to go. I've been there before. I can see it in her eyes.

Wow.

Yeah. It was kind of nice not to know. It's like the apocryphal story of the missionary and the Eskimos. When he had taught them all about heaven and hell, they said to him, "Thank you for teaching us these things. If you had not come to us, we would have been surely lost!" The missionary replied, "Well, not exactly... you wouldn't be lost if you never heard." And the Eskimos said, "Then why did you tell us?"

Do you feel, perhaps, that you gained great insight about women, but at the cost of a measure of innocence?

That's a great question. Yeah, I think so. I have known the loveliest of women, and I would rejoice to see any one of them again, but there is not one woman on this earth that I think about when she is not around. Is that sad? I'm not sure. Maybe you can't fall in love anymore when you have studied it for so long. Maybe you can't fall in love anymore because you have lost the mystery of it all.

You're not searching for it?

For what? A girl? Girls are everywhere. I don't want a companion. I want an angel. I don't want to date. I want to revere. I don't want a casual encounter. I want an exquisite encounter. I don't want to fill some supposed void in me. I want to step into a shared light.

For love, perhaps?

Oh, we're all searching for love in some way, I suppose. But I feel no need to thrash about looking for someone to save me. I don't know. I mean... sure. I would love to fall in love again. It's exciting to think that there's a woman out there who will someday surprise and enchant me. I like to imagine a simple girl with the same simple gypsy spirit as me, dancing before me in the moonlight, in the firelight, flowing and free. Maybe... maybe that's all I really want... to watch her dance, to hear her voice, to close my eyes as she forever strokes my hair.

Maybe you just haven't met the right woman yet.

Maybe.

Or maybe you left her behind.

Ah... now there's a thought...

A slow rocking train, a smiling radiance, a delightful, inviting beauty... what else is there in this life? Outside... out there... a fleeting, furtive landscape... everything a blur. In here, in this lucid stillness... there is only her.

You're asking me all these questions... questions I haven't asked myself in a long, long time, he said.

Yes.

Who are you, really?

Just a curious girl... sitting here across from you.

Are you really writing an article?

Maybe.

Maybe?

No.

⁮ℓ⁮

We've lost focus. Women and men simply don't get invested as deeply today as they once did. Marriage, once a sacrament, is now a quotidian contract. Intentions are still noble, dreams are still dreamy, "happily ever after" is the story we still share. Yet everywhere we look, as far as we can see, is smoking wreckage, the detritus of relationships strewn across the landscape.

And why? Good question. Relationships have devolved into a series of manipulations and mind games and a contest of wills. We all feel it in the air; we taste it like a metallic coating in the mouth. It's not the fault of the men. It's not the fault of the women. It just is.

The result is a large, tepid wading pool full of single men and women and a deep-seated hook-up culture. Instead of mindful commitments, a switch is flipped on and we are in a relationship, and after a few weeks or months or years, the switch is inexplicably flipped off again and, just like that, it is done.

We don't give fully. No matter how sincere and happy and excited we are at the beginning. What usually happens when we enter into a relationship is that we tend to hold back just a little, because some part of us is still unsure. Are we really willing to give up all others forever? For her? For him? Yes, of course we are... but really? *Forever?*

And when our partner says, "I love you," they notice a slight hesitation in our reply, and then they get a little more nervous about the depth of *their* commitment, and now they hold back a little more. So the relationship begins and continues with the two of us only ninety percent present. The other ten percent is a withholding, a wariness, a simmering, suspicious insecurity.

In all of our wanderings, in all of our longings, what we want is simple: to be loved, to be respected, to be adored. And we can't understand why we are *not* loved, when we are so sincere, so kind, so accommodating. Oh, how many glad promises have we made to ourselves and to others? If love were a business venture, we would run away, fast and far. What other enterprise do we undertake with such hope and optimism? The failure rate is so predictable and recurring that it is amazing how excited we are every time we begin anew. No matter how spectacularly the last relationship crumbled into dust, no matter how stacked the odds, we do it all over again. Because look how strong our love is *this* time! Look how aligned we are, how compatible, how different we are together than anything we've ever experienced before! Those other relationships? Mere dress rehearsals. This is the real thing. How can it not last?

And when this one crumbles to dust? What are we to believe now? If *that* love could die, when we believed in it so much, when we thought it was exactly what we dreamed of finding all our lives, then what hope is there for future love? So here we sit, discouraged and bewildered, staring at the impossible Gordian Knot of relationships before us, and none of us with a sword.

හ)ભ

Why do relationships end? Who knows? We look at our great-grandparents and we scratch our heads. Why was it so easy for them? How did they manage to stay together for fifty years? Some might say it was because they had little option. They stayed together through good times and bad because they needed each other to survive. They grew some potatoes, raised a chicken or two, had a bunch of kids. Oh, and don't forget there was a universal stigma back then about separation and divorce. So even if it was a little messy, they stayed together because they pretty much had to.

Sometimes relationships end because the mediocrity of our lives hits us in mid-stride, like a clear-sky bolt of lightning. Men have a mid-life crisis. Women have a quarter-century crisis. Woe to a man with a girlfriend who is just about to turn twenty-five years old! Twenty-five… this is a critical time in a woman's life. Her thoughts about her future intensify and she examines everything about her life. Do I still want to be a party girl? Is it time that I get serious about my life? Some of my friends are getting married. Some of my friends are having children. What about me? And what about my career? Is it what I really want? Should I move to another city? Maybe it's not too late to change, but it soon will be. I'm halfway to thirty! And on and on. The man in her life needs to put his seat belt on because he is going for a ride. She's going to be distant and wistful and wondering, questioning everything about him, about herself, and about her entire life. It's just the way it is.

Sometimes relationships end because… they just end. Entropy. The 2nd Law of Thermodynamics. *Everything in order tends to disorder*. If a relationship settles into routine, with the two of them half-splashing about in the bathwater of their daily lives, trudging to and from their daily work like dust-choked, travel-stained, and mile-weary pilgrims, slumping down nightly in front of the television, and never taking the time to come together as a team—winking at each other, caressing each other, clinking glasses together—the relationship will surely fail. It's just a matter of time.

Sometimes relationships end because of a natural and graceful parting, like we are traveling together along the freeway of life and one of the lanes just… diverges. It's just the way it is. All kinds of reasons come into play. People change, desires change, beliefs change, lanes change.

ରେଓ୍ୟ

How radiant she is upon a blue pillow! She is a beauty, all right... a beauty in the conventional sense, sure, but seeing her on this pillow in this light on this morning, the true wonderment of her being unfolds.

"Wow," she says, "I can't believe I slept with you on the very first night. I just met you. I've never done anything like that before."

Yes well, I can believe it, sweet girl. It makes complete sense to me. We are believers, are we not? Was there any other way we could experience each other, except for experiencing each other entirely? No, I don't think so. And if we had artificially distanced ourselves from each other, staying out of each others arms, wouldn't that have been a betrayal of the great and honest desire we both feel, and the loftiness of our mutual connection?

"And why did you?" I say, "With me?"

"I don't know. You were different, I guess. It just felt right, and somehow... necessary."

Has it ever been any other way? No, not really. Every passionate relationship began passionately. There is no other way. In every single one of the long-term, loving relationships I have experienced (oh joyous remembrance!), we were intimate on the very first night. Every single one. And these were women who all said it is something they "would never do."

It is a postulate that men will not respect a woman who sleeps with them on the first night. For me, the opposite is true. In fact, when I have connected with a woman on such a profound level, with such an alignment of our hearts and minds, I am mildly shocked (and amused at my shock) if something doesn't occur on the first night. I chalk it up to logistics or circumstances and not to any supposed societal consideration on her part. That particular roadblock was bypassed long ago.

I respect a woman more if she honors the closeness, the intimacy, the alignment we share, with the full knowledge that she can trust me and she shows it with her actions. It makes me respect her completely. It makes me like her immensely. It makes me realize that she, like me, believes in the beauty of life and the everlasting gifts it brings.
— The Alabaster Girl, *page 150*

ഌർ

Relationships almost always follow a typical and predictable path. They have a series of stages, a life-cycle that repeats itself over and over again.

Stage one: The man and woman meet and start to date. As they spend more and more time together, they begin to desire exclusivity with each other. They both want to move forward to…

Stage two: They become exclusive. Now they are "seeing" each other. They might refer to each other as boyfriend and girlfriend. They stop seeing other people and this is either directly agreed upon or tacitly understood. Either way, they are both under the impression that they are now exclusive with each other.

Stage three: They are completely comfortable with each other. This is months or years down the road now. They are happy together; they do a lot of fun and exciting things together. They have wonderful communication, great sex, they go for drinks, they dance, they merge their friends. This is a blissful time when the relationship is the most euphoric. They are very much in love.

Stage four: They settle into the routine of daily life. They know each other so very well, they can finish each other's sentences. They have their ups and downs, of course, the normal vicissitudes of life. They go to their separate jobs, they attend their various classes, she has coffee with her girlfriends, he watches football with his buddies.

Normal life, but routine is starting to settle in. They have the intention and the desire, but life, as life does, gets in the way. In this stage, they start to long for the days of stage three, when they had more time to spend together, when they did fun and exciting things together, before they got bogged down with routine and bills and general busy-ness. Sex is happening less and less often and when it does happen, it tends to be dispassionate, unremarkable, and uninspired. Their focus is no longer directed toward each other and their plans together. A quiet unrest is simmering underneath. They start to question what it is they really want. They say things like "Where are we going to be in five years?" and "What am I to you?" and "What do you want from me?"

Stage five: They realize that all their best intentions—about communicating more, having a date night once a week—are not really working. They become more and more frustrated. Sex is sporadic and perfunctory, or non-existent. He is sick of her constant nagging and she feels she has been reduced to feeding and watering and cleaning out his cage. They are starting to resent each other, and they are surprised to discover that the things they absolutely loved about each other at the beginning are the very things that repel them the most now. She might have loved his independence; now, she can't stand his independence. He might have loved that she was fun and liked to party; later, he hates that she likes to party. She might have been delighted that he is always upbeat and joking; later, she wonders why he can't be serious for once.

This is the stage where they cast about, looking outward, looking for relief. And this is where affairs somehow seem to just… happen. The relationship at this stage is held together by proximity and fear alone.

Stage six: Things are getting nasty. Blame and accusations start to fly. One of them is bitter and confrontational and the other just doesn't give a damn anymore. They are holding on to the last ragged edge of their discontent. Can the relationship be restored? Good question.

Stage seven: This is where the rubber hits the road. They decide on a trial separation. They are still technically connected, but they are taking a "break." Drastic measures are needed and drastic measures are taken; everything, in fact, is drastic. They may try to get back together, but only, one of them insists, if they get counseling. They go back and forth, sad and hurt, until they either end it, or shakily get back together and try again.

৪০৫৪

Society says we must create a box for our relationships. It should conform to a certain shape and size and have a solid foundation and sturdy walls. So most of us construct this society-approved box for our relationships, this framework that is expected of us. We toss all kinds of things into this erstwhile bed of Procrustes: expectations, promises, demands. We climb in together and close the lid. Hello forever, we think. Then we are shocked and dismayed when we both feel stifled and can't breathe and have an overwhelming urge to kick the side out.

Surely a relationship should never be constructed? Surely it should never be examined, never be analyzed? Am I the only one who thinks this way? We say we need to "work on the relationship." An oxymoron! What an ugly phrase! What unfathomable loss of life-force, loss of redemption, loss of passion, loss of everything that can be considered good and beautiful, is contained in that vitiating, soul-numbing phrase.

But, some will say, relationships *are* work. They are, by definition, sacrifice, compromise, a willingness to abdicate certain freedoms in exchange for security and longevity. This all sounds wonderful. Then we discover that our partner is not living up to the fifty-fifty bargain we thought we had negotiated. Rarely do relationships find this equilibrium, this ideal. We look around us one day and realize that the relationship is no longer a refreshing oasis but a meandering, repetitive slog through a dry and dusty desert.

Two shall become one, we say. But there are three distinct entities at play here: the man, the woman, and the relationship itself. The relationship is its own entity. It stands alone. It needs its own space, its own agenda, its own boundaries, its own room to breathe. Our mistake is in trying to blend everything together into one big, amorphous pile.

Oh, to have relationships that are pure and free-flowing and natural, without needing to be propped up by compromise and marriage-counseling, without having to "work on the relationship." Like the Observer Effect in physics, the moment you attempt to examine it, you change it. As soon as you question where a relationship is going or what the plan is, you change it forever.

୫୦୯୨

Forever is a myth. Why? Because we don't really believe in it. We make long-term promises on short-term feelings. We are so suspicious, so nervous, that we try to capture the future, to force "happily ever after," to set it in stone. We seal it with a contract, desperate to convince ourselves that yes, it will last forever. But this is simply blind optimism, wishful thinking, paper promises. It will never work because the future—being only a half-imagined, liquid dream—can never be captured or contained.

Forever only exists for those who don't try to force it. Forever only exists for those who truly believe in it. When we believe in forever, we eschew the artificial, contrived, and expected edifice of conventional relationship and instead, let the light shimmer on the path just ahead of us. This is the secret to co-creating and nurturing a relationship, because now it is real before our eyes, and only then might it last.

Oh, and praise. The other secret to a beautiful relationship is praise. Little, beautifying words and actions every day, at the place where two hearts coalesce.

There is an upward-sloping curve to the journey of a soul, my love, a spiritual line, and when it is transgressed the whole body suffers. A relationship can only last if the two of them view it—with all the requisite wonder and curiosity and communion—as a *spiritual* journey. And by spiritual, I mean spiritual in the broadest sense of the word: soul-searching, celebration, salsa lessons. A side-by-side, albeit *individual*, quest for greater understanding.

‟⌘”

Every relationship has an arc. It might last a lifetime or a few years or months or days or even a quiet evening on the shore. A relationship with someone who draws your heart is always real, no matter what its arc through time. It is as real and strong and romantic as any that has ever been.

Relationships never end. A contradiction? No. Relationships are eternal, no matter how long they last. A true lover is connected to the women in his life for all of his days. Their shared experience lives out of time, and their interrupted conversation is forever poised to resume where it left off. He was authentic and honest and clear, and that clarity touches a woman so profoundly that she will always carry him around in her heart. She will defend him forever because she understands him, and because he didn't lie to her.

A woman will only say bad things about a man, will only feel disappointed in him, will only feel cheated, if she thought he promised something to her that she never received. If a man buys flowers and chocolates and opens the door for her early in the relationship, and then he no longer does those things two or three years down the road, well then, he lied about who he is. He misrepresented to her how the relationship was going to go. That is why she feels cheated when it ends. That is why she despises him. That is why she calls him her "ex."

Women move in and out of my life, a constant stream. I cherish them when they come and I cherish them when they go. A mutual parting, an eternal knowing, a secret winning, and a love and respect that transcends everything mundane... we will meet again someday with glad tidings and hearts!

Maybe it's semantics, but it seems to me that I have never broken up with a girl. Is that true? Yes, I think so. Women left me, of course—in the early years because I was pathetic and needy, in the later years because it was time.

I miss every girl I have ever been with. They never say a bad word about me. There is no animosity toward me. There are no hard feelings toward me. There is sadness, but never regret. And any sadness is temporary. How in the world is this possible? It's because I gave them room to breathe. It's because I respected them so much that I let them go with gratitude, grace, and ease. When a man can gently let go of a beautiful woman, all things are possible with women.

Oh, chiaroscuro love affair! An attempt to discern light from shadows. Let's you and I be different, my love. Let us never analyze this "us." Let us just be. Let us trust our love. Let us not expect or demand. Let us stay amazed. Let us only say to each other, "I love you today, and I want to see you again tomorrow." Is that not enough to say? Is that not complete enough to sustain a relationship through an entire lifetime? Or even a quiet evening on the shore?

೩೦೧೩

When we sat together that day, on the long, slow flight between those two magnificent cities, you talked to me of hurtful loves and unresolved liaisons. There was a sadness in your eyes from the betrayal you felt from the last man you trusted and loved, and even though the words you spoke and the stories you told were all about him, I knew that hidden here were all of your loves longed for and lost...

the slow and inexorable reduction of the dreams of young women everywhere.

Suddenly, you were angry at him (at them)! Your soft face, normally so beatific and clear, twisted then into a lurid caricature of you, like a curious Cubist painting, with dark lines of betrayal and bright colors of despair, exaggerated and clashing and juxtaposed all over your face.

Did you notice then how I softened your countenance with the tips of my fingers? Did you notice that I stayed? You resisted, looking away, shaking your head a little, tearing up a little, just a little, but I stayed... I stayed right there with you, calming you down with the warmth of my eyes and the warmth of my voice and the warmth of my fingers tracing lines on your cheek.

I have no answers for you, I said.

Love is a mystery, I said.

But I stayed.

— The Alabaster Girl, *page 152*

৪৩০৫

It's like swimming in the ocean, underneath the surface. Ah, it's beautiful there, a beautiful time for us, refreshing and fun, for it is delightful to swim in the ocean. So wonderful, so life-giving, and not a care in the world.

Near the surface, it is light and there is little pressure. It is easy to swim fast and have fun in this beautiful water of translucent blue. The sunlight is rippling on the surface right there above you, and you know you are always close to the way out. There is no pressure. All you have to do is swim up and you're out. It's an easy, light blue experience.

Deeper down, the ocean becomes more vibrant and rich. There is much more to see. Here are crayoned fish and pink coral and dancing plants. How beautiful and vibrant! It's a little slower going and it's not so easy to get to the surface. There is a lot more pressure down so deep. But it is a far more serene and reflective experience. It is, you could say, more profound.

Picture yourself in this ocean, my love. Feel the water on your skin. Look around at the sights you can see. Now then, here's the question: How deep would you go? Do you picture yourself near the surface where it is easy and fun, translucent and free? Or would you commit to a depth more colorful, variegated, and vibrant?

Either way is fine, but each of us tends to prefer one or the other. The man you love might like to swim deep but you might not be so comfortable there, preferring to swim a little closer to the surface. If he encourages you, you may swim down a little deeper with him, because you love him and want both of you to be happy. But if you find you cannot breathe or the pressure is too much to bear, you will have to return to the surface. Or you might convince him to swim with you, light and easy, near the surface, and he will do it because he doesn't want to lose you, but it will never be as satisfying to him as his preferred depth.

That's what relationships are like. We all like to swim at different depths at different times in our lives. There is nothing you can do about it. We can swim together for a time, but we can never change the depth the other prefers. Therein lies a lot of our problems with relationships: trying to convince our partners to swim at our preferred depth, then blaming them when they don't. Finding someone who can swim comfortably at the same depth as you is not easy, my love. You might even wish you could *change* your preferred depth because you are so in love with him and want it to work. You can't.

No one is right and no one is wrong. It's just one great big, glorious ocean. Each depth is beautiful and unique and interesting. The best we can do is swim where we are most comfortable and happy. Sure, we might lose each other as the current drifts us apart. But if we try to force the other to stay at our chosen depth, then loss is certain.

৪৩

Open relationships are in vogue today, with shared intimacies and shifting layers of commitment. Why now? I wonder. Are we jaded? War on monogamy? Have we given up on the idea that traditional one-on-one relationships can work? Do we no longer believe there is a "lid for every pot"? Or are we in such an advanced and enlightened stage of consciousness that this is the next logical step in the way men and women connect? Are open relationships something that we should learn to embrace, to even celebrate? Or is it just a sign of our times? After all, modern man has explored everything else *ad infinitum*: every possible hairstyle, every possible political ideology, every possible philosophical rabbit-trail. Is this current trend toward open relationships, therefore, just another logical extension of our post-modern societal exploration, a trying on of every possible combination and permutation of love and sex and relating to one another? I don't really know.

A woman may willingly and enthusiastically embrace an open relationship at first. But can it last? Only for a time, I suspect. For if she grows to know and love him, that clear enthusiasm shifts, imperceptibly, confusingly, into a secret yearning to be with him and him alone, a desire to take care of him, to relax into his arms, to rest in the quiet assurance of his embrace and their shared vision of the future. A disquieted, albeit pleasant, tolerance sets in.

This tolerance can sustain for a time, maybe even a very long time. And though she might be only peripherally aware of her heart's desire, she certainly can't express it or explore it, for it will undermine the very lifestyle she has been openly advocating and celebrating with him all this time.

I may be wrong, of course, but I don't think so. Many have tried to describe to me in infinite detail just how wonderful their open relationship, their arrangement, truly is. She is free to see other men, he will say to me, and he, of course, is free to see other women, as long—and this is crucial—as they both play safe. Ah, but somewhere along the way, she fell deeply in love with you, my illustrious friend! I look at her and she nods her head and smiles and agrees with him, but I see something else in her eyes… that she wants only you and the two of you and no one else.

Surely he sees it too? Ah, maybe not. Maybe he is blithely—blissfully!—unaware of this infinitesimal shift in her. Maybe he still thinks she is excited to maintain this open relationship with him, this status quo. After all, their communication about all this was crystal clear from the beginning, was it not? And she enthusiastically embraced everything up front, you see, and look how enthusiastically she still agrees with this arrangement today! Yes, he marches cheerily along, and though he may not see this quiet, encompassing desire in her, bless his heart, I can.

There are some who think the whole pursuit of man is a desire to increase his sexual options. If none, then one. If one, then more. If more, then different. Who knows? If this is so, then it lends credence to my half-facetious theory that fashion seasons were created by women to give the illusion of a new and different sexual partner, so that a man is fooled and stays transfixed on her. If this is so, then polyamory is slanted toward men. If this is so, then an open relationship is something that is ideal for a man, and something a woman can only ever tolerate. Open short-term love affairs can work. Open long-term relationships? Not so much.

I will, of course, get thoroughly skewered for saying this. What specious and uninformed romanticism, silly and archaic! Ah well, perhaps some things are better left unsaid. It is not my place to judge him and besides, I have little energy for the onslaught of exposition that he will surely pour forth upon me.

Look here! he will say. Advocates abound, men and women of authority and powerful suasion. Look at all these examples of successful open relationships. And look at all these studies from science and psychology and evolutionary biology. And look also at our entire history of harems, polygamy, hidden affairs, kept mistresses. It's all there and there is nothing new under the sun. Yes, yes, you may be right. And yet... I can see her heart.

₧)⁖

There is a general consensus about self-centered independence: in order to be happy with someone else, you must first have an overall sense of happiness with yourself. You can't find your happiness in another. Yes, yes, true, but let's dissent a little, shall we? Among other things, happiness is a direct result of our relationship to others. A great deal of our happiness comes from *shared* experiences. We are creatures of community, of connectedness. In this context, we can indeed experience happiness in our lives through others. We accomplish things faster and better when inspired by others. We share laughter with others. We all benefit from a muse, whether real or imaginary. Is this not a source of true wonder and joy that is outside of ourselves?

So what now, my love? What shall we do with our ridiculous, delirious relationships? How shall we go forth? How shall a man and a woman number their days together? How shall it be? Is there a better way?

I want to love my muse. I want to love my relationship with you because you inspire me. I want to love the way you make me laugh, and the way you surprise me every day in little ways. This gives me joy. This brings fun into my life. This fulfills me. All experiences in life are amplified once shared.

There is a quiet greatness in the heart-connection between a man and a woman. There is a knowing and a not knowing. There is a mindfulness, a hopefulness, and even a curious trepidation. There is also a sense of looking out together at the hazy horizon of life and saying, "This is what I want. I want this with you."

That's all we really know. When we relax into our relationship and just let flow the sweet grace of continuance, it might last forever. To not know and to not analyze it. However long it lasts, it is amazing.

ಌღಌ

We have been sitting here for a long time, contemplating. A single room with a single bench, centered, equidistant from every wall. This entire room is devoted to only one thing, and that one thing is right there on the wall in front of us. Right there. There is nothing else here but this bench and that one thing.

'Water Lilies' by Monet, before us in this room, before us in this stillness, before us in our contemplation. A triptych as large as, and larger than, this room that contains it.

Who were you, Claude Monet? What were you trying to capture in life? What were you trying to steal? What were you trying to possess? You never really managed to capture it, did you? And oh, you tried. You spent the last half of your life painting the same bridge over and over again, at different times of the day, different angles, different seasons. Over and over again. The same bridge. And as you aged and your eyesight worsened, your paintings became more blurry, more diffuse, more, well... impressionistic, one might say. Same bridge, a little bit harder to make it out, but there it was... the same old bridge that you always painted.

We say nothing, sitting here, holding hands. Me and my lovely girl. What are you thinking in this space, my lovely girl? What is Monsieur Monet saying to you? What do you think he desired the most? And for that matter, what do you desire the most? A relationship? With me? A life-long love affair? Ah, my lovely girl...

We enter into the same relationships over and over again. We think this one will be different, but it's just the same old bridge we've always painted. We repeat our patterns, the same scene over and over again, losing clarity and insight

as time goes on, each new relationship less carefully painted.
Because we are slowly losing our ability to see.

Earlier today we encountered Vermeer, the 17th-century
Dutch master who painted ordinary scenes of ordinary
people in ordinary clothes doing ordinary things. Sublime
images, haunting and beautiful.

Vermeer tried to capture light. In fact, maybe the only
thing he ever painted was light, and not at all the subjects
you see in his paintings. He painted the light. Only the light.
He didn't see a table, he saw a table that reflected light.
To him, the light was supreme, the only really interesting
element, the most important theme of the picture. If there
was no light, nothing else in the picture would make any
sense or even exist. Without the light, the wonderful light,
nothing else mattered.

Oh, my lovely girl... to paint our relationship like Vermeer...
to capture the light... and only the light.
— The Alabaster Girl, *page 155*

৪৩৫৪

What draws our hearts, my love? Symmetry... The ones you love are
the ones who love you. The ones you truly delight in will delight in
you, the ones you celebrate will celebrate you. If all our issues and
expectations and presumptions were somehow magically removed,
the ones we find ourselves attracted to would be the ones attracted
to us. That's the way it works. Love is symmetrical. This is a secret
that no one knows.

How can this be? we say. There are times when I am attracted to
someone who is *not* attracted to me. And the ones who want me are
not the ones I want at all. There is a French proverb that translates to
"In every relationship, there is the one who kisses and the one who
offers the cheek." Another way it has been said: "The one who loves
the most is the one who waits." We think about this and agree; it
aligns with our experience. Love certainly *appears* to be asymmetrical.

Yes, I hear you, and let me say it again: *The ones you love are the ones who love you.* Those who you are truly attracted to—on a heart level—are the ones who are attracted to you. The problem is that most of us cannot make a distinction between what we really want for our lives and our surface impulses. Thus, we end up in asymmetrical situations and relationships.

A typical single man has a sexual desperation billowing all about him, obscuring his vision like a cloud. It's not his fault; he is just not getting the quantity of sex he needs. Yes, men need sex, and lots of it, and no, that's not a bad thing.

So a man is sexually frustrated and that is all he can see; it informs all his choices. And because he can't see clearly, his impulses are all-consuming and every pretty woman he encounters masquerades in his mind as what he wants. Through his *cloud of horniness*, all he can discern are amorphous female shapes, like Plato's shadows on the wall. Every woman who looks reasonably pretty to him becomes an immediate, must-have object of desire. It is asymmetrical, a numbers game, a shotgun spread. Maybe that one. No? Okay, then maybe that one. He chases everything.

Then when a woman agrees to go on a date with him, his desire to have her in his life crashes headlong into his fear of not being good enough for her, and a familiar and pervasive paralysis sets in. The whole time he is with her, all he can think is, "Wow, I really like this girl. But I will surely mess it up like I always do."

He is sexually frustrated, lonely, and certain of impending loss, so he attaches himself to her, craves sex from her, craves her in every way. He holds tightly to any positive affirmation from her, no matter how insignificant, like a drowning man holds onto a small stick. He puts her on the proverbial pedestal. He casts all his expectations of future happiness directly upon her. She becomes his entire hope for the future. She replaces any vestige of purpose he might have had for his life. And not even her, actually. Merely the *shadow* of her projected on the wall, the impossible image of her he has built up in his mind. And that's only after the first date!

This man, bless his heart, is sincere. He has simply mistaken his impulses, his sexual frustration, and his loneliness, for his true desires in life. He believes that she is the only one he will ever want, but in truth, she is interchangeable. When she finally tires of his over-weening attention and breaks up with him, when she shakes off the wet and heavy shroud of neediness he has draped across her shoulders, he will simply pick it up, ready to drape it upon the next reasonably shaped female form he encounters. He is continually chasing a mirage, attaching himself to the nearest pretty girl, and projecting onto her his own distorted version of reality—only to be disappointed and bitter when she tears herself away from his grasp.

And women? Women have a similar cloud obscuring their vision. It is not a cloud of horniness. Yes, I know that women are perpetually horny, and that they desire and think about sex even more so than men. No, it is not *quantity* of sex that women lack, it is *quality*, and once a woman discovers a source of quality sex, she will put up with almost anything to retain it.

The cloud across a woman's vision is the *promise of a shared future*. This is the filter through which she sees every man she meets, dates, or loves. She considers him in the context of shared possibilities: a shared vision, a shared future. If she does not see that possibility with a man, she either accepts him as just a temporary sexual partner (because why not?) or turns away from him forever.

The promise of a shared future. Women become convinced that, in order to have a meaningful connection, it is important to share not only the present, but the future together. Which is quite a tall order. After all, most of us don't know how to fully share the present with each other, let alone the future. In fact, if a man does not share her expectation for the future, some women will dismiss him as not a real man or needing to grow up.

It is not a bad thing to hope for a dreamy, happily-ever-after story. It is only troublesome when it degrades, as it often does, into desperation. Then this intense need will cloud her vision just as surely as the sexual frustration of men. This is why some women become clingy and suffocating and needy, and it causes men to run fast and far.

I said it before: *We make long-term promises on short-term feelings* Women believe a future together is only possible with a promise. But perhaps a future together is only possible if there is *no* promise. A living in the present with one another, a delighting in each other in small ways every day.

My point is that none of us can see clearly. Our relationships do not last because our vision is obscured. Women see everything through an obscuring cloud of wishes and expectations and repeated patterns and men see everything through a cloud of sexual frustration. So we find ourselves attracted to anyone who bears a passing resemblance to what we think we want. We try everyone on for size.

What draws our hearts, my love? Again, I say it: Symmetry. The ones you love are the ones who love you. If the clouds were somehow magically cleared away from our eyes, the ones we'd find ourselves attracted to would automatically be attracted to us. That's the way it works. Because we can now see clearly, we will recognize the ones who will love us the most, the ones who will desire us the most, the ones who will celebrate us the most. These are the only ones who will delight our hearts and we will be drawn to them across any space, any time, like the sea is drawn to the sky.

※◎◎

Plato talked about the idea of the perfect "chair" that we all have in our consciousness but none of us have ever seen. We have all seen chairs, of course, but Plato asked a further question, "What is the one perfect ideal of a chair?" According to Plato, we can never know, for we have only seen approximations of a perfect chair, inexact shadows of the ideal. Although no two chairs are exactly alike, they all share the same essence of "chair."

Every man has a vague notion of the perfect girl, my love, a subconscious image that he carries in his heart from his earliest years to his dying day. She is a symbol of all that he holds dear and cherishes in his soul, a compilation of all the traits that he desires in a woman. She is truth to him, and justice and beauty and love and life.

His perfect girl might be sharply drawn in his imagination, well-considered, or she might be vague and undefined, nothing more than a diaphanous collection of approximate curves or a preferred color of hair. His perfect girl might resemble a film star or someone he saw in a magazine or a dream conjured up from books he read in his youth. On the other hand, he may have no idea at all what the image of the perfect girl for him might be, but there is an outline resident in his heart all the same.

The media, of course, with its smoke and mirrors, does not help. All those carefully constructed women, artfully airbrushed and perfectly posed, leading us astray like the Sirens of yore. "There, see? I told you there are perfect women in the world. It says so right here in this magazine."

The perfect girl is one a man can show off to his friends, the one he can drape over his arm as he enters a room. A man daydreams this scenario all the time, in living color and detail; he can feel the surge of natural confidence and grace that only a woman like this can impart to him, this beauty who is with him and no one else. She is the one that he imagines would make him forget every other woman forever.

Over and over again, time after time, we believe we have found "the one." This is because every woman a man encounters throughout his life—the one he saw in the bookstore, the one dancing so seductively on the stage, the one he saw walking across the street, the one who is going on a date with him tonight—he subconsciously compares to his image of the perfect girl. He squints and scrutinizes, and in his eagerness to convince himself that this new woman is indeed his ideal woman, he blinds himself to everything about her that doesn't quite match. Then over time, it dawns on him that this latest obsession of his is just a girl, nothing more. A girl with as many faults, fears, and insecurities as his own. She is no longer shiny and new.

When the realization hits that she is just a girl, that she is not what he has made her out to be, that she is not perfect at all, men deal with it in all kinds of different ways. Some men settle, accept their lot, and, rolling their eyes, dejectedly soldier on. They give her nothing of themselves from that day forward. They commute to their tired cubicles with their tired briefcases on their tired feet and return to their tired homes. Every single day. Except weekends, of course, when they mow the lawn and watch the game and fill their time with other things, other things, anything really. Unremarkable in every way. Some men get angry or mean-spirited and take it out on her—through neglect or verbal violence or physical abuse. It's not her fault, yet he blames her and relentlessly sets out to punish her. Other men, well, they just abandon her.

The perfect girl is a myth. We will never find her. It is a search without end. Men have conquered the business world, they are captains of industry, they have interesting friends and fascinating hobbies, they build, they create, they do great and wonderful things. But they feel in their hearts, that they haven't yet found *her*. The perfect girl whom we desire so intensely, who would make the world feel whole again, who would make us believe in love again, who would complete us, is forever out of our reach. This is a vision so perfectly formed and so lovely and so complete that no real woman could ever come close to actually being her.

The answer we seek can never be found in a woman. This has a quiet beauty to it. This realization frees a man forever, allowing him the simplicity of looking into the eyes of his sweetheart, the wonderful woman who shares his life and who loves him. He looks into her eyes and he knows. He knows that she is just a girl, that she is not, nor can she ever be, that impossible ideal. And now he can accept her for who she is, now he can love her without expectation or restriction. She is not perfect, no, but she is perfect for him. And no, this does not mean that he is settling. Far from it.

෫෧෬

Way down south, along the irrepressible Caribbean shore, Lucía, when you lay on top of me, so close to me, wrapped tightly around me, so much a part of me, and before we fell asleep that way, without moving, without speaking, I cried a little because I missed you so.

I missed you and your heart, beautiful girl. I missed you all these many months since I last saw you here in lovely Las Peñitas.

You took all of me into you, my whole heart, my whole being, my hurt, my longing, you took all of me inside of you, Lucía, without asking for anything in return, healing me, and I had missed you so.

— The Alabaster Girl, *page 157*

෫෧෬

What is love? What is love? Do we even know? Is it that tingling you get when you meet the right person? Is it just a pleasant feeling? Is it a knowing? What do we mean when we speak of love? Do we mean to love? Or to be loved? Do we fall in love with the other? Or with the *idea* of the other? With the person? Or with what they represent? Do we love the potential we see in them? Or the potential they see in us? Do we love their goodness? Or our perception of their goodness? Do we love because we are loved? Or do we love because we love? All of the above, perhaps? Well then, what about this… would we still love our chosen one if our family and friends despised them? Yes, of course, we say. But would we really?

Some will say that love is a bond that grows over months and years of staunch commitment between a man and a woman, a deep understanding, an unassailable mutuality that transcends such fleeting trivialities as sexual tension and desperate passion. But is this really love? Or is this just best friends?

When we talk about love, maybe we only mean one thing: to be loved. Maybe all of our discontent in affairs of the heart is really just the longing for someone to desire us, for someone to find us lovable. Men spend their time and money on accumulation of things. Women concentrate on their outward appearances. It is all for one thing, for one goal: to finally, *finally* be loved.

Some will say that love is caring for another's heart as much as we care for our own. That's as good a description as any.

෨෬

The notion of marrying for love is surprisingly new on this earth. It's only about two hundred years old or so. Tell that to people now and they are shocked. We can't imagine that it was ever any different, but it was. To us, love is the only legitimate reason for marriage, but until the early 19th century, parentally arranged marriages and a sober exchange of dowries, property, or influence were the order of the day, and in some places still are.

In the 1800s, a radical notion took hold: the idea that romantic love is the necessary foundation of a successful marriage. For the first time, personal choice was introduced and courting one another before marriage was not only allowed, but encouraged. A man could choose his betrothed; she, in turn, could choose to concur or demur, and if she did not demur, then after a whirlwind courtship of oh say, a year or two, they would marry.

This is not to say that men and women didn't fall in love before then. They just had the notion that something as fleeting and frivolous as romantic love and something as sensible and practical as marriage were two entirely different things.

We have always been influenced by romantic love in some form or another. Even the slightest glance at the literature and mythology of history will yield a multitude of examples: Jacob laboring fourteen years for his beloved Rachel, Solomon and his effusive Songs, Virgil's portrayal of the desperate passion of Dido for Aeneas, Paris and Helen and the destruction of Troy, the legendary shenanigans of Cleopatra, to name just a few.

Having said that, the idealized notion of romantic love and courtship in the modern sense first arose as a cultural force in the West only about a thousand years ago, at the dawn of the age of chivalry: knights in shining armor, lords and ladies, and all that. Fueled by Dante, the first lover of love, the modern concept of romantic love, once so suppressed by customs and culture, began to grow in earnest throughout the centuries until it wholly eclipsed every other myth, emotion, and sensibility of human imaginings. Romantic love is now—and has been for a long time—the predominant theme of all poems, books, and songs. It has coalesced in our collective consciousness as the most lofty of human emotions, the most exalted of aspirations, and the greatest influence on our lives.

From about the time of Eleanor of Aquitaine in the 12th century, troubadours, wandering minstrels, and various tinkers expanded upon and extolled the virtues of virtuosity, regaling the populace with songs and tales of courtly love, and spreading the idea of "my fair lady" throughout the land. The celebrities in those days were the knights-errant, and for them, ideal love was the unrequited kind, never to be fulfilled, never to come to fruition. The unobtainable love of a beautiful lady was heartbreaking, tragic, and above all, noble, for this truly was the height of sacrifice, of divine glory. This philosophy—the sublimation of courtly love—was central to the concept of honor, and honor was the greatest treasure a man could possess, more valuable than life itself.

All the way up to the Renaissance, futility in love was the order of the day. All love stories had to be tragic in order to have any resonance with the hearts and minds of the people. All the great myths from that time describe men of brave hearts and damsels of untrammeled countenance, and all have the theme of impossibility, hardship, and futility. Shakespeare, of course, capped the Renaissance with the ultimate lyric to the tragedy of romantic love: Romeo and Juliet.

Every age in Western culture has had distinctive notions about the ideal form of romantic love. We had the Puritans, self-righteous, pious, and dour, steadfastly covering their eyes and ears. We furthered the suppression with the Victorian prudes, abstinent, austere, and shaking their heads. We had the wispy era of the Romantic poets, lounging about and opium-laced, effervescing on and on about "my dearest" and "my beloved." We had the light-hearted flowering of women in the Flapper era—a revolt against their Victorian mothers—with their short skirts, bobbed hair, and jazz. We had the idealized '50s where households and women were picture perfect on the outside and thoroughly lost on the inside. The '60s and '70s brought us free love (free sex, actually), the burning of bras, the Pill, complete liberation and anything goes. That morphed into the me-first, what-can-you-do-for-me, frantic consumerism and ego-centric modernism of the '80s and '90s. And now we spend all our time trying our best to optimize our online dating profile.

What is next? Who knows? But make no mistake, my love, something is about to shift. It cannot remain the same. In every country, every culture, there is an unrest, a tingling, a vibrating undercurrent that wants to break forth. I talk to men and women all over the world, and it is palpable; you can feel it in the air. We are on the verge of scraping off our old century, of new ways of thinking and being. Every decade changes its views about romantic love and the coming decades will do the same. Not only will we witness it, we will create it, for we are leaders and we will lead.

୨୦୯୫

Permit me to wax philosophical, my love. Imagine three circles interlocked in the shape of a triangle, like a Venn diagram. In the first circle we are *Single*. In the second circle we are *Dating*. In the third circle we are in *Relationship*. These are the circles of our lives. They are entire. They contain our entire love story. Everybody is in exactly one of these circles at any given time. We might move from one circle to another from time to time, but we are in them until the day we die.

No circle is more special or important or valuable than the others. Only our *perspective* gives a circle any value, any desirability, any weight relative to the other two. And no one has a preference more important, more desirable, or more correct than our own. Oh, and also it is impossible to be indifferent. We are either happy with the circle we are in—maybe we like being single?—or we would rather be in one of the other circles. We are there because we want to be or we wish we were somewhere else.

In each of these circles, there are attendant problems and fears, and possible solutions to those problems and fears. The primary fear associated with the Circle of Single is the fear of being alone when we are old. The primary fear associated with the Circle of Dating is the fear of somehow screwing it up before the foundation has set. The primary fear associated with the Circle of Relationship is the fear that we might become stuck with the wrong person. Of course if we want to be pedantic, these fears are all essentially the same fear: the fear of being alone.

Now then, each of these circles has an entire industry of advice attached. There are volumes of books and programs and gurus and instructors all devoted to a successful navigation from one circle to another. There are dating coaches, approach coaches, life coaches, relationship experts, and marriage counsellors, each focused primarily on just *one* of these circles, but almost never all three. Single and want to meet someone? Dating and want to figure out how to keep him? Marriage broke up and you suddenly find yourself single again? No problem, join a support group, take a workshop, buy a book.

Now then, here's a question, my love: If we imagine a larger circle that surrounds all three of our circles, our imagined Venn diagram, encompassing them, then what is *that* circle called? Is there a word in English that circumscribes or describes them all? All three circles? What is the word for the whole thing? There is none. So what shall we call this whole enterprise, this mystery, these ineluctable affairs of the heart?

We need a new word. *Love* is too broad. Love of family, love of pets, love of pasta. *Connection* is too generic. *Romance* is too specific. And after passing through the hands of Plato, Schopenhauer, Scheler, Freud, Jung, and countless others, we're not quite sure what the Greek word "Eros" means, with definitions ranging from love of beauty to love of genital activity.

So what are we left with? Relationship? Limerence? Interacting? Dating? No, they are all too narrow, I think. None of these will suffice. None of these accurately describe the whole thing. Thus, we need a new word.

Well, maybe we don't and I am being ridiculous, but permit me, in my painted presumption, to suggest a new term: *Ars Amorata*. Now then, where did that phrase come from? Many years ago, a reporter misquoted me when I happened to mention I liked the works by Ovid called the *Ars Amatoria*, which, when translated from the Latin, means the *Art of Love*. The misquote she printed? The *Ars Amorata*. Beautiful. I absconded the phrase and have used it ever since. So, why not? Let my naive contribution to the lexicon be this: The *Ars Amorata* is all the aspects of the Single, Dating, and Relationship circles combined, a term for the art and philosophy that describes the entire "intimate" portion of the human condition—everything from love to loneliness, from seduction to beauty.

ഏറൠ

What shall I do, shall I do with you, my dear, my beautiful, my darling girl? You sit with me and hold me close. I love you, you say, and I see that it's true. Not the love frivolity of a desperate need, not the love emptiness of a wounded soul. A real love and calm, from deep within, and I marvel at the pure dispelling, the pure peaking power of your love for me. You know what you want, your heart's desire, and I see in your eyes that all is true.

What shall I do, shall I do with you, my angel sent to hold me close? How can I be the one that you love above all? Can you not see that my love for you is cast against your bronze desire with a forged patina of indeterminate hue? How can I give of my heart, my mind, my gypsy countenance, to you? Oh, your pure, untrammeled love for me... it makes me pause, makes me turn toward you, and I have waves of wanting to be the hero for you.

How shall I be, what shall I do, my dear, my darling, my beautiful girl?

— The Alabaster Girl, *page 159*

ഏറൠ

There are four stages in a man's love for women. The first stage is the simple love for a simple girl, a day-dreaming desire for her and her alone, a belief that she is all he needs to be happy for the rest of days. This is the stage where he is wishing and hopeful and excited, with heel-clicking delight and measured anticipation. What joy! How wonderful she is! This is also the stage that hurts the most when it all falls apart, when his heart is torn asunder, when he spends his days and nights lying prostrate and despondent and heartsick on the floor.

The second stage in a man's love for women arrives when he has experienced the euphoria and heartbreak of the first stage a few times. He has fallen in love. He has had his heart broken. Now he

tells himself that he is wiser, that he will just date for a while, nothing too serious, play the field, keep his options open, plenty of fish
in the sea, and all that. If he starts to see someone and it ends, sure
it hurts a little, but it doesn't cause him to sit in the dirt in despair.
Most men spend their entire lives floating somewhere between stage
one and stage two: they date a few times, fall in love a few times, get
in a relationship a few times, get disappointed a few times.

The third stage is a rarity. Most men will never discover it. But the
third stage, if discovered, is a wonderful stage indeed, for a man's
love for women now becomes love of the *essence* of women, the
love of the goddess in women, the love of the divine feminine and
everything that this life-giving spirit creates in this world. It is no
longer about one woman or even about multiple women. He has
had all that before. No, now he is fascinated by the gifts of the
female spirit; he is in love with all women, but obsessed with none.
He explores this love for women and their elegance and beauty in a
spiritual sense, in a whole sense, in a holistic sense.

Now then, is there perhaps a fourth stage? What else could there be?
After all, what is more profound and complete than the love of the
goddess in women? I don't know, but sometimes I think I can see a
fourth stage on the periphery of my understanding.

This possible fourth stage is the stage where the only thing that
can ever fulfill a man is *one woman*. One woman who embodies
everything he has ever learned to love about women in general. One
woman who is the goddess for him, personified. One woman who
represents to him the very height of feminine grace and elegance.
One woman who understands him and his nature better than he will
ever understand himself. One woman who cares about his whole
being—his fears, his dreams, his half-hopes, his halting and cart-
wheeling aspirations. One woman who sees the greatness in him that
he can't see himself, and his true potential in ways he never would.
One woman who inspires him to all loftiness. One woman who is
his muse, his sanctuary, his place of rest.

The fourth stage is a full-circle return to the sincerity and honesty of a simple love for a simple girl—exactly what he had in stage one, but stripped of all neediness, obsession, and fear of loss. A calm knowing that she is his girl, and will *always* be his girl.

Desire for a specific woman, then desire for women in general, then desire for the essence of women, then desire for a specific woman again. This theory rings true to me. Memories are only complete when shared. Maybe life is better as a duet and not a solo affair. A duet, after all, creates harmony.

₧⁗

What about *true* love? A concept that philosophers, troubadours, and poets have tried to capture for centuries. We say, "I thought it was true love, but it ended badly. I thought I was in love, but now I'm not so sure. Maybe it wasn't true love after all." But what else is there? If we thought we loved, we loved. Is there any greater heart-desire than that on this earth? Surely the love we felt was as "true" as any that has ever been, as any we will ever know.

Does true love exist? Some scientists will harrumph and point to rational charts and erudite studies. Look here, they will say, and proceed to list off all kinds of sixteen-cylinder words to describe the butterflies in our stomachs: evolutionary biology, endorphins, oxytocin. A chemical explanation. A cause and effect.

Maybe true love is its *own* cause and effect. To the 11th century French theologian Bernard of Clairvaux, "Love seeks no cause beyond itself and no fruit; it is its own fruit, its own enjoyment. I love because I love; I love in order that I may love."

Maybe true love is a free-fall, a euphoric loss of sensibility, a clash with logic, an exquisite madness that takes over all our senses. It's kind of like building a boat alone in the middle of a desert and the people passing by say to you, "What in the world are you doing?"

And you say, "Well, see… I'm building this boat," because it kind of makes sense to you, but not really if you think about it at all.

Maybe true love is an ancient sentiment, as described by the greatest Italian poet, Dante: "The moment I saw her I say in all truth that the vital spirit, which dwells in the inmost depths of the heart, began to tremble so violently that I felt the vibration alarmingly in all my pulses, even the weakest of them. As it trembled, it uttered these words: Behold a god more powerful than I who comes to rule over me."

Maybe true love is grace. A generosity of spirit. A willingness to allow others to be what they choose to be for themselves, without any insistence that they fulfill some unfulfilled part of us.

Maybe true love only exists for those who believe in it. If you don't believe in true love, then there is no such thing.

Maybe true love is new love. It is that and only that. Like your first love all over again. Every passionate relationship began passionately. As Marlowe wrote: "Who ever loved, that loved not at first sight?"

Which of these theories describes true love? All of them and none of them, of course. All we really know is that love *is*. That is enough to say. Love is a mystery. *Love is a mystery!* Oh lofty, divine mystery! There is a greatness in that thought, a great beauty. It is as wonderful as the stars that, in spite of the best efforts of all those poets, storytellers, and scientists, love remains a mystery. A mystery that trumps all.

eight

The Way of Salvation

Oh, who invented time and why?
And why such furious pace?

So intent, so perceptive, so knowing... who is this enigmatic girl? Outside the window, a cascading sensory wonder, a horizontal deluge, a synthesis of memory and color, so familiar, so familiar, so familiar.

The name of your book, she said.

Yes.

The Alabaster Girl...

From a poem I wrote—

A poem?

—when I was young.

I would love to hear it.

Well... it's kind of, you know... I've never really shared it with anyone.

Will you share it with me?

Yes.

We leave it all behind on a journey: our onion-skin intentions, our star-less, sleepless nights, the dreams we had as dragons. This girl on this train in this moment in time... her eyes are like chrysolite diamonds, her voice clear as a running stream.

Okay... here's my poem, he said.

> *Man has only ever searched*
> *For three things in this world*
> *The source of light*
> *The perfect note*
> *An alabaster girl*

We dream in vagabond splendor... of loves left behind... of summers draped languid around our shoulders like a shawl... and sudden memories that you stop to pick like a daisy.

Alabaster as in white? she said.

As in pure.

The perfect girl?

Perfect for me.

Like a dream?

Like a dream.

୨୦୧

The Bible says that this earth shall wax old like a garment, and surely there is no greater description of the state of the world today. Something is lost—lost from the hearts of men and from the hearts of women. Society is fragmented, there is no longer any joy, there is no longer any sense of community, of belonging, of ceremony, of giving thanks. There is disquiet in our emotions, a heaviness permeating our thoughts, a dissonance, a *weltschmerz*, a lassitude, and we all feel it.

The whole earth is out of balance, cloaked in an aggressive masculine energy, a systematic obliteration of the feminine. It is a dark and cataclysmic energy, bereft of any of the beautiful components of masculine energy—empathy, generosity, charm—and devoid of the countervailing saving grace and healing of the female spirit.

Our relationships are mean-spirited, me-centric, entitlement-laced, and perniciously moribund. Women are suspicious of men and their motives and men accuse women of being manipulative and dismissive. Everyone is tired of the games, the half-hearted attempts at commitment, the general dispassion and uncaring, and the utter banality of it all.

We tolerate a lot of ugliness. The media swaddles us in mediocrity and increasing infantilization, appealing to the lowest common denominator and in the process, driving that denominator ever lower. We endure talk-shows with no heart and sitcoms with no soul. We are obsessed with celebrity, glutted with sticky-fingered consumption, and herded into our stalls to stare glassy-eyed and slack-jawed at the pointless spectacle that unceasingly passes before our eyes. Bread and circuses. The Internet is the Tree of Knowledge of Good and Evil of our time. Eat of it and your eyes are opened, yes, but you are forever banished from the Garden. Pornography abounds, yet so little intimacy. We wander aimlessly like dogs, sniffing each other's asses in public, we "hook up" without a thought, we penetrate each other in all kinds of ways, but we have no concept of true connection or communion whatsoever. We manipulate each other endlessly. We wallow. We settle. We read the labels on each other and, ah, whatever… it's good enough. It's been said that even drowning is kind of pleasant once you relax.

Here we are in the twilight of the Information Age. Emerging is what? The Instantaneous Age? Where everything on earth happens at once. Where every event, large or small, downloads into our collective consciousness in nanoseconds. Our attention spans surrendered long ago to the ceaseless onslaught of minutiae. The reality television aesthetic. Instant updates. Trivial snippets of mostly useless information. The brevity of text messages dampening, homogenizing, and stripping our language of any inflection, nuance, or hue. Noise, noise, noise and very little signal, going everywhere, going nowhere. Knowledge at our fingertips, but very little wisdom. Open your phone and stare at it like a fish. We are stimulus-stoned, anesthetized, bored; we spend more time deciding what to consume than actually consuming.

Our society is wired together, inter-connected, hyper-linked. These are chains that bind us, under the illusion of making us more free. We are connected in "real time," and the result of all this real-time connection is confusion and self-help and medication and woe-is-me and complete and utter disconnection. One of the ironies of our hyper-connected age is how astonishingly disconnected we've actually become. We are so synchronous that we have become asynchronous.

So what is it? What is lost from the earth? *Beauty*, my love. We are missing beauty. Always and forever beauty. We no longer recognize beauty. Oh, but we must pay for our sins against beauty, for beauty is holy above all.

All have a longing for beauty. Atheists, theists, agnostics—the desire for beauty binds us all, a single defining common denominator. Beauty is the great equalizer, the Philosopher's Stone, the Fountain of Youth, the Grand Unifying Theory that Einstein dreamed about all his life.

છ৫

You were sad last night and still you gave. You wrapped your arms around me the moment you saw me, and you touched my hair, and I could feel your sadness. And when you put your fingers in my hair, touching me the way you did, I dared not move. I could not move.

Everything was there in your touch: a distance, a despair, a kindness.

Why am I drawn to you? I don't know you at all, and yet I do. You and I so new, and yet your touch so familiar, an invocation, an invitation... a beauty in you... and oh, you whispered my name like a sacred incantation, and you pulled away a little, but wondrous.

Yes, you were sad last night... and still you touched me... so giving... so nurturing...like you were channeling all your hurt into me... how can you give so much... how can you love so much... how can I return it to you... I don't know... I don't know...

There is something about you... and it breaks my heart. Thousands of women I have known in my life, and yours is the touch that gives me pause.

I move through layers toward you, I move through layers
away from you. I am hidden behind the door of desire...
beyond the place where it is possible to see.
— The Alabaster Girl, *page 161*

℘

There is a regnant Cult of Self-Help that permeates the earth today,
a multi-billion dollar industry, with wearisome and noisome man-
tras. Do we really need this? Should we not reject this whole sordid
conspiracy with all the righteous indignation and force that we
can muster?

I am not talking about mindful therapy or careful counseling. I
am talking about the drive-through, *à la carte*, self-help mentality
that consumes us today. Meaningless platitudes, trite quotations,
endless words, words, words. We want quick answers and we want
them now. Read a book, take a workshop, and bam! now we are
enlightened. Well, at least we *feel* enlightened, for a time, and then
it's the same-old, same-old. But oh well, there is always another
book, always another program, right? This next one will surely
have the answer.

A never-ending cycle, searching for a former clarity. And when it
doesn't work, we blame ourselves. We feel like we just don't get it,
that we aren't learning fast enough, that we are somehow doing it
wrong, that we're falling behind in life, that we're actually taking
steps backwards, and that everyone else is way further along in their
understanding. So we buy another book and place it on our shelf.
It is not necessary to actually *read* it; the important thing is to *have*
it. Yes, my life sucks, but hey look, at least I have done something
about it. I have the answer right there on that shelf, inches from my
fingertips. *Right there.* Bought and paid for.

Oh, this is how we spend our days, this is how we spend our days,
spinning in circles like a dog making his bed, until we come to the

realization that our spinning is not doing much of anything really, the bed is exactly the same no matter how many times we spin, nothing is really changing… and we flop down weary, empty, and done.

∞

This is the era of the so-called Second-Wave Equality Movement, a relentless groundswell, an epic chorus for equality of the sexes. This movement (along with the Pill, of course) has afforded women unprecedented mobility and independence.

Societies that honored the feminine and worshiped the goddess in our collective histories are so rare that they stand out only as interesting anthropological curiosities. Women today have risen up against that lack of recognition. How? By declaring God a woman, by taking up arms to fight for their long-suppressed rights, and by making forays into career realms traditionally occupied by men.

It has not been smooth. Women have had to adopt a masculine energy in order to be successful. Men looked up one day and discovered women sitting on "their" side of the table. Small-minded men can't stand it, sitting in their huffy pile of ashes, scraping themselves with pottery shards, and whining about how abused they are, how the pendulum has swung too far in the opposite direction, how they have been forcefully emasculated, and how women have become too powerful for their own good. Men still want to be on top, prancing around and in control, but the women have managed to somehow wrestle themselves out from the bottom. Almost.

The battle of the sexes can get incredibly violent at times. There are strident, bellowing voices on both sides, dominating the discussion, polluting the media, and drowning out the reasoned discourse of the rest of us. There are men's advocacy groups out there that barely mask their agenda of utterly destroying the aspirations of women and "putting them back in their place," and there are women's advocacy groups out there whose thinly disguised mission is to not only strangle and choke man and his motives into complete submission, but to continue to stomp on him until he is reduced to a quivering pulp on the ground. Then stomp on him some more. The best thing we can do is shunt these people aside, ignore them. Let the militant, frothing men and women on both sides yell and scream and throw rocks at each other and leave the rest of us alone.

So now then, if we disregard the multitudes of disgruntled, Luddite men and clamoring, bellicose women, I think we can all say that the Equality Movement has been a good thing. It's opened up all kinds of possibilities—for both men and women.

It's also killed a few. The goal of the Equality Movement was noble: to do away with the old patriarchal system, to remove the gender barriers and ceilings, to create an equilibrium, a balance between the sexes. The goal was *equality* but we didn't get it. We got *sameness*. Men are more like women. Women are more like men. Same, but not equal at all. A complete and utter loss of the beauty of polarity. So women lose and men lose. We all lose.

∞≪

Look at any university in the Western world: everyone wearing the same nondescript, shapeless, gender-erasing garments, all blended together, hanging out, hooking up, humping each other's legs. We graduate from these universities and move on to antiseptic and litigious workplaces, scrubbed clean of any inflection of gender, with equalized business attire and joyless fluorescent expressions on every face.

We go to our vacuum-sealed workplaces where we are politically correct, neutered, asexual, then we are supposed to somehow… *turn it on in the evening*? As the ad campaign says, "Business by day, Bacardi by night." How in the world is this possible? We've washed it all away. Any sense of the polarity of men and women is blended down, watered down, gone.

In some regions of the world today (Scandinavia, for example), young people get blistering drunk at home, go out and meet someone, then have sex. This pretty much sums up courtship there; the two of them are now considered to be "dating."

And if we want something more measured, more paced, more traditional—less drunken—our only option is meeting and dating through a computer. We meet each other online, which is to say, apart. Actually having to leave our houses to discover new people? How quaint.

I once went to a cowboy bar with a cowboy band, and the guy in the cowboy hat who played the cowboy guitar called out to us before they began their songs, "Welcome to Texas, y'all… where we still dance with our women!" *With* our women. Indeed. We, the modern, the neoteric, the *au courant*… we meet apart, we date apart, we dance apart, then we have sex. There is nothing in between.

And we call this intimacy? Why does everything have to end up in bed to have any meaning? We automatically go there. It is easy to give of our bodies, but not so easy to give of ourselves. We are naked with each other a lot, but we don't share our essence. We hope others see us as nude, lush, and sensual, and instead we are just plain old naked and exposed.

"Pornography!" some will cry. "Pornography has destroyed our sense of balance, our sense of intimacy. It is ruining marriages! It is clouding our expectations!" Well, notwithstanding the flagrant pornography that was *everywhere* throughout all of history, I suppose they might be right. I have no idea. Oh sure, I have no doubt that, because of its ubiquitous nature, pornography must have *some* effect upon the way we view each other, upon our concepts of intimacy, and upon our relationships. And if you were to argue that the right-at-our-fingertips accessibility of pornography has wiped out any vestige of sexual imagination, you will get no counter-argument from me. But in truth, I have no opinion.

I have no opinion because I spend my days *thinking of other things*. I am not interested in the slightest in studying the effects of pornography. I have no time to furrow my brow and wax philosophical or analytical or parenthetical about the rampant state of pornography and what it is doing to our society today. Let others opine and study and address the issue of the commodification of sex. There are plenty of voices out there attached to the issue. No one needs to hear mine.

Yes, I know I am generalizing in this, my screed, and speaking in absolutes. And yes, I know I am simplifying some shockingly complex realities, that gender issues are not all black and white, that there is a gradient, a difference between "sex" and "gender," and that most of us will identify—in various degrees—with both energies. It doesn't change my rant.

My point is that we all feel the thudding inertia of our modern culture, blending us together, graying everything out a little. We are starved for polarity... the dance, the seduction, the tension, the attraction, the dreamy, irresistible force. We've lost the *beauty* of polarity. We've lost the beauty and simplicity of the feminine spirit, just like we've lost the beauty and simplicity of the masculine spirit.

୫୦୯ୟ

We are standing four feet apart, and it is strange. You are in the sunlight and I am in the shade. I ask you to come closer to me. It is sunny in this spot, you say, and then we stand like that: four feet apart. And it is strange.

I missed you so much, you say, but now I have someone else in my life. I nod my head and I look down at the ground between us, to the edge of the bright sunlight that surrounds you. Is he a good guy? Yes, he is a very good guy. Are you happy? Yes, I am. I look back up to you, my sweet, sweet girl. I missed you, too, I say. You bite your lip to stop the hidden tears.

I stand here in the shade, and you in the sun, four feet

apart. *What do I know to be true about you and me? Do I love you? Yes, I do. But not in the way you want. Why am I not jealous? Because I know I am not the man for you, whatever the hell that means. Because I know that this new guy releases me, allows me to ride away... away, without worrying that you are sad. I am happy that you are happy.*

And yet... well, I didn't really think about you at all when I was gone. And now, of course, because there are ancient gods of retribution, I do. I look at you now, I think of our times together, and I miss those times. I miss you. You are wonderful. You are kind.

I want to give you the vision for the future that you desire, but the truth is... I really don't. We want different things. If you hadn't met this guy, we would already be laughing and talking and singing and sleeping together, like we have always done, a glass of wine, a warm embrace, a hand in my hair. Our time together would be bright and sunny... but you want something more, more than I give, and the gray clouds of our different desires would hang low over the hills all around us. You would resent my distraction. I would resent the quality time you require, the conversations about "us," wishing I was somewhere else, anywhere I could be alone to think and write. What the hell?

It is best. I could reach out to you, yes I could, and you know I could, and you are keeping four feet between us because you know I can convince you of anything, because any less than four feet and you would be back in my arms.

What is the correct way, I wonder? What is the most truthful thing I can say to you in this moment? What is the path of no agenda whatsoever? My only desire is to grant you your silent request, to release your heart with the same grace that you have just released mine, to create something pure and clear and radiant with you, like the sunlight that is all around you now.

My quiet song once had a name... and beauty had a face. My heart lies elsewhere, out there somewhere. This is

my truth. And I love you, and I will miss you, and I am on
a different path, my angel, I am off through the mountains,
and I will think of our times together and I will delight in
seeing you if ever we meet again somewhere, someday, and
I must let you go, and I want to do it now with no agenda, no
manipulation, no careful words or actions, nothing deliberate,
just pure and clear and radiant honesty, like the sunlight
that is all around you now.
                    — The Alabaster Girl, *page 163*

ഇന്ദ

Men long for female energy. They want nurturing spirits; instead
they get women with semi-accessible holes. There's a reason men talk
about the "girlfriend experience" with prostitutes. Men are starved
for sex, but more for the greater energy of what sex represents. I
heard a prominent female public speaker say that women need to
stop withholding sex from men, to stop using it as a kind of currency.
But it is far more than just a withholding of sex; it is a withholding
of the healing, life-giving gift of the female spirit.

I shall be prudent and make a careful distinction between the event
of a woman actually *withholding* sex (which means that she would
very much enjoy it if she let it happen but she's deliberately blocking
it in a manipulative tactic) and the event of a woman not having sex
because she feels the emotional connection with her partner has been
severed and it has to be restored before she would enjoy having sex.
This distinction is rarely made but without it, the use of the word
"withholding" immediately sparks a blame game.

Women are equally at a loss. Men seemingly want it all: subservient
housewives in the home, and nymphets everywhere else. I remember
an artist named Lorette in a Brussels gallery who had tried all her
life to capture on canvas the dichotomous nature of the female spirit.
Her pieces were profound diptychs of light and dark, front and back,
saint and harlot, dove-white and sin-scarlet. "Men want women to

be either innocent or dirty," she said in a quiet voice, as we stood side by side looking at her paintings. "*But I am both*!"

Either or. One or the other. The madonna or the whore. The hidden truth is that every woman is an amalgam of *both*. Every "fallen" woman retains in her heart the fundamental facility of mother instinct that is the exclusive province of women. And every chaste and innocent girl has a secret, dirty side. I don't care how prim and proper and innocent she may appear, every woman has a little bit of whore in her—*for that one guy!*

Good luck trying to figure out how to be both in the eyes of men, my love. Very few men have the courage to accept the totality of the female spirit. Thus, the experience of women is left hollow and without identity, floating forever between these two ideologies—or not, and to hell with it.

₧℣

I knew a man who had everything. All the trappings of success. He had houses and lands and businesses and cars. He had all these things and more. One day, as he related it to me, he happened to see a poster hanging on a wall somewhere, a poster that changed his life completely.

The poster was a photo of a sun-drenched meadow, a country path, flowers and birds, buzzing bees, bucolic and serene. Beside the country path was a man sitting on the ground in the grass, with his back to the viewer, looking up to a woman who was standing beside him. She, too, had her back to the viewer, and she was wearing blue jeans and nothing else. She was looking down at the man, in this field of sunshine, smiling down at him, the picture of perfect stillness and bliss, quiet, calm, the two of them together in God's field, a field of dreams, looking at each other, smiling and knowing.

He saw this picture and it made him pause, greatly pause. He thought of it for many days, he told me. It took hold of him, some part of him, in some mysterious, half-understood way, and it made him cry. "Why?" he asked, "Why do I not have that? I am successful by any measure of man. I have all these things that all men desire. I have women who orbit around me, who want what I provide. I have everything and can have anything. But I don't have *that*. Why? *Why?* What is the point of a life? Where is my serenity? Where is my lyrical meadow? Why don't I have a woman smiling down on me like that? Why don't I have a woman who loves me in such a simple way? A woman who is happy with me and the sun and the flowers and the bees?"

ஐ‍ஒ

We lack nothing. And yet, we think we lack everything. Our relentless pursuit of more, better, different, yet nothing fulfills us. We are given one life and we use up every minute of it chasing something we think we don't have, a frantic pursuit of what we think we lack. And this is how we end our days, used up and spent, our bodies and minds slumping slowly.

Our Religion of Rush. Accumulate more and more. All of the requisite desire but none of the requisite beauty. In the West, we are just beginning to feel the hangover pangs from the binge of consumerism we partook of in the '80s, '90s, and '00s, the *fin de siècle* mood redux. In some emergent parts of the world, the consumerist wave is just beginning, a curious admixture of old and new, the latest gadgets superimposed upon ancient ways of living—an old man bent low under a large bundle of sticks with ear-buds in his ears.

We are worn out, hung over, from the consumerist orgy of the last fifty years, where we gorged on things, packing it in, never enough, cramming it all down our throats like desperate feral cats, accumulating more and more stuff just because we can: canoes, barbecues, hot tubs, pool tables, things we own and never use. Oh, but you never know. Just in case. We have it all right there! We constantly seek to *have* more instead of to *be* more. And we yearn to find the answer, reaching into every nook and cranny, putting our hand into every jar, hoping to pull out a cookie and hoping that it is a good one.

We overestimate how happy something will make us in the long term. We think things like, "If only I get that raise, then I will finally be happy," or "If I get that fancy car, then women will want me and I will finally be happy," or "Maybe if we have a kid, then our marriage will be good and we will finally settle down into domestic bliss," or "If only I had a girl like that… wow, with a girl like that, I would finally and forever be happy."

But the truth is, if we did get that new fancy car… in six months, it's just a car. It's not as fun anymore. It's got scratches… If we did get that fancy girl, same thing… in six months, she's just a girl. A girl that we depended on to make us happy. That's too much to ask of anyone. She's just a girl.

Relationships are just like everything else we buy and sell. Nothing is ever good enough. We thought we were getting top quality and sure enough, once again we are disappointed, jaded. What to do? Go out and look for a new girl with that new car smell. Repeat.

Our outlook on life defines who we are. We've all heard stories about someone winning a lottery, yet it didn't make them fundamentally happier than they were before. For a short time, yes, they seem to be on top of the world, but after a time the people who were already happy in life, who already had a zest for living, and who were already pleasant to be around, are pretty much the same way a year or so later. The only difference is that they have lots of money. Conversely, anyone who is a miserable pessimist, who blames the world for letting them down, is going to be a rich, miserable pessimist.

Think how many rock stars and movie stars have wanted so, so badly to make it, to get fame and fortune. Why did they want it? Girls and money, of course. And yet why are so many of them still so unsatisfied once they have "made it"? Because they realize that the moment they can get any woman they desire, the moment they can buy anything they wish, it loses its appeal. When you have enough money to buy five impossibly expensive cars, the concept of "car" loses its luster. And similarly, when you can walk into any room, club, or party and, because of your name alone, you can leave with any woman there, you suddenly don't want to.

From Ecclesiastes: "I have seen all the works which have been done under the sun, and behold, all is vanity and a striving after wind." We are waking up in the West, looking around us, surrounded by all our *stuff*, and we are just now beginning to ask, "Is that it? Is there nothing more?" We have everything and nothing. We have all the trappings of fulfillment but none of the fulfillment. Vanity of vanities, all is vanity.

Simplify, simplify, simplify. Or as they say in the aeronautics industry, "Simplify and add lightness." Or as Thoreau so wonderfully put it, "As you simplify your life, the laws of the universe will be simpler; solitude will not be solitude, poverty will not be poverty, nor weakness weakness."

ℬℬ

Sometimes in the morning I like to walk out on a balcony, consider life, consider morning, watch the world. It is cold out here but I like it, knowing warmth is only three feet away.

Morning is a promise. Everything I desire is contained in this day.

This day.

The thought makes me smile. Alone on a balcony, every man becomes Kierkegaard... Kant... Spinoza.

The city below me is awakening—stretching and yawning and scratching itself. The people, far below and small, begin once again their frenetic routines, well-rehearsed parts in a carefully choreographed danse banale. They did the same thing yesterday and the day before, and they will do it all over again tomorrow and the day after. To me, they look so small and distant and defeated, although of course, not all of them are.

I watch them flow. In and out of coffee shops, with all necessary accoutrements—newspapers, briefcases, folders—tucked under various arms, and I wonder what it is we believe in anymore.

I look up to the sky. I look down to the city. I feel mighty on this morning on this balcony.

She calls to me.

"What are you doing out there?"

"Go back to sleep," I laugh. "I am floating out here above this great city."

"Come back to bed. It's too early."

"But you don't understand. I am being mighty on a balcony!"

This makes her laugh and laugh. "Come back to bed, silly. You are anything but mighty."

It is in the quiet moments that the relationship is defined.

I love mornings.

I love mornings with her.

          — The Alabaster Girl, *page 165*

„)‣

It's not our fault, we say. Our childhoods were miserable, we say. Okay, fair enough. But how long will we continue to tell that story? For the rest of our days? We go through life hoping our past will change. Here's the news: our past is never going to change. Ever. And that's okay.

We devote significant portions of our adult lives to the resolution and correction of our childhoods. Is there really anything to solve? Have we not all had a difficult past, everyone, in all of history? Has not every child for thousands of years seen hunger and war and abuse and disease and death? Was there ever a time of idyllic childhoods?

I'm not saying that we should just amputate the dark experiences of our past and act like nothing happened. It did happen. The hurts in our past were real. The betrayals were real. The abandonments were real. We can't just flick them off our shoulders like so many specks of lint. It is hard to look back—the violence, the guilt, the withheld affection, the tears, the fears—our heartbeat slows, heavier and heavier, as we recall. No, it is necessary to mourn the innocence that once was, a cry for what is lost.

And yet… the past is always created in the present. The past is an interesting story, but it's just that: a story. Nothing more. The excellent thing is that nothing from the past can touch us now. Nothing from our past has any influence on the way our life is about to go. Not a single thing! We get to choose the perspective we inhabit and how our story will go from this moment forward.

Some will say, "Is it really that simple?" Yes, it really is that simple. It is simple, but not easy. Some will then say, "Maybe you just happened to stumble across the right opportunities." No, opportunities are entirely created. Some will then say, "But sometimes circumstances override opportunities, right? Our childhoods create our belief systems." Yes, and what of it? Do you want redemption and a life-change or a baby-sitter and an excuse?

Circumstances swirl around all of our childhoods, yet we get to inhabit any world that we desire. Sure, past choices we made might limit our opportunities in some way. After all, a guy who robbed a bank as a youth can't just decide to move to Bali to open a tiki bar on the beach. So there are reasons, to be sure. Reasons are good. Excuses are excuses.

I heard a guy on a television talk show say, "Hey, don't blame me. I beat up my woman today because that's all I saw as a kid." All I could think was, "Huh? That's all I saw as a kid, too." The way we live our lives is all a choice. A love of life is something you consciously choose. It is no accident. You create it out of thin air.

Bad experiences, painful abandonments, negative assumptions, fears, and misfortunes… all of these might make us hesitate, to be sure, but they are not what holds us back. What holds us back is our tired excuses. All we have to do is shake hands with our past, take the lessons, and leave the excuses.

Too many of us are using the wounds of our past as excuses for our failures today. We blame our childhoods or our circumstances for our mediocrity today, but that's a tired, tired story. We live a life of excuses. We hope that somehow, miraculously, our past will change. We have been telling ourselves and others that tired story all our lives. No one wants to hear it anymore. It's time to put it away. If not now, when?

To escape from casting blame, to never settle, to always strive for something better, is all a choice. The world is not going to do anything for us. We want others to solve all our problems, then bitterly blame them when they don't. As George Bernard Shaw wrote, "This is the true joy in life, the being used for a purpose recognized by yourself as a mighty one; the being thoroughly worn out before you are thrown on the scrap heap; the being a force of Nature instead of a feverish selfish little clod of ailments and grievances complaining that the world will not devote itself to making you happy."

We were there and now we are here. And here is where everything is possible. We get to choose the way we see our past and the way we see our future. We get to choose, from this day forward, how our life is going to go. What a wonderful gift! Nothing can take the soaring loftiness of choice away from us. Because of choice, the past is no longer a burden; we will lift it easily, we will carry it lightly, we will put it behind us where it belongs.

There is a delightful light that surrounds the present. To head toward the light and only the light, to exhilarate in the gift of life we have been given, to stop hoping our past will change, to include our experience into who we are today, seeing it as a strength and not a weakness, to celebrate our past instead of running from it. The entire journey through life, from there to here, is what makes us the vibrant, passionate, unpredictable, creative, lovable adventurers we are today. Our past gives us wings.

ෂ☾

We are propelled through our lives in one of two ways: desire or fear. The carrot or the stick. We are either driven by the things we "have to do": our obligations, our promises to ourselves and to others, or we are enticed by a compelling vision ever before us.

We dread the future and despise the past. We live in wishes in all directions. Rarely do we consider the miracle that is the moment surrounding us right now. Emerson again: "These roses under my window make no reference to former roses or to better ones; they are for what they are; they exist with God today. But man postpones or remembers; he does not live in the present, but heedless of the riches that surround him, stands on tiptoe to lament the past or foresee the future. He cannot be happy and strong until he too lives with nature in the present, above time."

The size of your problems is the size of your life. If a man's greatest problem is how to get a girl to text him back, or how to pay his phone bill, well then, that's as big as his life is ever going to be. However, if his greatest problem is how he can help to get clean water to a village in Africa, or how he can become the greatest lover a woman has ever known, well then… things like a girl not texting him back or paying his phone bill make no difference to him whatsoever. Those are trivial problems, that melt away before his eyes like so much inconsequential dross.

The quality of your life is determined by the quality of the questions you ask. It's as simple as that. Small minds sit in answers, great minds sit in questions. Always ask the greater questions and nevermore the small.

Most of us don't design our lives at all. We live our lives in constant reaction. We wait for life to happen, then we react to whatever comes our way. We are overwhelmed. We wish for change in our lives, but we have too many things to deal with first. "I want to do *that* but I can't because *first* I have to do *this*."

The truth is, *we don't have to do anything*. The only thing we have to do is die. All the rest is optional. What a realization is this! Knowing this, there are only possibilities spread out before us. We can do anything we desire in this life. We can create the kind of life we deserve and desire, craft it like a piece of art. Out of nothing.

Oh, but first we need money, right? Wrong. I once asked an old, wise, and renowned Korean business man about the secret to success. His answer? "Never think about money again." Notice he didn't say to never *worry* about money again. He said to never *think* about money again. Step out in faith and money will *always* find you.

The wonderful thing is that we are all on the same, simple journey from cradle to grave. No one is enlightened, no one has the answers, no one has arrived. We can forgive ourselves any confusion. And we get to choose! We get to choose how we are going to move forward through the rest of our days.

We will never have it all figured out. This is the beauty of life. We will never arrive at some mystical vantage point where everything is now clear before our eyes. And that's okay; it's not important. The only important thing is to love the *mystery* that surrounds our journey, to find ease and delight in the learning that comes to us, to quest without ceasing for our own authenticity and relevance, to seek out beauty—always and forever beauty—in all its forms.

ଛଓ�03

Coincidence is time shuffled around and replaced, like playing cards disappearing and reappearing in surprising places, like masterful sleight of hand.

The peripheral flash of red catches my eye, is strangely familiar, and then is gone. Startled, I turn my head, but there is only the bustling energy near the wine counter: the wine man, the wine racks, and the wine purchasers all mixed about and normal. The swash of red (did I imagine it?) that streamed through my consciousness from right to left, has disappeared. But there was something about it...

I turn and thrust into Camila's hands the bottle of Capstraadt Shiraz, the label of which, an infinite moment before, we had been casually and warmly perusing together, shoulder to shoulder. "Hold this," I say, without looking back, and I hurl myself toward the door and out onto the street.

Nothing. I look left. I look right. Nothing. I bolt and whirl myself around the corner of the building. And there she is... a woman walking away, in a long red coat, a coat that is vastly familiar to me... the long, black hair... no, it can't be.

"Simone!" And now she is turning around and now she is looking at me and now there she is. It is Simone. She stands and looks at me and I at her, our mouths and eyes opened wide. How on earth? I last saw her four months ago in Montreal, a city three thousand miles away.

Well, there we are. She walks slowly to me, throws her arms around me, and we hold each other tight. "What are you doing here?" I say, standing back and holding her shoulders firmly at arm's length, looking her up and down, astonished, then sweeping her tight to me again.

"I... I just arrived here three days ago," she says. "I can't believe I am seeing you! I decided at the last minute to join my boyfriend on his business trip. I remembered you were here in Vancouver and, for some strange reason, I knew I would run into you."

I am still trying to comprehend all this, and I shake my head in wide-eyed wonder and laugh. "I saw the flash of your red coat out of the corner of my eye in the wine store and I thought, 'Wow, I know that color. It looks just like the coat I bought for Simone.' And so it is!"

"Yes, I was in there buying this bottle of wine—" she says, holding up a brown bag without looking at it, her eyes fixed on mine, "—for a get-together with my boyfriend and his client." Ah, I say, but my mind and hers are on other things, on the wonderment of happenstance, of chancing upon each other this evening, of walking into the exact same wine store at the exact same time of evening, in this wide city brimming with millions of people and millions of possibilities.

"Come!" I say, remembering my poor Camila, whom I so unceremoniously left behind, like a trussed up bride left at the altar, and I lead Simone by the hand back into the wine store.

Camila is still standing where I left her, thoroughly puzzled, still holding the bottle and looking at the door. I guide Simone over to her and with a wide grin I say, "Camila, look who I found... believe it or not, this is the beautiful Simone."

Eyebrows rise all around and the two women look at each other curiously, as if they should have recognized each other all along. Camila cocks her head, smiling, processing this information. "Really?" she says. "Yes, really," I laugh, and I expand my introductions. "Simone, this is the lovely and impeccable Camila..." And the two of them step toward each other and embrace each other like long-lost friends.

"I have heard so much about you," Camila is saying, genuinely excited and genuinely pleased. "He talks about you all the time," she says.

"Ah, yes... this one," Simone replies, cocking her head toward me with a sparkle in her eyes. "I feel sorry for you." And they both look at me and laugh. "This crazy man is trouble!"

"Yes, I know," Camila replies.

We continue talking and laughing for, oh, ten minutes or so. The girls in collusion, conspiratorial, and me excluded, on the periphery, but exceedingly loved and loving it. The perfect dynamic.

And then, lo and behold, the boyfriend arrives, for we are taking far too long, I suppose; and he is not pleased, I also suppose. He sees me and recognizes me from a photo, I suppose. Hey, he says, and shakes my hand, limply, half-heartedly, and turns to Simone. We have to go, he says. People are waiting, he says. And Camila, dear Camila, oh sweet Camila, who knows me so well, says, Perhaps you two can join us? And he says thanks anyway, but we can't and Simone says but maybe a little later we can join you both for a quick drink, and the boyfriend says no, no, it's not possible, we have things to do, people to see.

Simone turns to me now with a hint of welling tears and Camila looks at me with a look of is-there-anything-we-can-do, and just like that, Simone is gone.

Camila and I talk about this strange encounter all night. What does it mean? Nothing perhaps, we conclude... Or...?

Oh, I believe monumentally in moments like these, in the encounter, in the shuffling of the cards, and in the flash-recognition of our chosen card revealed to us again, in the majestic coincidences that make us believers in love and believers in life.

— The Alabaster Girl, *page 168*

ഇൻ

We live our lives as a reaction to what is coming our way, full of worries, excuses, complaints, frustration, even depression, because life is not treating us as we think it should. It is a life concentrated on what others are doing to us, and what others think of us. A life devoted to making other people feel comfortable, so we do not have to stand up and express ourselves.

We try to make others feel comfortable out of fear and not out of love, and because we do not want to deal with the responsibility of making our own choices and speaking our truth. We are afraid to put a stake in the ground. We are afraid to stand up and be noticed.

We are afraid of what others will think of us and so we hold back, we hope everyone is okay with our choices, few though they may be. We spend our lives following the "proper" path, making sure that everyone else around us is comfortable and happy with our decisions.

Here's a glorious thought, a liberating, life-giving idea: *Stop making other people comfortable.* Stop worrying about what others think. This includes friends, co-workers, and yes, this includes parents. Others may not understand, and that's okay. It is not our responsibility that they understand. It is not our responsibility that others are comfortable with the way we choose to design our lives.

Others will shake their heads and say to us, "Who do you think you are? To try to rise above the crowd? Be realistic! Get your head out of the clouds!" Oh, but the world needs more of us with our heads in the clouds. It's been said that we are the average of the six people we hang around with the most. Those that insist on keeping us small must be left behind. There is no other way.

It is not easy for those of us who dare to step away from the wide, well-trodden path. But we must do it anyway. No matter what others think. No matter what others expect. No matter how uncomfortable others may be. It is a wonderful thing to realize that the approval of our friends and family is not at all our responsibility. Our sole responsibility in this life is to seek our authentic desire with all our hearts and to dare to express it to the world. To ask this and only this: What is needed for me? Blake said it like this, "I must create a system, or be enslav'd by another man's." Create yourself or you will be created.

This quote from Joseph Campbell (in turn referring to Chretien de Troyes' description of the Knights of the Round Table and their quest for the Grail) says it all: "They thought that it would be a disgrace to go forth as a group. Each entered the forest at a point that he himself had chosen, where it was darkest and there was no path. If there is a path it is someone else's path and you are not on the adventure."

ଚ଼ଦ୍ୟ

Well, someone will say, I have a strong reason why I can't live the life I want to live. Not everyone can be like you and wander the earth at will. Some of us have a family and responsibilities. To which I answer... and? How is there any discrepancy between you living your life in wide-eyed wonder and your family and responsibilities? Why is not your whole family caught up in a life of magic and adventure?

But not all of us can live a free-wheeling lifestyle like you, some will say. Not everyone can just give up possessions and home. Yes, well, those who say that are missing the point. Saying that life-*meaning* is about life-*style* is like saying *The Grapes of Wrath* is about fruit. I am not suggesting that everyone should give up everything and become a vagabond, or run around the world with family in tow, eating beans and wieners from a can. I am not advocating a certain type of lifestyle in any way, but I sure am advocating a type of *spirit*. Our lifestyle (how we choose to spend our physical and mental energy) is merely a layer over our spirit (how we choose to spend our spiritual energy).

To live in a quiet town in a quiet suburb with a quiet job is a wonderful thing—if it is mindfully chosen. This might be a great life, if that is what we truly want. But it should never be a result of personal ennui or obligation or because we settled. It should be because we have examined our life and this is what we want above all the other things we want. There is no discrepancy between a man working hard all his life at a simple job he loves, and that same man living with the singular spirit of freedom in his soul. That man is a fulfilled man.

A mindful choice is a beautiful choice and the only honest choice. Mindfulness, choice, clarity. A friend of mine once told me of the monks he spent time with in Burma. They had a peculiar way of speaking, a way of setting intention into their requests. They framed mindfulness around their sentences. They would say things like, "Would you like to go for a walk with me *happily*?" or "Would you like to go to the market with me *merrily*?"

හ○ය

But what about sacrifice? Ah yes… sacrifice. A fundamental tenet of our beliefs about relationships is that they need to be based upon mutual compromise… fifty-fifty and all that. We must sacrifice our individual desires and impulses for the greater good of the whole, for the growth and sustenance of the relationship. We call this "commitment," proclaim it to be necessary, and move on to the next subject. But wait, wait, wait! How can this be? Who dared impose this upon us? Who decided that the word "commitment" is synonymous with compromise and obligation?

A man once said to me, "You say that the only meaningful question in life is 'What do I want?' But it's not that easy. Sure, I know what I want… I saw a woman yesterday who was gorgeous to me. I want *her*. I would love to have her! But I can't have her because I have a wife and kids. So there you go. I know what I want but I can't have it. I have no choice. I have to sacrifice what I want because of what I have."

Sacrifice? What sacrifice? When on earth did his wife and kids become an obligation instead of a choice? A burden instead of a delight? What a thought! This is what happens when we don't examine our hearts, when we don't pause to consider what it is we truly want. Life flows around us like a crowd on a busy sidewalk and we feel we have no control. We just stand there in the middle of the rushing crowd, bowed low and silent.

There is no discrepancy at all between what this man is saying and what I am saying. He underscores my point with his example. It is not a bad thing to want what we want. There are two things he wants: to have the woman over there, and to retain the harmony of his family over here. Two options before him, both beautiful, and he has to make a choice.

We always have a choice and we always make a choice, whether we know it or not. The secret of great men and women in this world is that they always stay connected to what it is they want, then they make choices around that. They make *mindful* choices.

His choice, however, is not mindful. He did not examine his heart and ask himself, "Who am I and what do I truly want? Do I want that woman over there or do I want my family over here? What is most important to my heart?" Because he feels trapped and obligated and fearful of consequences, he chooses neither. Which is to say, he chooses nothing. Which is to say, he still makes a choice. Choosing nothing at all is still a choice. His was a passive choice, a choice rooted in feelings of frustration and obligation and burden, a choice that serves no one whatsoever. Yet it is still a choice.

He doesn't choose the woman over there and he doesn't choose his family over here. He chooses neither and consequently, he loses them both. In fact, everyone loses. The girl loses, his family loses, and he loses. One might say that his family, at least, still has him. But no, not really. His heart is elsewhere, his focus distracted and fuzzy, his attention span on something else. He's around all right, but deflated in spirit. He may not be gone, but he is *absent*.

"Who am I and what do I want? What is the best expression of my life on this earth?" Only when we ask ourselves questions of this magnitude can we make meaningful choices. A meaningful choice for this man might be, "My desire to stay connected to my family is greater than my desire to get together with that woman over there. So I choose my family." This is a mindful choice, a great choice. And so is the other one. It doesn't really matter which option he chooses as long as his choice is conscious and mindful and informed—by his morals, for example—and as long as he has examined his heart about what he really wants for his life.

There is a great power in being mindful, making conscious choices, and recognizing that we have chosen. A mindful choice toward his family creates a spirit in him that they will all feel every time he walks through the door, an energy that is exciting and welcoming and life-giving. He is fully present with his family, and they are no longer an obligation. They are his choice.

Where is the sacrifice in that? Where is the compromise? What has been given up here? Nothing. There is no need for sacrifice. There is no need for compromise. There is no need for obligation. There is only what we want over here and what we want over there. There is only the beauty of choice.

೮ාೞ

Whenever I come to San Francisco, I always stay with you in your tiny apartment, don't I, dear Sophie? What wondrous times we have!

But I won't be staying with you... not this time. You have a man in your life now, a man you dearly love. You are excited to see me again, to tell me all about him, and you were so excited for me to meet him but he happens to be out of town this weekend and oh well, someday I will.

We come together for a glass of wine, you and I, and we drink the wine and we enjoy the neon-lit evening and the stories that catch us up. He is a good man, you say. You would get along with him wondrously, you say. It is important that you approve of him, you say, and I laugh. Of course, I say. I would love to meet him. Bring him around next time.

I can see it in the sparkle of your eyes, how happy you are, how joyous is your love. Ah, Sophie, life is so good when you are in love, n'est-ce pas? A woman in love is the most beautiful she will ever be in her entire life. And you, sweet Sophie, are marvelous in the lambent light of your love.

No more trysts for us! No more late-night, playful, laughing caresses. I don't mind. I will gladly sacrifice our sweet little love affair for your greater bliss. To me, it is the most wonderful thing in the world that you are happy. I raise my glass again, I toast the night and you and him and young love.

I don't feel a sense of loss in this moment. Instead, I feel a sense of peace. Ours was a time, a beautiful time, a time that ends, and now that it is ending, let it end well, end joyous, end complete.

You feel it, too. I can see it in your eyes, oh my beauty. We had a torrential affair, you and I! In the misty haze of San Francisco, we had a monumental, life-giving affair.

I dream of days of you and I... a dream of me and you.

And now the evening is done. The rain comes in from the bay with its gentle ministry. We share a cab, heading in the same direction toward our separate lives. You sit close beside me and you kiss my cheek and you thank me and you rest your head on my shoulder. And we are silent together for a time, and then you take my hand gently and guide it inside your blouse and place it wholly upon your breast—the ultimate parting gift of grace and gratitude—and we sit like that together in silence and contemplation, along dark and shiny streets.

Fare thee well, darling Sophie, go in love and laughter. Never again will I taste the rain... the way I did with you.
— The Alabaster Girl, *page 172*

SOCR

None of us has it all figured out. We are all broken. We all desire understanding, meaning, and excellence, but our thoughts crowd in, tormenting us with confusion and doubt. We analyze and second-guess everything. We feel we are not making progress in our understanding. The journey of understanding is difficult and the journey takes time and we don't want it to be difficult and we don't want it to take time, we want answers now, and so we sit in the back seat and sulk, asking, "Are we there yet? Are we there yet?"

I certainly don't have it all figured out. I am not at all perfect. I will never be perfect. I make colossal mistakes. But I regret nothing. Regret is a sin. Guilt is a sin. As long as I am aspiring, as long as I remain a student of life, as long as I am moving faithfully toward the vision I see before my eyes, I can forgive myself everything. I can be curious about my mistakes, saying, "Okay, that didn't work out so well... what can I do better next time?" Something doesn't go according to plan? I can stand outside of myself, observe my reaction, the shift in my countenance, and say, "Hmm, that's interesting... well, I guess I'm doing something else."

I trust the process, the journey I have embarked upon. As the actor Lee Marvin once said, "Give me my span of years and knock me down when it's all over. You've got to make room for the other guy. I've had the simple pleasure of being present when the sun was shining and the rain was falling. I've had mine, and nobody can take it away from me."

It is a great place to be, to embrace confusion, to embrace uncertainty. To simply be where you are. We are exactly where we need to be. Great questions do not lead to answers. Great questions lead to greater questions. It's like Wagner's famous *Tristan Chord*, a surprising dissonance, an unbearable tension, a longing for resolution, and a lush promise of harmony to come.

Everything is illuminated by the soft light of awareness. Awareness will save us. Awareness is curative. Awareness is entire, a seed that contains its own solution. Awareness *is* the solution. Awareness is the first step in understanding how we view the world and how the world views us. You can't undo awareness.

ഇരുഓ

Some of us write down our goals—one-year, five-year goals, those Christmas wish-lists of our lives. Dear Santa, please bring me a bike. We write them down and we fervently wish for them. We're sincere.

We really do want fundamental and profound changes in our lives. We make a list of New Year's Resolutions, and this time it's going to be different. These are the promises to ourselves that we make and break. And we spend our lives in despair, looking back over our days, our months, our years, realizing that we have failed in our resolutions once again and, ultimately, failed ourselves.

The problem with resolutions and goal-setting is that as soon as we write them down, we set about figuring out how we are going to make everything on the list happen. We make a plan. And this is how it fails. We are so attached to a certain way that we want our resolutions for this year to materialize that we miss the subtle shifts and changes that are required from us to explore new possibilities. We miss the opportunities. Our eyes and ears are opened only if we take time to listen and see.

Ah, my love, our well-intentioned goals are just glorified wishes. For at the same time we are writing them down, we don't really believe that we can have them. Or we say, "I really do want this, but I don't know where to start." We swear we want change and understanding in our lives but do we really? Is it not easier to make excuses? We buy self-help books that promise change and they sit on the shelf. Even if we do read the book and get all inspired, that only lasts a few days, and next thing we know, we are sitting around scratching ourselves in front of the television again, and wondering—if we wonder at all—where it all went.

৪০৫৪

We nag ourselves out of bed each day, grab a coffee, and rush out to our lives. Then begins the navigating, transacting, consuming, meeting, moving things around, hoping, planning, moving things around some more, squeezing every hour, nothing wasted. We struggle with our paper piles and email backlogs and soul-numbing meetings. We squirm at the thought of the obligations we made to others, knowing we really should call, should get together sometime soon, should reciprocate for all the little invitations we receive every day. An onslaught. Things we have to deal with. Things we have to do. Things we should do.

We have been conditioned to always be doing something. "Don't sit around doing nothing," we are told when we are young. "Be productive," we are told. "Stop wasting time," we are told. And we learn this, cramming every corner of our lives with activities and obligations. The daily grind, shackled forever to the oars. We rush here and there. We never stop. And then we collapse at the end of each day, collapse into our "down time," into our "me time," and turn on the television and feed, feed, feed. And then we do it all over again tomorrow and the next and the next. Sisyphus and his accursed rock.

We never take time to be still, to sit with ourselves quietly. It is amazing that we will spend thirty minutes watching a sitcom we don't really care about, and yet we won't take that same thirty minutes to sit quietly and consider our future, what it is we really want, and our place on this earth.

I have a simple routine. As soon as I awake in the morning, I sit quiet and still and ask myself, "Who am I today? And what do I want?" I close my eyes and observe myself ninety days from now. Ninety days is all it takes to change everything in a life completely. One hundred percent. Career, friends, location. One needs no more than that.

Where am I standing on this earth ninety days from now? How am I dressed? What am I doing? Who is around me? I imagine this future scene in vivid, freshly-washed colors. I smell the smells, hear the sounds. I visualize it with all the clarity and emotions that I would have if it was real right now, today. Then today, on this day, I simply head toward that vision. No matter what the cost. My path will be made clear. Luck favors the lucky, does it not? Luck is an attitude. I think it was Louis Pasteur who said, "Chance favors the prepared mind."

There is an immense power in stillness. To pause. To start each day with intention. To take time every morning to be still, and in that time, to ask, "Who am I today? And what do I want my life to look like?" This simple daily routine is the greatest thing we can do to create the changes we desire, to create the lives we deserve, deliberate, mindful lives.

ೞೱೞ

There is a distance that distance creates. All those miles and months between us. It is inevitable and I feel it now (can you?). I am lying here beside you and I love you so much and yet I can feel it going away. Ours is not meant to be. "Something there is that doesn't love love," as the poet once said.

It has been long months since I last saw you, and I thought about this reunion every day in recent weeks. I could not wait to see you. I tried to pretend that I was not that excited— to myself really—but I was enchanted at the thought of seeing you again.

I had no illusions that you and I would just fall into each other's arms and pick up as lovers again. This is not our story. This is not our future. You and I came together one tumultuous summer, alternating between worship and attack, clashing and clinging to each other like violent magnets. We kissed the passion of it all with a fury. That summer.

Now here we are again after these many months, and something has slowed down in me (in us?). Something has calmed. I have rational eyes now. I have logical, dispassionate observations. You are a girl I love completely, yet strangely—well not strangely, I suppose—I don't need you. I don't need you at all. I am ready for the next phase, for the next girl.

I have a memory of you in a white dress. An unbelievably expensive evening gown, sophisticated and elegant. You loved it and, of course, we both wanted you to try it on. The lady in the shop was firm: "We have a strict policy of not allowing dresses to be tried on." But I could tell she secretly wanted you to try it on, too, and so she was effortlessly persuaded. And when you came out from behind the heavy, olive-green damask curtain, wearing that white dress like a snowy dream, the radiance in the air was almost audible.

Is there anything truly like true love? What is it? How can I be so in love and yet have it drift away from my grasp so surely, so easily? Are the pundits right? Is love a compromise? Is love even sustainable for a gypsy pirate like me? Do I really love you? Did I ever love you? Is there another reality about love that I don't even know?

I have another memory of you beside a pool... you in your floppy, white hat and me with my head in your lap and the sun shining down. I think I fell in love with you there.

— The Alabaster Girl, *page 174*

୫୦୯ଓ

Once upon a time, we believed in ceremony. Everything we did had meaning. Everything we did was mindful. Everything we did was imbued with ritual. We were storytellers. We used to gather around the fire and tell the stories of the day. We used to pause, to wonder, to give thanks for our meals. Yes, we once believed in the beauty of mindful ceremony, of being still, of coming together.

We have lost this from the earth. We no longer have ceremony, we no longer have mindfulness, we no longer have quiet contemplation. We no longer gather. We no longer take time to pause, to wonder about our lives and be amazed.

What a loss! We have pushed aside the very things that will fulfill us, that will make us whole, that will make us worthy. In a typical modern family, the father and mother crash separately into the house at the end of the workday, the kids crash into the house after school, they root around separately in the refrigerator, one after another, then they rush off to their respective rooms, computers, televisions.

If families were to do only one thing: *gather together every day*, the world would change. The simple expedient of checking in with one another on a regular basis is, in my mind, the single most important thing that will keep a family united and strong. If a man would gather his family around him every evening—even for just a few minutes—what wondrous harmony might be created! To have daily *Vespers*, a family ceremony, a checking-in with one another, a ritual of separating the day from the evening, the work from the rest. This is what will keep relationships alive. This is what will keep families together. Gathering together every day fosters communion, empathy, and curiosity. And *then* let everyone run off to their chosen, separate distractions. It is enough, and the evening can now commence.

One could imagine that daily *Vespers* is like a checkpoint in a video game. We are playing the game of Life on the 'Hard' difficulty setting, but because we saved the game at that point yesterday evening, because we reconnected with what is truly important, we can always fall back on that point again any time in the future.

Gathering together around the virtual fire and telling the stories of the day. The way we used to gather, through time immemorial. Anachronistic? Simplistic? A throwback to quieter times? Yes, indeed. And so very needed in our disconnected, miscommunicating age, our last defense against mediocrity and the religion of rush.

ෆ☙

Fear is a bad adviser. It has been well said that there are no atheists in foxholes. We've seen these conversions before. The man sentenced to die and now, only now, does he seek meaning and God. The celebrity afflicted suddenly with some debilitating condition who then goes on to be a great supporter, spokesperson, advocate for that very affliction. To be sure, their eyes have been opened to something they knew nothing about before, but is this the only way we will slow down, reflect, see things in perspective? Is this the only way we will wake up and consider our lives and how they should be lived? Must we be struck down and blinded in order to truly see?

We want transformation, a redemption, a salvation, but the truth is, we really don't. We don't want it badly enough. We are wallowing in wishes, scratching at our lassitude, lost in feeble velleity. We create nothing. We invent nothing. We live in the shadow of our unattained but attainable self, sitting around all day and staring out of the window, waiting desperately for the promise of a new tomorrow when we can sit around all day and stare out of the window.

It's like the apocryphal story about the man who is moved to tears by a heavenly piano concerto and after the performance he rushes up to the virtuoso to thank him and to gush. "I would give *anything* to play like that," he says. The pianist looks at him and says, "No, you wouldn't."

Ω

There is a curious energy in the air today, a hunger, a thirst. We are seeking something. But what? Ours is a secular type of spirituality, with little bits and flecks of all the major and minor religions—pantheism, monotheism, science, creation, evolution—thrown in. We refuse to be pinned down to anything specific. We are "spiritual but not religious." What does this even mean? What is this secular spirituality? All the world's religions were invented by men, we say, and as such, should be cast aside. Does this mean we no longer worship? Do we still believe in the concept of worship? Does being spiritual mean we worship nothing? Or everything? What do we worship? Stuff? Self? Science? Universe? Gaia? Angels? Cows? Do we even know?

We invent new ways to describe old things and then proclaim them as revelation. What is the difference between Putting our Intention into the Universe and Praying to God? Nothing, except that in our secular brand of spirituality, we can't say God, so we say Universe; we can't say Prayer, so we say Intention.

All pursuits are holy pursuits. All quests are spiritual quests. All systems, whether religion-based or science-based, concern themselves with the search for our origin. The Big Bang, the Creation Story, quantum mechanics, the stars, the earth, the sun, the universe... why are we here? This occupies the minds of all critical thinkers: theologians, scientists, philosophers, poets, artists... *the source of light*.

Now that we have established that we are, in fact, here, how do we do it best? What is the purest ethos we can imagine? How do we maximize the quality of life? How do we traverse from cradle to grave in the most profound and meaningful way possible? Should we strive for personal happiness? Or the greater good? Are the existentialists right? The absurdists? The nihilists? The theists? The atheists? Is there meaning? Or do we invent our own meaning? Music, art, laws, politics, justice, ethics, morals, wars, economics, communities, meditation, prayer. All these are concerned with the creation of the highest quality of life possible... *the perfect note*.

Beauty. This is what we seek from the day we are born to the day we die. The essence of wholeness, completeness, belonging, togetherness, newness, and enchantment in our lives. It is our desire for relationship, for communion, for intimacy, for procreation, for immortality through our children. It is the fight of our lives... the fight against the darkness, against our fear of being forever lost and alone. It is our fundamental longing to be included, to be wanted, to love and to be loved... *an alabaster girl*.

༺ও৪ঌ༻

She weeps reluctantly on my chest. I lie silent beside her on a blanket beneath a tree, holding her as the day slowly empties.

Her past was full of pain, she says, and I hold her close, for I know this to be true. I can feel it in her body, in her breath, in her soft and halting surrender in my arms, in the rhythm of her despair, in the easing in and easing out of her imperceptible sighs. Her emptiness washes over me with the coolness and power of a baptismal cloth. Hers is a beautiful heart and it is not fair what happened to her. Is there anything more sad in this life than the quiet anguish of a stolen past?

I say nothing and look up to the sky, through the lattice leaves of the tree that wafts above us. I hold her close, sheltering her. The tree shelters me and I shelter her, circumscribed, like a simple kind of ecosystem. I listen to the sound of the wind in the leaves. I feel her despair tears on my chest.

Because I do not judge, as I lie beside her in this quiet time, she feels comfortable enough, or compelled enough, I suppose, to tell me all manner of clandestine conceits. I am glad that she senses she can let go in my arms and cry a little, knowing I will never steal this moment from her, never betray it, and never appropriate it to my own advantage, as others have before.

It is always a shock when a pretty girl says she doesn't feel pretty at all. This oh-so-quiet girl in this oh-so-quiet moment tells me how she once felt pretty as a child, but now feels small and inadequate, like she has been robbed of something vital, and now she is afraid that she has become little more than a robber herself. Unable to give of herself completely, she opens the curtains to her heart ever so slightly—but never the door, never the door—you can look in but you can never enter.

We have a curious notion that time is a one-way path. We stroll through the gardens of our lives contemplating things we see along the way. Nous étions la et maintenant nous sommes ici. We were there (and we point) and now we are here (and we point). And oh, how we wish we had been given a different path through the garden!

The past is always created in the present. Here she is, the girl I adore, wishing she had a different past. And I think, could it be any other way? When I first saw her that day at the outdoor café, there was something in the air, was there not? Yes, everything about her on that day—her smile at my smile, her mischief-flashed eyes, her skin like poured cream—everything about her took my breath away, and I was drawn to her like a bee to a daisy.

What if she didn't have those terrible times of her past? Would her beauty and her humor and her spirit be the same? Would I still be attracted to her? Would I even like her? Would I even notice her? Who knows?

Everything that has happened to her in the past has created the girl she is today. All the good things and all the bad things—everything that hurt her, excited her, abandoned her, loved her—have created her, the way she is right now, her ideas, her dreams, her personality... all of it. This is the girl I discovered, the girl I was attracted to on that fine spring day, the girl I adore. Because of her past—not in spite of it—I love who she is today.

"What are you thinking?" she says.

I look up to the sky through the leaves, looking through, looking past.

I tell her what I am thinking.

I can feel her eyelashes brushing softly on my skin as she listens.

"Embrace it all," I add, "for it is you."

She lies still for a few seconds, saying nothing.

And now she sits up slowly, bunching the blanket around her knees. "I've never thought of it like that before," she says.

I smile up at her and the sun and the leaves.

Yes, well... I think about it like that all the time, my love, all the time.

— The Alabaster Girl, *page 177*

෨෮

Every great life has had in it a great renunciation. Let me say that again: *Every great life has had in it a great renunciation.* There is no other way. We simply can't continue our lives the way they are if we want to be great. Small incremental changes are no longer enough. Reading a few books, taking a few workshops, and taping a few affirmations to our mirrors is no longer enough. If we want to be great, great changes are needed, great strides forward, a great distance placed between ourselves and all the ways we have, up until now, conducted our lives. We need a new perspective. A grand perspective. A world-changing perspective. If we want to be excellent then we have to stand on this earth in excellence.

Renunciation! A bold examination of our hearts. To stand on the earth and ask, "Is this what I want my life to look like? At this age in my life, is this where I wanted to be?" If the answer is no, then we must renounce everything, immediately and with great force. We must remove everything that holds us down in any way.

Oh, but I'll just sit this one out, we say. Tomorrow, we say. Next time, we say. Yes well… no more small measures. Our life begins when we are born but our life story begins *when*?

We are given the gift of the Book of Life and we stay forever on the first page. We have everything and we have been given everything, yet we deplore everything. From Shakespeare: "But thou contracted to thine owne bright eyes… Making a famine where abundance lies…"

Carl Jung said this: "I asked myself, 'What is the myth you are living?' and found that I did not know my myth, and I regarded this as the task of tasks." If we really want change in our lives—and we say we do—it is not enough to periodically consider the path, or to view it as a part-time endeavor. It's going to take everything we've got, and more. It is the fight of our lives, more important than anything else, forever.

౭౦ఇ

Maybe I am not realistic. Okay, I accept that. Maybe it's part of my own delusion, my diffuse, pointillist view of the world. So be it. I have my eyes so firmly fixed on what I want and where I want to go, that anything that gets in the way is simply that: something to go around.

In this world of constant stress and obligations and broken promises, I keep my gaze steady before me. I am no flagellant, whipping my own back, shuffling along on my knees, and bewailing my lack of progress. "Ease and delight" is the slogan of my life. I *never* rush. Goethe said it best, "Do not hurry. Do not rest."

Do I feel happy? I feel aligned. Some of us have a mini-crisis, an existential angst, every time another birthday rolls around. Wow, we say to ourselves, another birthday, the year *flew* by. We feel it right here… that slight but familiar twinge in our stomach, a diffuse despair. It's the same feeling we get when we realize the summer is gone and now it is winter again and we didn't go to the beach and the gym and camping and all the other things we promised ourselves we would do, any more often than we did the summer before. And now we have no choice—our birthday is here again whether we like it or not—so we gamely celebrate it, making the most of it, hiding our dread of mortality behind a cake and a card.

Here is something amazing: When you fill every day with the best memories you can possibly make, when you visualize the life you want to live and then move toward it no matter what the cost, that twinge of regret is forever gone. You are aligned. You are exactly where you need to be. You can't see the future, but that's okay. You just take another step forward into the mystery, the unknown, knowing that your foot will *always* hit something.

It is a wonderful thing to be free of the feeling of the marching of time; to have the ability to welcome it; to know that all your adventures, small and great, are creating you, a glorious you; to discover that when you love and celebrate your life, others will love and celebrate your life, too.

This is all, of course, retroactive advice to my young self, my love. "Walk forever in the aleatory wonder of discovery. Embrace confusion. Love mystery above all. Trust the God of your youth. Retain the audacity of your youth. Smile, wink, tease, and play. Make glorious fun of yourself. Engage everyone with equal equanimity. Give thanks every day for how delightful life really is. Look all around you in curiosity and wonder. Turn up the volume. Become more and more animated. Take a deep breath. Relax into the arms of life. Let it all go... let it all go. Ease and delight. Ease and delight. How can you possibly fail? You can only win."

ဆၢလ

I open my door at the end of the day and there she is, my glorious girl. "Surprise!" she exclaims, and I am surprised. She is laughing and clapping and excited, and the room is full of people. Today is my birthday. Today I am forty years old.

I walk into the room, tentative, excited, anticipating, like a little boy on a diving board. The room is alive with celebration, streamers and balloons floating all about, glasses of champagne and wine raised high in toast, a cornucopia of food spilled all over the table, and small photos of me taped to the wall (in the shape of the number 40!). It is absolutely fun and absolutely lovely. And loveliest of all are the people who are here to share this evening with me.

Here is a small wonder of the world: a woman who knows me so well (and loves me anyway). For she, my dear girl, my clever girl, because she knows me so well (and loves me anyway), has invited to this surprise birthday party all of the former lovers and girlfriends of mine that she could find. And here are twelve of them! With their current boyfriends and husbands. Surprise, indeed!

And because my girl knows me so well (and loves me anyway), she has decided that the best kind of party for me is a lingerie party! Surprise, again!

A surprise lingerie birthday party filled with pretty women whom I adore! All for me. Yes, she knows me so well. And here are twelve of my former loves, beautiful, beautiful, adorned in various negligees, chemises, lingerie. And their husbands and boyfriends, regal, complicit, in their pajamas and robes and slippers.

Even my great friend, Bill, whom I love, who is still a scoundrel, who is still alive with the spirit of ease and delight at the age of eighty-four, is here. With his heavenly wife, Patricia, of course. And even they are in their silk night robes and slippers.

I look at her, my girl who knows me so well, my eyes wide, and she throws her arms about me, laughing and kissing and caressing the bewilderment on my face. I love my girl.

I hesitate for a moment or two, then dive into the midst of it all, like a little boy on a diving board, waiting shyly and proudly until everyone is watching before he jumps. I kiss all the girls, shake hands with all the men.

Everything flows and blurs. There is celebration here, and I love it. Everyone congratulates me on making it this far, and I love it. Jokes about my "faltering and decrepit old age" and "soon needing a wheelchair" fill the air, and I love it. Stories are told and retold. Former strangers, who have all been introduced, are wonderfully comfortable with each other.

The women dance with each other in the center of the room. The men stand around with their drinks, admiring the dancing maidens, talking and chuckling and nodding as men do, la band of happy thieves, like the Merry Men of Sherwood Forest.

Everything at this sumptuous medieval feast is admired and happily consumed: the wine, the food, and the sight of the dancing maidens en dishabille.

At some point, in the midst of the merriment, needing a moment to consider everything quietly and alone as I often do, I slip out onto the balcony and look back at the party effervescing inside. The scene, framed by the glass door, reminds me of a painting by Brueghel the Elder (or Younger), one of those typical ones called "Soldiers and Laughing Girls in a Tavern" or something like that.

Today I am forty years old, a man, and yet I don't feel like a man. In fact, I don't feel any different than when I was eighteen. I feel no more aches or pains or slowness than I did back then. I think I could take off running just as fast and as far and jump just as high as I always did. I think I could still effortlessly climb all those dangerous trees of my youth. Perhaps, I can't. It is strange to have the feeling that you are still on this side of the wall of maturity, still just a wet-behind-the-ears kid, when logically you know you are not.

I see Bill holding court near the food, regaling everyone with his well-oiled and time-tested tall tales. And I wonder, does Bill still feel a youthful spirit in his heart at eighty-four? Does he still think the adults around him seem so old? Will I still feel young when I am eighty-four? Is there ever a time when you become tired of it all and decide it's time to... just be old?

No, I think something else must be possible, for although Bill is obviously eighty-four and is obviously slow, I have never seen anything but mischief and youthfulness in his crystal-blue eyes. This man has lived a spectacular life: he speaks seven languages, he was a code breaker in the second World War, he was a translator in the Vietnam War, he was a raconteur, a perpetual traveler, and a notorious lover and friend to women. His life is full of stories, grand stories, spectacular adventures. And he is always in a good mood, always happy and pleasant. It's as if his memories are enough, giving him a chance to live those dashing years all over again, filling him with untold volumes of energy and *vitality, enough to sustain him forward forever. He is not a bitter old man at all. He has no guilt. He has no regret. He is ashamed of nothing. He admits it all.*

When I grow up, I want to be just like my old friend Bill, no regrets, proud and grateful and enormously happy with the life I have lived and the loves I have loved.

I look at the scene again and I see my girl, my beauty, twenty-four years old, so radiant, in the middle of the tavern painting, hovering about, entertaining, so in charge of everything, and I am in awe of the power and creativity of a beautiful mind.

I look at the scene again and I see the women who have shared my life, all dancing together. And the men... for some reason, men are never jealous of me. Maybe it's because I always try to be gracious and reach out to them, if given a chance. Or maybe it's because she says something to him like, "Okay, I love you and I only want to be with you, and you can be jealous of all other men, that's fine... but not him. He doesn't count, for he is my dear friend, and will always be in my life." Whatever the reason, men seem to accept me and part out of my way.

A beautiful scene before me. Everyone together, men and women, laughing, talking, and celebrating. I love this night. I love this moment. Everyone is here this evening, gathered around, to celebrate me. Me! How profound! How stunning! How absolutely humbling! I am celebrated by these women because I celebrated them. I am respected by these men because I respected them. I am honored because I honor. I am revered because I revere.

What a pretty moment in my life, what a pause, what a demarcation, what a profound landmark, what a happy memory to cheer me on my deathbed. When it is time, I can wink one last time at those around my bedside and smile and say, "No matter what else happened to me in this crazy old life, well hey... at least I had that."

— The Alabaster Girl, *page 180*

ളാരു

Find your purpose! This is the clarion call of today. You are nothing without your purpose. You're twenty-nine years old, for Pete's sake! What are you going to do with your life? Find your purpose and all is solved.

Find your purpose. A meaningless, albeit well-intentioned phrase, similar to "follow a budget." Yes, we all kind of get what it means, but very few of us can actually incorporate it into our lives. Are we missing something? Are we not trying hard enough? We have no idea how to discover our purpose, that grand, unifying reason that we were thrust upon the earth at this time and place in history. And yet we are told that if we don't somehow discover it, if we don't find the silver briefcase that contains the documents for our secret mission, we will have spectacularly failed. And the years go by and inertia kicks in and we get old and sick and die.

And so we try. We wrack our brains for years, wishing we could craft that one perfect, grand "mission statement" for our lives. We try to commit it to paper, but we usually end up with something generic and all-encompassing and watered-down like: "My mission is to inspire others to excellence in every blah blah blah and to empower myself and others to blah blah blah while maintaining positive relationships with blah blah blah." That's nice, I guess. To me, it sounds too similar to those loathsome, wordy, all-things-to-all-people Mission Statements that are *de rigueur* in modern corporations.

Maybe we don't really want to inspire others to be all they can be. Maybe we just want to grow a garden or build a cabin in the woods or raise a child. Not grand enough? Not doing your societal duty? To grow a garden or a child is as grand a mission statement as there has ever been. It's just as noble, just as life-giving, just as world-changing as any enterprise in the history of man. As Kundera wrote, "It's a terrific relief to realize you are free… free from all missions."

"Wait a minute!" wiser ones will cry out. "Forget trying to find your purpose. Instead do this: *Follow your passion!* Do what you love. Discover within your heart what you are most passionate about and then do that. And only that. Turn your love of food, photography, or crafts into your career." A lovely sentiment, to be sure, but soon we discover that we also like to eat.

Because it is so difficult to stay afloat on our "passion," we cautiously seek out something a little more substantial to cling to in the ocean of life. Parents say, "You want to be a painter, yes, we understand, being an artist is good, but perhaps you should study for a few years first to become a dental hygienist or something. That way you will always have *something to fall back on.*"

Something to fall back on. Security. Safety. From Tacitus: "The desire for safety stands against every great and noble enterprise." From Steinbeck: "We spend our time searching for security, and hate it when we get it." From Tennessee Williams: "Security is a kind of death."

Maybe the better advice is this: "Fly, my son, as fast and as far as you can toward your dreams. Go and live a grand life, the life you see in your mind. Never hesitate. Never settle. Never dabble. Never play small. *Never have anything to fall back on.* Your one life on this earth, and it is to be lived in fear? In shame? In hesitation? In wishes? In regret? I don't think so, my son."

The great artist Turner, the "painter of light," was once asked how he managed to capture, with such striking imagery, the remarkable personal emotion and immense impersonal fury of a storm at sea. His answer was that he went one day to the coast of Holland and hired a fishing boat captain to take him out to sea in the next storm and bind him high upon the mast. The storm was so violent and terrifying that he was certain he was about to die. That storm went right through him until he was forever a part of the storm and it was a part of him. And when he came back, that is what he painted.

৪০৫৪

The incomparable Joseph Campbell wrote the perfect mission statement for us all: *Follow your bliss!* Find your purpose? Follow your
passion? No, follow your bliss. This makes sense to me. In work, in
play, in rest, follow your bliss. This, to me, is the only guiding light
we ever need.

Bliss does not mean happy and bouncy all day, or overbearing perma-
grins. It contains within it contemplation, mindfulness, gratitude.
It means we have the courage to face the challenges of life head-on.
It means that we trust our own center of gravity. It means that no
matter what comes our way, we have what it takes to handle it. Nor
does bliss mean we should just relax and do nothing. An essential
component of bliss is fulfillment, a great work ethic, a desire to
provide for our families, and a love of projects great and small that
act as stepping stones for our lives.

Bliss does not mean avoidance of the uncomfortable. It does not
seek distraction. Bliss means staying the course, even when it hurts.
It reaches its arms around the whole experience that we call life and
embraces it all—good and bad—with equanimity and grace.

Bliss means to do whatever, in this moment, brings you into alignment with your true nature. Bliss means to fill your days only with
things that have heart and meaning to you. Bliss means to follow
your gut, your intuition, that still, small voice. Your head is a great
tool, but sometimes it thinks it's the master. Your head needs all the
information—all the pros and all the cons—to make a great decision.
Your gut, however, is *never* wrong; even with only a fraction of the
information, it is always right.

৪০৫৪

*How I delight in her by my side! What mischief, what
scandal, what fun are we about to discover today?*

I follow her through the mazy streets of London, for this is her town. I am taking you to Westminster Abbey, she says. I think you will like it, she says. You will see what I mean, she says.

And now we are here outside this great edifice, and I stand back and gaze at the augustness and grandeur of this centuries-old place of worship, and my mind fills with a myriad of questions. Where is the grandeur in the architecture of our buildings today? What edifice have we created lately that will last a thousand years? Is architecture dead? Has kitsch won? Our buildings are shiny and sparkly—glass wonders, to be sure—but arrow-straight, cookie-cutter, utilitarian, banal. Our religion of rush extends even to our architecture. Our buildings today are not built to last. They are a symbol of our age, of our short attention spans, our pop culture, our love of kitsch.

Suburbia is a nightmare to me. It is mediocrity on a grand scale—bureaucrat-approved and stamped in place. Our communities are just as disconnected and directionless and inattentive as we are ourselves. There is no longer a focal point in anything, a locus, a centrality around which communities gather. We have replaced our town squares with shopping malls, and all the roads mere conveyor belts leading to and from—and this is where we now gather. Or is it? Who knows?

Everywhere are strip malls and chain restaurants and mega-stores. Our car culture in the West necessitates bewildering arrangements of dividers and barriers and road rage on all the streets; you can see your destination right there... beside you... to your left. Right there! But you can't get to it, for there is no way to turn left, or so it seems. And I think, can this really be by design?

What are you thinking, she says, and when I tell her she laughs and kisses my cheek. Silly man, she says. Only you would think about such things, she says. You are only content in the heart of a city or the heart of the wilderness, she says. Nothing in between, she says. Let's go inside, she says.

And now we are inside. And now I know that mischief and scandal and fun will have to wait for another day, for there is a wonderful hush here in Westminster Abbey, a reverence, in the way we used to use that word.

We wander ponderously upon the foot-worn stone, like the millions before us through the centuries, amid the flowing sculptures and majestic tombs of long forgotten rulers, knights, discoverers, warriors, poets. Yes... the poets.

Joseph Brodsky said, "There is nothing as dear as the sight of ruins." I understand this completely. Do we feel any connection to our past at all? Do we aspire to anything anymore? I stop near a stone embedded in the floor with a life-size etching of a knight, worn away like an old penny. Others in the Abbey are celebrated still. Not him. His name is long gone, whiled away, there is no helpful placard, just a dark gray stone worn completely down, a faded relief outline of him, worn completely down, and the shape of his shield worn completely down, a knight whose name is gone, whose achievements are gone, whose remembrance is gone, everything gone. And I think... this is us. This is how we end our days.

If I see a photograph of a pretty young woman a hundred years ago, smiling, calm... I can look at it for hours. I am amazed by her, mesmerized, for some reason. I think it's because everything she ever was, everything she ever dreamed, every talent she ever possessed—maybe she could sing, or maybe she could speak languages, or maybe she loved to dance—is gone, all gone, one hundred years later, and it matters not at all, the way she dreamed and what she loved. And I think... this is us. This is our one slice of life.

We are remembered for a few years after we are gone, but not many. We are thrust upon this earth like the pop flash of fireworks, and some of us might sparkle a little more brightly than others and all the people ooh and ahh, but only for a moment, and then it is dark once more and the people get in their cars and go home.

In Westminster Abbey, on this day, there is a single ethereal note floating in the air that I will never forget. Deep and low and heavy and filling the entire space. From somewhere above us or below us or around us or inside us I can hear the single note of a pipe organ, as deep as any bass sound I have ever heard. And it lingers and sustains, like mist, like magic, floating heavily about our feet. And then, to my surprise, it shifts down a halftone to another note, lower still. And I think, how marvelous. And then, interminable seconds later, it shifts down again. And I think, how is this possible? Surely it can't go any lower than that. And then it does. And then it does again. And again. Lower, lower, a downward spiral, and yet it seems to float higher and higher, like an anthem or a hymn (or a dirge). It's sparse and lonely, violent and quiet, lyrical and bizarre, vile and poetic, ancient and modern, and I find myself humbled and calmed and deeply overwhelmed by this single ethereal note with no bottom, as it slowly descends lower and lower, calling to me somehow, bidding me follow, and I do, stepping lower and lower into my thoughts, into my self, stepping down, down, all the way down.

— The Alabaster Girl, *page 184*

80CB

I knew a man who loved to fish. All he would talk about was fishing. Every chance he got, he would go fishing. For years, fishing was his first love. He could not wait to retire. He worked hard every day at a job he did not love, waiting for his retirement. For then his dream of fishing every day all day long would be realized. You can guess the rest of this story. A month after he retired, he was diagnosed with terminal cancer and in six months, he was gone. What was the point of any of it? I thought about this man for a long, long time.

A doctor friend once told me about the way old men die. In one room, he said, a family has gathered together, from various parts of the country, reluctantly and tentatively, around an old man. Some members have not spoken to each other—or him—in years. They are plotting in secret against one another for estate or esteem. There is discord and distrust and long-standing resentment hovering in the air, a harrowing darkness that permeates the atmosphere, a cold and dismal mood descending all around. The doctors, nurses, and interns can all feel the onerous and steel-trap energy of the room, and they avoid it as much as possible.

In another room, a family has gathered, from various parts of the country, with rejoicing and celebration, around an old man. They come together in harmony, a family unified once again. There are tears in their eyes but a song in their hearts. There is nothing but profound gratitude to their beloved patriarch for the values he has bestowed upon them, for his gentle guidance throughout the years, for the gift of life he has passed along to all of them. The room is light and serene, inviting and life-affirming. The doctors, nurses, and interns all delight in the ambient blessing of a life that was well-lived and well-loved.

The remarkable thing, my doctor friend said to me, is that in all his years of observing old men die, there is nothing in between. It is either phenomenally dark and drear in the room, or phenomenally light and love.

ⅮⅯ

In 1958, Samuel Beckett wrote a remarkable play about "a wearish old man" named Krapp. Every year on his birthday since he was twenty-four, he has recorded his thoughts on a reel-to-reel tape machine. By listening to these past tapes, he can relive and contemplate his life, looking back at who he was and considering who he is now. And here he is today, sixty-nine and jaded, and reduced to a confusion of aches, incontinence, and regret.

He sits alone beneath a single, stark light, framed in interminable darkness, and listens to a tape of himself at thirty-nine. The voice on the tape is describing how he has just listened to an even earlier tape from his mid-twenties and oh, how idealistic and ridiculous and unrealistic he was in his expectations: "Hard to believe I was ever that young whelp. The voice! And the aspirations! And the resolutions!" He listens and ultimately joins his middle-aged self in dismissive laughter. He was a fool back then; in fact, he was a fool at every age, including the present one at sixty-nine. Nothing worked out as planned. None of it matters. Everything is dross.

He changes the tape, listens to another passage and, unable to bear the optimism in his voice, changes it again. He listens, fast-forwards, muttering to himself. He listens again, fast-forwards again, listens again, fast-forwards again, each time more and more agitated.

Suddenly he hears his voice saying these words: "...we drifted in among the flags and stuck. The way they went down, sighing, before the stem! I lay down across her with my face in her breasts and my hand on her. We lay there without moving. But under us all moved, and moved us, gently, up and down, and from side to side." He pauses the tape, sits in silence for a while, then rewinds the tape and listens to this passage again. Then rewinds it and listens again And again. And the curtain descends.

The only thing we will have when we are old is our memories. And the only thing we will remember are those we loved and those who loved us. We won't remember that car we bought or that raise we got. We will only remember the moments in life we shared, the hidden moments when we lay in the bottom of a boat in the reeds and rested our head and hand and heart on the breasts of a girl we loved. That's it. Nothing else matters in this whole, wide world.

Creating memories is the only meaningful goal in life. When faced with two courses of action, two different paths before my eyes, and I have to make a decision, I do not ask which path will offer greater security, or which path will be better off financially, or which path will be approved of by family or friends. I ask only one question: *Which path will give me the best memories?* That's it. What are the best memories I can possibly make? Which path will give me the best stories when I am old? This is a wonderful guiding principle in my life—the only one I ever need—basing all decisions on creating the best memories I possibly can.

ଃଠ୧

If I close my eyes in a quiet place, backing out of the frenetic, hurtling traffic of life and into a calming lane, I can see her.

She is wearing a simple dress as she comes to me, unadorned and soft, and the dress floats about her body as she moves, and the sunlight shines right through that dress, tracing the outline of her legs, her shape, her form, like a painting en plein air.

It's that kind of dress.

Her hair is gathered in the sublime and effortless way of all women who gather their hair.

She comes to me like the sun and I cannot breathe, but then she takes my hand and I can only breathe. My vision is fading, blurring, swirling, but then she looks into my eyes and, for the first time in my life, I can clearly see. Her smiling face calms me, forgives me, lets me know that everything is okay. I reach out to touch her face; she reaches out to touch my soul.

Who is she? Who is this quiet woman in this quiet lane of my reverie, in the distant corners of my consciousness?

Oh my alabaster girl... I linger on your wine lips.

I will build a hut for us on a deserted island, marooned and lost together forever, and even cause the shipwreck myself if need be. I will sing songs of angels, songs of eternity, songs of songs, and all for you, my alabaster girl...

— The Alabaster Girl, *page 187*

೮೦೦೪

My purpose in life is women. Is that a purpose? I have no idea. All I know is that I have dedicated my entire life to women. I have arranged everything else in service of that vision. Beauty is my *leitmotif*, my horse, my hound, my guiding light.

Years ago, because it suited me, I decided to wander off the beaten path, to check out of society, to "let slip the surly bonds of earth," to become, for the most part, itinerant, a wanderer, a gypsy. I gave all my possessions away, erasing everything that might hold me back from my search for treasure. To this day, I have no home or hearth, no pillow or towel. I have moved away from everything that we usually consider to be safe and secure in this world. I am mindfully homeless… or rather, *homefree*.

I devoted my life to creating the very best memories I could possibly make—both for me and for those around me. I sacrificed material-worth in order to maximize my relationships. My whole being is caught up in this exhilaration of adventure, of living in the wind. Because, why not? What's the point of making a living if you are not living?

I accept all invitations, if possible. If I am invited, for instance, to a party down the street or to somewhere as far-flung as Istanbul, I am going. How? I have no idea. But that doesn't matter. I'm going anyway. Isn't that what I asked for? Most of us, when faced with a new invitation, tend to second-guess our intuition. We get an invitation and we reason it out, try to make sense of it. We think we are being prudent by soberly considering all the angles, but in reality, we are killing the essence of creation.

೮೦೦೪

Freedom, fame, fortune… are these not the prime motivators in life, my love? Picture a top executive who spends sixty hours or more a week in the office or the boardroom. His motivation is fortune. And on that altar of fortune, he is willing to sacrifice all kinds of freedom. Let it be said that I value freedom above all. I will sacrifice all fame and all fortune on the altar of freedom. Freedom, always and forever freedom, the essence and the glory of freedom, the freedom to exist, the freedom to just be. This, for me, is the only sensible ethic.

I am unabashedly and joyously itinerant, a wayfarer, a sojourner, living in the wind. It might seem like I am careless or mindfully drifting, unfocused and without direction. But not so! I am the most focused man I know. I know exactly what I want. I know exactly where I am going. I have no idea how I am going to get there, but I'm sure going anyway. I don't have time to think about how. All I know is what I want.

Let me make a clear distinction between obligations (our have-to's and should's) and commitments. Obligations are obscene, a distraction, an imposition. I will not explain myself to anyone on this earth. I will not tolerate the gnawing, numbing pang of obligation to anything or anyone in any way. Obligations are tyrants, the assassins of our soul.

Commitments, on the other hand, are glorious. Commitments are mindful. Commitments are the manifestation of our conscious choice. Commitments are our desires put into action. Commitments are good. Commitments should not be broken. Commitments are the very foundation of freedom. Commitments draw us forward like a sail upon the seas.

Relaxing into the arms of life is the greatest possible commitment I can imagine. Stretched out before me as far as I can see is a vista, a horizon, something that calls to me, something that is stronger than me, something that I love with all my heart. Casanova described it like this: "I never had any fixed aim before my eyes, and my system, if it can be called a system, has been to glide away unconcernedly on the stream of life, trusting to the wind wherever it led."

ଚଙ୍କ

This has ever been my heart and my joy: to spend my days in a magical place, in the spirit of dancing and fire and music, and with the
vitality of female energy flowing everywhere, from the balconies, the
bars, the cafés, the terraces, and into the streets, to be caught up in
space and time, unbounded by mere location, to inhabit a concept
rather than a place, a gypsy caravan, a "movable feast," a safe haven
for wayward girls and urban gypsies of every kind.

From about the *fin de siècle* through to the 1920s, artists and writers
flocked to Paris to be around the Impressionists and the Cubists and
the "stream of consciousness" writers. There was a great buzz in the air
in those years and people wanted to be a part of it. Amateur artists
and writers would hang around the cafés of Paris, hoping to catch a
glimpse of Hemingway or Joyce. Gertrude Stein actually brought all
these great minds together in her extensive home on the Left Bank:
Hemingway and Joyce and Picasso and Braque and Apollinaire and
Rousseau and Pound and Bowles and Fitzgerald and Matisse, among
countless others. That collective energy, with everyone looking over
the shoulders of the others, raised the art of all involved.

The Paris of the 1950s saw a similar gathering, with Sartre and de
Beauvoir and various other philosophers. Over in America, Burroughs
and Kerouac and Ginsberg gathered together in Greenwich Village,
challenged each other, and inspired each other, helping to shape
the Beat mentality. They were joined there by the artists Pollock,
de Kooning, and Kline.

All of these "gatherings" facilitated great leaps of inspiration, imagination, and art—the collusion of minds creating something greater
(whole movements) than an individual ever could.

My long-winded point is this… where is that gathering happening
today? You might say, "The Internet," and you might be right. But
something is lost, I think, in the notion of virtual communities.

There is something good and right and necessary about looking into the eyes and shaking the hands of our peers.

So where is this locus on earth, this creative energy field, this gathering place that draws our hearts and minds? How come we missed out on the creation of a movement? So, to hell with it… let's build it.

೮ಌ

There is a greatness in men that the world is waiting for. That women desire. Everywhere are men without direction, without conviction, without masculine beauty. What are we waiting for, a fuller moon?

We think we need more money, more time, more energy, before we can cast off from the shore and live a life of beauty. There is no time to wait any longer. Self-help is done. No more dabbling. No more playing small. No more time for the old story. No more. No more. No more. Everything we desire is outside of our comfort zone. Otherwise we would already have it. Here is not where it is. It's out there somewhere… away.

Do we truly want to be magnetic, dynamic, and attractive? When we move toward the things in our life that have heart and meaning to us, attraction is automatic. This is the only thing that will make us truly mesmerizing to others. We will discover that simple things like phone numbers are everywhere around us. We will discover that women of truly transcendent beauty are always in our lives. This is grace. This is masculinity. And this is true attraction.

Make no mistake… this is a call for leaders. Men of character are needed, men who stand on this earth without apology, with their feet on the ground and their heads in the clouds. A few will heed the call, many will be left behind.

Can you feel that in the air? That urgency? For there *is* an urgency. There is no time to waste! Let the trumpet sound throughout the land!

A clarion call for a new way of being. Head toward the light, and only the light. Destroy your options. Cross your personal Rubicon. Burn your ships. Ride your horse as far as it can go, then dismount and carry on. Forward! Never settle! *Dregs* settle. Lead! Lead! And *never* follow again!

ഇൻയ

And so this part ends. I can always feel it. Not right away, but then like a tide-pool rising, flowing inward, absorbing sand and shells and little bits of things, I can feel it grow and well up all around me. There is great beauty here, great dangerous beauty. The sea shocks you in that it never ceases to fiercely crash, never a respite from the roar, day or night, never a calm. I came here to the jungle by the sea to find God, I asked for him by name, politely, and then I waited in a plastic chair in the lobby. God is busy, it seems. Great volumes of eons and events happen, but no God. I sit and wait and look around and lightning crashes, great scare-you-blind-you flashes, and frightening, forbidden clouds thunder down all around, churning, flickering, menacing. God? Great breaking waves pound the rocks, reaching up to punch the sky, defying God, punching at God, but forever missing, like a prize-fighter who tries from the ground, until futile and feeble and fizzling out in white froth and bubbles, sad and spent, on the sand.

I was a child then... sneaking through the forests of my youth... in love with the birch-pine essence, the ambrosia of the north... I had nothing... a bed and a book. Oh, how I wanted nothing else forever. Run, run, run... return to the forest...return... a return... a return to the simplicity of those times. Once you have the wild in your blood, it never goes away.

The nature of God and the Great Controversy... It takes faith to believe in God. The question we ask ourselves and others is "Do you believe in God?" but maybe the greater question is "Do you believe in the Devil?" Is there really Good and Evil? Maybe there is only God on the one hand and the absence of God on the other hand... and nothing else? I've never been afraid of the Devil or demons or minions or what have you. I've always thought that if confronted by demons or some other unspeakable entities, I would defy. As in "Do your worst. Destroy me utterly. I am not afraid of you!" No, I am not afraid of the Devil. I am afraid of the absence of God. Surely the absence of God is worse than the presence of the Devil?

An extreme hangover is caused, they say, by extreme dehydration, a lack of water in the body. Thus, it would seem that dying of thirst—in the desert, for example—would be equivalent to the worst imaginable hangover. All the same symptoms. The absence of water. In other words, the torment of the damned is not the fires of Hell that Joyce so vividly described; it is the absence of God... and worse, the knowing that there is no way back to God. And if there is no way back to God, then what's the point? Why do we care for others if there is no God to care about them, too?

Something incredible here, something indescribable, glorious. The dogs are completely, visibly, disturbingly covered in fleas, but bound happily along. The iguanas are skittish and, interpreting the slightest movement as imminent, apocalyptic doom, run and hide.

The people are the poorest I've ever seen, and yet there is an incredible lack of lack, a shared joy of life and living, a freedom and generosity of spirit. They sit outside their houses all evening with their backs against a wall. Just sit there, doing nothing. Like they are waiting for something... an event? a miracle? the rapture? No, they are not waiting for any of those things at all. They are waiting for tomorrow when they can sit outside their houses all evening with their backs against a wall.

Damascus? Huh? No... nothing so dramatic, it seems. No knocking me off my horse in the middle of prideful prance *on the way to Damascus. It's more like I'm just sitting here waiting in a white lobby in an aluminum-rimmed, plastic chair waiting for God. For months. And a young girl here beside me near the sea, a girl who paints nails, who has as her highest ambition to paint nails, and can't afford to stay even one more month in her twenty-dollar-a-month nail-painting school because she needs to go to the big city to find a way to survive for her and her little hija, a darling, sweet, little girl with the word "ya" constantly on her lips, as she points at things and holds out little flowers and bits of things to you that she found in the dirt. This girl and her beloved little hija need, what? Two hundred dollars per month? Just to survive here, to stay alive here, an obscenely trifling amount. God? Hello? Is she your angel sent to guide me? Or am I hers? Where are you, God? No waiting room for you? Do I need a horse and a mission?*

— The Alabaster Girl, *page 190*

෨෬

It is time. It is time to be magnificent. To live our lives in bold and vibrant colors, crayoned against the sky. To look around us through all of our days in continuous awe and wonder and reverence. To romance our women again. To seek beauty and art and grace and nothing else forever. To float above and apologize for nothing in this life.

The greatest women are the ones who can see the potential in a man, where it is possible for him to go. If there is to be a meaningful men's movement on this earth, it will be led by men, but inspired by women. We can't do it alone. Shiva is useless unless Sati dances around him. Men need to be surrounded by the magnificence and inspiring light of women in order to be great. It is not possible without it. Women have given birth to us all, and it is women, truly feminine women, who will give men the rebirth that the world so desperately needs.

God has bestowed His favor upon us. The only thing we can do is to ask Him for more. We will be saved by beauty. We will be saved by the essence of the female spirit. We will be saved by feminine grace. We are real men in the presence of the intimate, inspiring, connecting essence of women. We are builders of empires, we are warriors, destroyers, we are masculine, powerful, alive, invincible. We can do no wrong. We can only win. It is because of you, my love, because of you.

How wondrous and vast is this life! What a gift it is to be still! To sit on a balcony with you, a pomegranate, and a glass of champagne… like a still life painting… to me, there is nothing else. A return to romance. A return to beauty. Beauty is holy. Beauty is all. Always and forever beauty.

Let us sit beneath the stars and set in stone a clear intention, let us pray for grace, in this moment, this day, this time in our lives, let us lift our eyes to the heavens, let us open our minds to the thunderous call of the firmament, let us feel the wind on our faces, let us find the courage to design our lives. For once! Let us be willing to give our lives for our own cause. Let us go forth toward our heart's vision, no matter what the cost. Let us be captains of our own ships, and let us careen those ships madly, delightfully, gracefully past the rocks of mediocrity and onward, ever onward to the bountiful horizons we see in our minds. Let us take up arms, and rush headlong into the fray, pressing on forever forward, toward the multitude, through the multitude, beyond the multitude, above the multitude, and the multitude will marvel and the multitude will rejoice and the multitude will cry out, "There is no wasteland in him!"

Everything is in balance. Everything is as it should be. Life is vast. Life is grand. The stream of life flows on with an ease and delight that carries us gently forward forever.

nine

The Way of Beauty

Oh Beauty, my dream, my sea, my sky
I so loved loving you
a thousand silly little things was all that I could do

The train is arriving now... an inevitable, elysian station... a secret slowing... a damascened layer of memories... fading, fading, fading...

We've come a long way, he said.

Yes, we have.

To the very end, he said.

Yes.

I have limned all my volumes to you. I have spoken my heart of hearts to you.

Yes.

What is this place?

I think you know...

The sun is blazing soft through the window... soft white blazing... sundust floating all around... she is leaning forward, reaching out, beckoning, inviting, come closer... come closer... smiling... serene... soft white blazing...

Do you believe in Beauty? she said.

I only believe in Beauty.

Do you *truly* believe in Beauty?

With all my heart.

Yes... I can see that you do.

Oh my love... oh my love... oh my love... oh my love...

ഏരു

For I will go into the deepest of dark
to steal out small diamonds
to place on your skin
in velvet arrangements
in trembling rows of three

I will call down great rains
of wonder and silver fear
nailing my very soul to the sand
only to seek out that one lucid drop
that forever reflects your eyes

I will rage through the torrents
of proscribed rivers piercing
the night in their undulant bliss
to cling to the sound
of your voice on the mist

I will climb the laughing rocks
between the sea and the sky
with my hands on sharp clouds
to bring you baskets of flowers
to lay in a dish

I would like to acknowledge (for various and sundry reasons) the following people:

Hans Comyn
Clare Kent
Lorelei Erho
Braden Kiefiuk
Kelly Mulzet
and
William Iler

About the Author

Zan Perrion is internationally recognized as one of the most original and insightful voices on dating and seduction in the world today. A regular media commentator, he has been widely featured in the international press. Zan is the founder of the Ars Amorata philosophy, a "celebration of the art of seduction, the rebirth of romance, and a lifelong quest for beauty and adventure." He is also co-founder of the Amorati network of men.

www.arsamorata.com

www.zanperrion.com

ARS AMORATA